GREAT-TASTING WRAPS

Publications International, Ltd.

Microwave Cooking: Microwave ovens vary in wattage. Use the cooking times as guidelines and check for doneness before adding more time.

CONTENTS

Appetizers with Attitude

Smoked Salmon Appetizers

¼ cup reduced-fat or fat-free cream cheese, softened
1 tablespoon chopped fresh dill *or* 1 teaspoon dried dill weed
⅛ teaspoon ground red pepper
4 ounces thinly sliced smoked salmon or lox
24 melba toast rounds or other low-fat crackers

1. Combine cream cheese, dill and pepper in small bowl; stir to blend. Spread evenly over each slice of salmon. Starting with short side, roll up salmon slices jelly-roll fashion. Place on plate; cover with plastic wrap. Chill at least 1 hour or up to 4 hours before serving.

2. Using a sharp knife, cut salmon rolls crosswise into ¾-inch pieces. Place pieces, cut side down, on melba rounds. Garnish each piece with dill sprig, if desired.

Makes about 2 dozen appetizers

Smoked Salmon Appetizers

Savory Sausage Mushroom Turnovers

1 (12-ounce) package frozen bulk pork sausage, thawed
1 cup chopped mushrooms
⅓ cup chopped onion
½ cup shredded Swiss cheese (2 ounces)
⅓ cup GREY POUPON® Country Dijon Mustard
2 tablespoons diced red bell pepper
½ teaspoon dried thyme leaves
2 (8-ounce) packages refrigerated crescent dinner roll dough
1 egg, beaten
Sesame or poppy seed

In large skillet over medium heat, cook sausage, mushrooms and onion until sausage is cooked, stirring occasionally to break up sausage. Remove from heat. Stir in cheese, mustard, bell pepper and thyme.

Separate each package of dough into 4 rectangles; press perforations together to seal. On floured surface, roll each rectangle into 6-inch square. Cut each square into quarters, making 32 squares total. Place 1 scant tablespoon sausage mixture on each square; fold dough over filling on the diagonal to form triangle. Press edges with fork to seal. Place on greased baking sheets.

Brush triangles with egg and sprinkle with sesame or poppy seed. Bake at 375°F for 10 to 12 minutes or until golden brown. Serve warm.

Makes 32 turnovers

Mexican Roll-Ups

6 uncooked lasagna noodles
¾ cup prepared guacamole
¾ cup chunky salsa
¾ cup (3 ounces) shredded Cheddar cheese
Additional salsa (optional)

1. Cook lasagna noodles according to package directions, omitting salt. Rinse with cool water; drain. Cool.

2. Spread 2 tablespoons guacamole onto each noodle; top each with 2 tablespoons salsa and 2 tablespoons cheese.

3. Roll up noodles jelly-roll fashion. Cut each roll-up in half. Serve immediately with salsa or cover with plastic wrap and refrigerate up to 3 hours.

Makes 12 appetizers

Savory Sausage Mushroom Turnovers

Vietnamese Summer Rolls

Vietnamese Dipping
    Sauce (recipe follows)
8 ounces raw medium
    shrimp, peeled and
    deveined
3½ ounces very thin dry rice
    vermicelli
12 rice paper wrappers,*
    6½ inches in diameter
36 whole cilantro leaves
4 ounces roasted pork or
    beef, sliced ⅛ inch
    thick
1 tablespoon chopped
    peanuts
Lime peel for garnish
    (optional)

Available at specialty stores or Asian markets.

1. Prepare Vietnamese Dipping Sauce; set aside.

2. Fill large saucepan ¾ full with water; bring to a boil over high heat. Add shrimp; simmer 1 to 2 minutes or until shrimp turn pink and opaque. Remove shrimp with slotted spoon; transfer to small bowl.

3. Add rice vermicelli to saucepan. Cook according to package directions until tender but still firm, about 3 minutes. Drain in colander and rinse under cold running water to stop cooking; drain again.

4. Slice shrimp in half lengthwise.

5. To form summer rolls, soften 1 rice paper wrapper in large bowl of water 30 to 40 seconds. Drain and place wrapper flat on cutting board.

6. Arrange 3 cilantro leaves upside down in center of wrapper. Layer 2 shrimp halves, flat side up, over cilantro leaves. Place layer of pork on top of shrimp. Place ¼ cup cooked rice vermicelli over pork.

7. To form summer rolls, fold bottom of wrapper up over filling; fold in each side. Roll up toward top of wrapper. Place on platter with leaf design on top. Repeat with remaining wrappers and fillings.

8. Sprinkle summer rolls with peanuts. Serve with Vietnamese Dipping Sauce. Garnish with lime peel, if desired.
    Makes 12 summer rolls

Vietnamese Dipping Sauce

½ cup water
¼ cup fish sauce
2 tablespoons lime juice
1 tablespoon sugar
1 clove garlic, minced
¼ teaspoon chili oil

Combine all ingredients in small bowl; mix well.

Makes about 1 cup

Vietnamese Summer Rolls

Sausage Pinwheels

2 cups biscuit mix
½ cup milk
¼ cup butter or margarine,
   melted
1 pound BOB EVANS®
   Original Recipe Roll
   Sausage

Combine biscuit mix, milk and butter in large bowl until blended. Refrigerate 30 minutes. Divide dough into two portions. Roll out one portion on floured surface to ⅛-inch-thick rectangle, about 10×7 inches. Spread with half the sausage. Roll lengthwise into long roll. Repeat with remaining dough and sausage. Place rolls in freezer until hard enough to cut easily. Preheat oven to 400°F. Cut rolls into thin slices. Place on baking sheets. Bake 15 minutes or until golden brown. Serve hot. Refrigerate leftovers.
Makes 48 pinwheels

Serving Suggestions: *This recipe may be doubled. Pinwheels may be prepared ahead and frozen. (Refreeze after slicing.) When ready to serve, thaw slices in refrigerator and bake.*

Mexican Egg Rolls

2 cups (about 2 boneless,
   skinless breasts) finely
   shredded cooked
   chicken
2 cups (8 ounces) shredded
   Monterey Jack cheese
1¾ cups (16-ounce jar)
   ORTEGA® Garden Style
   Salsa, medium or mild,
   divided
¼ cup ORTEGA® Diced
   Green Chiles
10 to 12 egg roll wrappers
   Vegetable oil
   Sour cream (optional)

COMBINE chicken, cheese, *1 cup* salsa and chiles in large bowl. Scoop ⅓ cup filling down center of each egg roll wrapper. Fold one corner over filling; fold in 2 side corners. Moisten edges of remaining corner with water; roll up egg roll from bottom. Press to seal edges. Repeat with remaining filling and wrappers.

ADD oil to 1-inch depth in medium skillet; heat over high heat for 1 minute. Place egg rolls in oil; fry, turning frequently with tongs for 1 to 2 minutes, until golden brown. Remove from skillet; place on paper towels. Serve with *remaining ¾ cup* salsa and sour cream.
Makes 6 servings

Sausage Pinwheels

11

Gingered Chicken Pot Stickers

POT STICKERS

- 3 cups finely shredded cabbage
- 1 egg white, lightly beaten
- 1 tablespoon reduced-sodium soy sauce
- ¼ teaspoon red pepper flakes
- 1 tablespoon minced fresh ginger
- 4 green onions with tops, finely chopped
- ¼ pound ground chicken breast, cooked and drained
- 24 wonton wrappers, at room temperature
  Cornstarch

SAUCE

- ½ cup water
- 1 tablespoon oyster sauce
- 2 teaspoons grated lemon peel
- ½ teaspoon honey
- ⅛ teaspoon red pepper flakes
- 1 tablespoon peanut oil

1. Steam cabbage 5 minutes, then cool to room temperature. Squeeze out any excess moisture; set aside. To prepare filling, combine egg white, soy sauce, ¼ teaspoon red pepper flakes, ginger and green onions in large bowl; blend well. Stir in cabbage and chicken.

2. To prepare pot stickers, place 1 tablespoon filling in center of 1 wonton wrapper. Gather edges around filling, pressing firmly at top to seal. Repeat with remaining wrappers and filling.

3. Place pot stickers on large baking sheet dusted with cornstarch. Refrigerate 1 hour or until cold. Meanwhile, to prepare sauce, combine remaining ingredients except oil in small bowl; mix well. Set aside.

4. Heat oil in large nonstick skillet over high heat. Add pot stickers and cook until bottoms are golden brown. Pour sauce over top. Cover and cook 3 minutes. Uncover and cook until all liquid is absorbed. Serve warm.   *Makes 8 servings*

Gingered Chicken Pot Stickers

Sesame Chicken Salad Wonton Cups

20 (3-inch) wonton wrappers
1 tablespoon sesame seeds
2 small boneless skinless chicken breasts (about 8 ounces)
1 cup fresh green beans, cut diagonally into ½-inch pieces
¼ cup reduced-calorie mayonnaise
1 tablespoon chopped fresh cilantro (optional)
2 teaspoons honey
1 teaspoon reduced-sodium soy sauce
⅛ teaspoon ground red pepper

1. Preheat oven to 350°F. Spray miniature muffin pan with nonstick cooking spray. Press 1 wonton wrapper into each muffin cup; spray with nonstick cooking spray. Bake 8 to 10 minutes or until golden brown. Cool in pan on wire rack before filling.

2. Place sesame seeds in shallow baking pan. Bake 5 minutes or until lightly toasted, stirring occasionally. Set aside to cool.

3. Meanwhile, bring 2 cups water to a boil in medium saucepan. Add chicken. Reduce heat to low; cover. Simmer 10 minutes or until chicken is no

longer pink in center, adding green beans after 7 minutes. Drain.

4. Finely chop chicken. Place in medium bowl. Add green beans and remaining ingredients; mix lightly. Spoon slightly rounded tablespoonful of chicken mixture into each wonton cup. Garnish, if desired.

Makes 20 wonton cups

Taco Bread

1 loaf frozen bread dough, thawed
1½ cups (6 ounces) grated Cheddar cheese
1 package (1.0 ounce) LAWRY'S® Taco Spices & Seasonings
3 tablespoons butter *or* margarine, melted

On baking sheet, stretch dough into 14×8-inch rectangle. Sprinkle with cheese and Taco Spices & Seasonings; drizzle with margarine. Roll up dough in jelly roll fashion (lengthwise); place seam side down on baking sheet. Bake, uncovered, in 350°F oven 20 to 25 minutes until golden brown.

Makes 6 servings

Serving Suggestion: *Slice bread when cooled and serve as a spicy addition to hearty soups.*

Sesame Chicken Salad Wonton Cups

Pack Up the Poultry

Ya Gotta Empanada

- 1 package (4.4 to 6.8 ounces) Spanish rice mix, prepared according to package directions
- 1 cup shredded cooked chicken
- 1 cup (4 ounces) shredded Cheddar cheese
- ½ cup sliced green onions
- ¼ cup chopped black olives
- 1 package (15 ounces) refrigerated pie crusts

Combine rice, chicken, cheese, onions and olives in large bowl. Spoon half of rice mixture on half of each pie crust. Fold crust over filling. Seal and crimp edges. Place on baking sheet. Bake at 400°F 20 to 22 minutes or until golden brown. Cut each empanada in half. Serve immediately.

Makes 4 servings
(½ empanada each)

Favorite recipe from **USA Rice Federation**

Ya Gotta Empanada

Chicken Enchiladas

1¾ cups fat free sour cream
½ cup chopped green
   onions
⅓ cup minced fresh cilantro
1 tablespoon minced fresh
   jalapeño chili pepper
1 teaspoon ground cumin
1 tablespoon vegetable oil
12 ounces boneless, skinless
   chicken breasts, cut
   into 3×1-inch strips
1 teaspoon minced garlic
8 flour tortillas (8-inch)
1 cup (4 ounces) shredded
   ALPINE LACE®
   Reduced Fat Cheddar
   Cheese
1 cup bottled chunky salsa
   (medium or hot)
1 small ripe tomato,
   chopped
   Sprigs of cilantro
   (optional)

1. Preheat the oven to 350°F. Spray a 13×9×3-inch baking dish with nonstick cooking spray.

2. In a small bowl, mix together the sour cream, green onions, cilantro, jalapeño pepper and cumin.

3. Spray a large nonstick skillet with the cooking spray, pour in the oil and heat over medium-high heat. Add the chicken and garlic and sauté for 4 minutes or until the juices run clear when the chicken is pierced with a fork.

4. Divide the chicken strips among the 8 tortillas, placing them down the center of the tortillas. Top with the sour cream mixture, then roll them up and place them, seam side down, in the baking dish.

5. Sprinkle with the cheese, cover with foil and bake for 30 minutes or until bubbly. Spoon the salsa in a strip down the center and sprinkle the salsa with the tomato. Garnish with the sprigs of cilantro, if you wish. Serve hot!

Makes 8 servings

Chicken Enchiladas

Chicken and Black Bean Soft Tacos

1 package (10) ORTEGA®
    Soft Taco Dinner Kit
    (flour tortillas, taco
    seasoning mix and taco
    sauce)
1 tablespoon vegetable oil
1 pound (3 to 4) boneless,
    skinless chicken breast
    halves, cut into strips
1 cup chopped onion
1¾ cups (15-ounce can) black
    beans, drained
¾ cup whole kernel corn
½ cup water
2 tablespoons lime juice

HEAT oil in large skillet over medium-high heat. Add chicken and onion; cook for 4 to 5 minutes or until chicken is no longer pink in center. Stir in taco seasoning mix, beans, corn, water and lime juice. Bring to a boil. Reduce heat to low; cook, stirring occasionally, for 5 to 6 minutes or until mixture is thickened.

REMOVE tortillas from outer plastic pouch. Microwave on HIGH (100%) power for 10 to 15 seconds or until warm. Or heat each tortilla, turning frequently, in small skillet over medium-high heat until warm.

FILL tortillas with ½ cup chicken mixture and taco sauce.

Makes 10 tacos

Garlicky Chicken Packets

1 cup julienned carrots
½ cup sliced onion
¼ cup chopped fresh basil
    or 1 tablespoon dried
    basil leaves
2 tablespoons mayonnaise
6 cloves garlic, minced
⅛ teaspoon black pepper
4 boneless skinless chicken
    breast halves

Cut parchment paper or foil into 4 (12-inch) squares. Fold squares in half, then cut into shape of half hearts. Open parchment to form hearts.

Preheat oven to 400°F. Place carrots and onion on 1 side of each heart near fold. Combine basil, mayonnaise, garlic and pepper in small bowl; spread mixture on chicken. Place chicken, mayonnaise side up, on top of vegetables. Fold parchment over chicken; seal by creasing and folding edges of parchment in small overlapping sections from top of heart until completed at point. Finish by twisting point and tucking under.

Place parchment packages on ungreased baking sheet. Bake 20 to 25 minutes or until juices run clear and chicken is no longer pink in center.

Makes 4 servings

Chicken and Black Bean Soft Tacos

Spicy Lime and Cilantro Turkey Fajitas

1 pound Turkey Tenderloins
1 tablespoon paprika
½ teaspoon onion salt
½ teaspoon garlic powder
½ teaspoon ground red pepper
½ teaspoon fennel seeds
½ teaspoon dried thyme leaves
¼ teaspoon white pepper
  Sour Cream Sauce (recipe follows)
1 lime, halved
4 pita breads
  Shredded lettuce (optional)

1. Slice tenderloins open lengthwise, cutting almost through, being careful to leave halves attached. Open halves flat. In shallow flat dish, combine paprika, onion salt, garlic powder, red pepper, fennel, thyme and white pepper. Rub mixture over tenderloins; cover and refrigerate 1 hour. Prepare Sour Cream Sauce.

2. Prepare grill for direct cooking. Grill tenderloins, on covered grill, 10 to 12 minutes or until meat thermometer inserted into thickest part of tenderloin registers 170°F, turning halfway through grilling time. Place on clean serving plate; squeeze lime over tenderloins. Cut tenderloins crosswise into ¼-inch-thick slices.

3. To serve, top each pita with tenderloins and Sour Cream Sauce; roll up. Garnish with lettuce, if desired.

Makes 4 servings

Sour Cream Sauce

1 cup fat-free imitation sour cream
¼ cup thinly sliced green onions
¼ cup finely chopped cilantro
1 can (4 ounces) green chilies, drained
1 plum tomato, seeded and finely chopped
½ teaspoon black pepper
¼ teaspoon ground red pepper

In small bowl, combine sour cream, green onions, cilantro, chilies, tomato, black and ground red peppers. Cover; refrigerate until ready to use.

Favorite recipe from **National Turkey Federation**

garlic, gingerroot, lime peel and red pepper flakes. Cover and refrigerate for at least 1 hour.

2. Unfold lavosh; drain turkey mixture, if necessary, and spread evenly along lower quarter of bread.

3. Fold in bottom and top portions. Roll up from side to completely enclose filling. Cut into four equal portions.
Makes 4 roll-ups

Cooking Tip: *Lavosh is a round, thin bread that comes in both soft and crisp versions; it is available in Middle Eastern markets and in most supermarkets.*

Favorite recipe from **National Turkey Federation**

Chicken Fajita Wraps

 1 pound chicken tenders
¼ cup lime juice
 4 cloves garlic, minced, divided
 1 red bell pepper, sliced
 1 green bell pepper, sliced
 1 yellow bell pepper, sliced
 1 large red onion, cut into ¼-inch slices
½ teaspoon ground cumin
¼ teaspoon salt
¼ teaspoon ground red pepper
 8 (8-inch) flour tortillas, warmed
 Salsa

1. Combine chicken, lime juice and 2 cloves garlic in medium bowl; toss to coat. Cover and marinate 30 minutes in refrigerator, stirring occasionally.

2. Spray large nonstick skillet with nonstick cooking spray; heat over medium heat until hot. Add chicken mixture; cook and stir 5 to 7 minutes or until chicken is browned and no longer pink in center. Remove chicken from skillet. Drain excess liquid from skillet, if necessary.

3. Add bell peppers, onion and remaining 2 cloves garlic to skillet; cook and stir about 5 minutes or until vegetables are tender. Sprinkle with cumin, salt and red pepper. Return chicken to skillet; cook and stir 1 to 2 minutes.

4. Fill tortillas with chicken mixture. Serve with salsa. Garnish, if desired.
Makes 4 servings

Chicken Phyllo Wraps

1 pound ground chicken
1 cup chopped fresh
    mushrooms
1 medium onion, chopped
3 cups cooked rice
1 cup nonfat low-salt
    ricotta cheese
1 package (10 ounces)
    chopped spinach,
    thawed and well
    drained
1 can (2¼ ounces) sliced
    black olives, drained
¼ cup pine nuts, toasted*
2 cloves garlic, minced
1 teaspoon ground
    oregano
1 teaspoon lemon pepper
12 phyllo dough sheets

*To toast nuts, place on baking sheet
and bake at 350°F 5 to 7 minutes or
until lightly browned.*

Coat large skillet with cooking spray; heat over medium-high heat until hot. Add chicken, mushrooms and onion; cook and stir 2 to 4 minutes or until chicken is no longer pink and vegetables are tender. Reduce heat to medium. Add rice, ricotta cheese, spinach, olives, nuts, garlic, oregano and lemon pepper; cook and stir 3 to 4 minutes until well blended and thoroughly heated. Working with 1 phyllo sheet at a time, spray 1 sheet with cooking spray; fold sheet in half lengthwise. Place ¾ to 1 cup rice mixture on one end of phyllo strip. Fold left bottom corner over mixture, forming a triangle. Continue folding back and forth into triangle at end of strip. Repeat with remaining phyllo sheets and rice mixture. Place triangles, seam sides down, on baking sheets coated with cooking spray. Coat top of each triangle with cooking spray. Bake at 400°F 15 to 20 minutes or until golden brown. Serve immediately.

Makes 12 servings

Favorite recipe from **USA Rice Federation**

Chicken Phyllo Wrap

Meat Matters

Ham Stromboli

1 can (10 ounces) refrigerated
   pizza dough
1 tablespoon prepared mustard
½ pound thinly sliced deli ham
1 package (3½ ounces) sliced
   pepperoni
1 teaspoon dried Italian seasoning
2 cups (8 ounces) shredded part-
   skim mozzarella cheese

1. Preheat oven to 425°F. Unroll pizza dough on greased jelly-roll pan; pat dough into 12-inch square.

2. Spread mustard over dough to within ½ inch of edges. Layer ham slices down center 6 inches of dough, leaving 3-inch border on either side and ½-inch border at top and bottom. Top ham with pepperoni slices. Sprinkle with Italian seasoning and cheese.

3. Fold sides of dough over filling, pinching center seam, top and bottom to seal. Bake 15 to 20 minutes or until lightly browned.   *Makes 6 servings*

Ham Stromboli

Border Scramble

1 pound BOB EVANS®
    Original Recipe Roll
    Sausage
1½ cups chopped cooked
    potatoes
1½ cups chopped onions
1½ cups chopped tomatoes
  ¾ cup chopped green bell
    pepper
  ¼ to ½ cup picante sauce
  ½ to 1 tablespoon hot
    pepper sauce
  ½ teaspoon garlic powder
  ½ teaspoon salt
  4 (9-inch) flour tortillas
  2 cups prepared meatless
    chili
  ½ cup (2 ounces) shredded
    Cheddar cheese

Crumble sausage into large skillet. Cook over medium heat until browned, stirring occasionally. Drain off any drippings. Add all remaining ingredients except tortillas, chili and cheese; simmer 20 minutes or until vegetables are crisp-tender. To warm tortillas, microwave 1 minute at HIGH between paper towels. Place 1 cup sausage mixture in center of each tortilla; fold tortilla over filling to close. Heat chili in small saucepan until hot, stirring occasionally. Top each folded tortilla with ½ cup chili and 2 tablespoons cheese. Serve hot. Refrigerate leftovers.

Makes 4 servings

Calzone Mexicana

1 pound lean ground beef
    or turkey
1 package (1.0 ounce)
    LAWRY'S® Taco Spices
    & Seasonings
¾ cup water
1 loaf frozen bread dough,
    thawed *or* 2 cans
    (9 ounces each)
    refrigerated pizza
    dough
2 cups (8 ounces) grated
    Monterey Jack cheese
1 can (4 ounces) diced
    green chiles, drained

In large skillet, brown ground beef or turkey until crumbly; drain fat. Add Taco Spices & Seasonings and water; mix well. Bring to a boil over medium high heat; reduce heat to low, simmer, uncovered, 7 to 10 minutes. On floured board, roll dough into 14×8-inch rectangle. Spread taco meat mixture into center of dough, leaving 2-inch border. Layer cheese and chiles on top. Fold dough lengthwise in half, pinch edges together to seal. Place on lightly greased baking sheet. Bake in 350°F oven, uncovered, 30 minutes or until golden brown.

*Makes 6 main-dish or 12
appetizer servings*

Border Scramble

Calzone Italiano

Pizza dough for one
14-inch pizza
1¾ cups (15-ounce can)
CONTADINA® Dalla
Casa Buitoni Pizza
Sauce with Pepperoni
25 (3 ounces) pepperoni
slices or ½ pound
sausage, cooked and
crumbled
2 tablespoons chopped
green bell pepper
1 cup (4 ounces) shredded
mozzarella cheese
1 cup (8 ounces) ricotta
cheese

DIVIDE dough into 4 equal
portions. Place on lightly
floured, rimless baking sheet.
Press or roll out dough to 7-inch
circles.

SPREAD *2 tablespoons* pizza
sauce over each circle to ½ inch
of edge. Top with meat, bell
pepper, mozzarella cheese and
ricotta cheese. Fold in half;
press edges tightly to seal. Cut
slits in top of dough to allow
steam to escape.

BAKE in preheated 350°F. oven
for 20 to 25 minutes or until
crusts are golden brown. Heat
remaining pizza sauce; serve
over calzones.

Makes 4 servings

Speedy Beef & Bean Burritos

8 (7-inch) flour tortillas
1 pound ground beef
1 cup chopped onion
1 teaspoon minced garlic
1 can (15 ounces) black
beans, drained and
rinsed
1 cup spicy thick and
chunky salsa
2 teaspoons ground cumin
¼ cup chopped fresh
cilantro
2 cups (8 ounces) shredded
cojack or Monterey
Jack cheese

1. Wrap tortillas in aluminum
foil; place in oven. Turn
temperature to 350°F; heat
tortillas 15 minutes.

2. While tortillas are warming,
prepare burrito filling. Combine
meat, onion and garlic in large
skillet; cook and stir over
medium-high heat until meat is
no longer pink. Pour off
drippings.

3. Stir beans, salsa and cumin
into meat mixture; reduce heat
to medium. Cover and simmer
10 minutes, stirring once.

4. Stir cilantro into filling. Spoon
filling down centers of warm
tortillas; top with cheese. Roll
up and serve immediately.

Makes 4 servings

Calzone Italiano

Original Ortega® Taco Recipe

1 pound ground beef
1 package (1¼ ounces)
    ORTEGA® Taco
    Seasoning Mix
¾ cup water
1 package (12) ORTEGA®
    Taco Shells or (12)
    ORTEGA® White Corn
    Taco Shells
1½ cups (6 ounces) shredded
    Cheddar cheese
2½ cups shredded lettuce
2 cups (2 medium) chopped
    tomatoes
    ORTEGA® Thick &
    Smooth Taco Sauce

COOK beef in medium skillet over medium-high heat for 4 to 5 minutes or until no longer pink; drain. Stir in taco seasoning mix and water. Bring to a boil. Reduce heat to low; cook, stirring occasionally, for 5 to 6 minutes or until mixture is thickened. Remove taco shells from freshness pack. Heat shells in microwave oven on HIGH (100%) power for 40 to 60 seconds or place on baking sheet in preheated 350°F. oven for 5 to 6 minutes. Fill taco shells with 2 to 3 tablespoons beef mixture. Top with cheese, lettuce, tomatoes and taco sauce.   *Makes 6 servings*

Sausage Stroganoff in Puff Pastry Shells

2 (10-ounce) packages BOB
    EVANS® Skinless Link
    Sausage
1 medium onion, sliced
1 (10½-ounce) can
    condensed cream of
    mushroom soup
1 cup sour cream
1 (4-ounce) can sliced
    mushrooms, drained
2 tablespoons ketchup
2 teaspoons
    Worcestershire sauce
8 frozen puff pastry shells,
    thawed according to
    package directions

Preheat oven to 250°F. Cut sausage into bite-size pieces. Cook in large skillet over medium heat until browned, stirring occasionally. Remove sausage; set aside. Add onion to drippings; cook and stir until just tender. Stir in sausage and all remaining ingredients except pastry shells. Cook over low heat until heated through. Warm shells in oven. Spoon sausage mixture into shells. Serve hot. Refrigerate leftover sausage mixture and reheat slowly in top of large double boiler over hot, not boiling, water.   *Makes 8 servings*

Original Ortega® Taco Recipe

Steak & Pepper Fajitas

1 packet (1.12 ounces)
    fajita marinade
1 pound boneless steak,*
    cut into thin strips
1 bag (16 ounces) BIRDS
    EYE® frozen Farm
    Fresh Mixtures Pepper
    Stir Fry vegetables
8 (6- to 7-inch) flour
    tortillas, warmed
½ cup salsa

*Or, substitute 1 pound boneless,
skinless chicken, cut into strips.

• Prepare fajita marinade
according to package
directions.

• Add steak and vegetables. Let
stand 10 minutes.

• Heat large skillet over
medium-high heat. Remove
steak and vegetables from
marinade with slotted spoon
and place in skillet.

• Add marinade, if desired.
Cook 5 minutes or until steak is
desired doneness and mixture is
heated through, stirring
occasionally.

• Wrap mixture in tortillas. Top
with salsa.   *Makes 4 servings*

Prep Time: 10 minutes
Cook Time: 5 to 7 minutes

Serving Suggestions: *Serve
with guacamole and sour
cream, or serve mixture over
rice instead of in flour tortillas.*

Reuben Roll-Ups

8 (7-inch) flour tortillas
¾ cup FRENCH'S® Deli
    Brown Mustard
1 pound sliced corned beef
2 cups (8 ounces) shredded
    Swiss cheese
½ cup sauerkraut

Spread each tortilla with about
1½ tablespoons mustard. Layer
corned beef, cheese and
sauerkraut on tortillas, dividing
evenly. Roll up tortillas jelly-roll
style. Secure with toothpicks.*

Place tortillas on oiled grid. Grill
over medium-low coals about
10 minutes or until tortillas are
toasted and cheese begins to
melt, turning often. Remove
toothpicks before serving.
    Makes 4 servings

Prep Time: 20 minutes
Cook Time: 10 minutes

*Soak toothpicks in water 20 minutes to
prevent burning.*

Steak & Pepper Fajita

Oriental-Style Ground Pork

1 package (8 ounces) shredded carrots
1 tablespoon sugar
1 teaspoon distilled white vinegar or rice vinegar
2 green onions with tops
8 large mushrooms
1 teaspoon cornstarch
½ teaspoon chili powder
¼ cup chicken broth
1 tablespoon reduced-sodium soy sauce
1 tablespoon vegetable oil
1 pound ground pork
Boston lettuce leaves

1. Combine carrots, sugar and vinegar in medium bowl; set aside.

2. Slice green onions diagonally into 1-inch pieces. Wipe mushrooms clean with damp paper towels; slice.

3. Combine cornstarch and chili powder in small bowl. Stir broth and soy sauce into cornstarch mixture until smooth. Set aside.

4. Heat wok over medium-high heat 1 minute or until hot. Drizzle oil into wok and heat 30 seconds. Add pork; stir-fry until well browned. Add mushrooms; stir-fry until tender.

5. Stir broth mixture until smooth and add to wok. Cook until sauce boils and thickens. Add green onions; stir-fry 1 minute.

6. Line serving plate with lettuce leaves. Arrange carrot mixture in layer over leaves. Top with pork mixture. (Traditionally, the lettuce leaves are eaten as a wrapper to hold the ground meat mixture.)

Makes 4 servings

Tip: *Look for firm, fleshy mushrooms with no discoloration or bruises. To store, keep refrigerated, unwashed, in a paper bag or ventilated package up to 5 days. If damp, wrap mushrooms in paper towels before storing. Use as soon as possible for best flavor.*

Oriental-Style Ground Pork

The Seafood Scene

Ensenada Fish Tacos

10 ounces halibut *or* orange roughy,
 cut into 1-inch cubes
1 tablespoon vegetable oil
1 tablespoon lime juice
1 package (1.27 ounces) LAWRY'S®
 Spices & Seasonings for Fajitas
6 corn *or* flour tortillas,
 approximately 8 inches
2½ cups shredded lettuce
½ cup diced tomatoes
¾ cup (3 ounces) grated Monterey
 Jack or Cheddar cheese
2 tablespoons thinly sliced green
 onion
 Dairy sour cream, guacamole,
 salsa, and fresh cilantro
 (garnish)

In shallow glass baking dish, place fish. Add oil and lime juice. Sprinkle with Spices & Seasonings for Fajitas; toss lightly to coat. Cover with plastic wrap. Marinate in refrigerator 2 hours, occasionally spooning marinade over fish. Remove plastic wrap. Bake fish in 450°F oven 10 minutes, until fish just begins to flake; drain. To serve, evenly divide fish and place in center of each tortilla. Top with lettuce, tomatoes, cheese and green onion.

Makes 6 tacos

Ensenada Fish Tacos

Orange Roughy in Parchment Hearts

8 ounces fresh asparagus,
    peeled and diagonally
    cut into 2-inch pieces
Parchment paper or foil
4 orange roughy fillets
    (about 1½ pounds)
Butter
1 yellow bell pepper, cut
    into 16 julienne strips
1 red bell pepper, cut into
    16 julienne strips
1 medium carrot, cut into
    julienne strips
¼ cup dry white wine
3 tablespoons Dijon
    mustard
2 tablespoons lemon juice
1 teaspoon dried marjoram
    leaves
¼ teaspoon black pepper

1. To steam asparagus, bring 2 inches of water in large saucepan to a boil over high heat. Place asparagus in metal steamer and set into saucepan. Water should not touch asparagus. Cover pan; steam 2 to 3 minutes or until asparagus turns bright green.

2. Preheat oven to 375°F. Cut parchment paper into 4 (12-inch) squares. Fold each square in half diagonally and cut into half heart shape.

3. Rinse fillets and pat dry with paper towels.

4. Lightly butter inside of each heart. Place 1 fillet on 1 side of each heart. Arrange asparagus over fish. Place 4 strips each yellow and red bell pepper over fish; place carrot strips over peppers.

5. Combine wine, mustard, lemon juice, marjoram and black pepper in small bowl. Drizzle wine mixture over fish.

6. Fold parchment hearts in half. Beginning at top of heart, fold the edges together, 2 inches at a time. At tip of heart, fold paper up and over.

7. Place parchment packages on large baking sheet. Bake 20 to 25 minutes or until fish flakes easily when tested with fork. To serve, place packages on plates and cut an "X" through top layer of parchment, folding points back to display contents.
Makes 4 servings

Orange Roughy in Parchment Heart

Seafood Crêpes

Basic Crêpes (recipe
    follows)
3 tablespoons butter or
    margarine
⅓ cup finely chopped
    shallots or sweet onion
2 tablespoons dry
    vermouth
3 tablespoons all-purpose
    flour
1½ cups plus 2 tablespoons
    milk, divided
¼ to ½ teaspoon hot
    pepper sauce (optional)
8 ounces cooked peeled
    and deveined shrimp,
    coarsely chopped
    (1½ cups)
8 ounces lump crabmeat or
    imitation crabmeat,
    shredded (1½ cups)
2 tablespoons snipped
    fresh chives or green
    onion tops
3 tablespoons freshly
    grated Parmesan
    cheese
Fresh chives and red
    onion for garnish

1. Prepare Basic Crêpes.
Preheat oven to 350°F.

2. Melt butter over medium
heat in medium saucepan. Add
shallots; cook and stir 5 minutes
or until shallots are tender. Add
vermouth; cook 1 minute.

3. Add flour; cook and stir 1
minute. Gradually stir in 1½

cups milk and hot pepper
sauce, if desired. Bring to a boil,
stirring frequently. Reduce heat
to low; cook and stir 1 minute
or until mixture thickens.

4. Remove from heat; stir in
shrimp and crabmeat. Reserve
½ cup seafood mixture; set
aside.

5. To assemble crêpes, spoon
about ¼ cup seafood mixture
down center of each crêpe. Roll
up crêpes jelly-roll style. Place
seam side down in well-greased
13×9-inch baking dish.

6. Stir chives and remaining 2
tablespoons milk into reserved
seafood mixture. Spoon
seafood mixture down center of
crêpes; sprinkle cheese evenly
over top.

7. Bake uncovered 15 to 20
minutes or until heated
through. Serve immediately.
Garnish, if desired.

Makes 6 servings

Basic Crêpes

1½ cups milk
 1 cup all-purpose flour
 2 eggs
¼ cup butter or margarine,
    melted and cooled,
    divided
¼ teaspoon salt

continued on page 46

Seafood Crêpes

Basic Crêpes, *continued*

1. Combine milk, flour, eggs, 2 tablespoons butter and salt in food processor; process using on/off pulsing action until smooth. Let stand at room temperature 30 minutes.

2. Heat ½ teaspoon butter in 7- or 8-inch crêpe pan or skillet over medium heat. Pour ¼ cup batter into hot pan. Immediately rotate pan back and forth to swirl batter over entire surface of pan.

3. Cook 1 to 2 minutes or until crêpe is brown around edges and top is dry. Carefully turn crêpe with spatula and cook 30 seconds more. Transfer crêpe to waxed paper to cool. Repeat with remaining batter, adding remaining butter only as needed to prevent sticking.

4. Separate each crêpe with sheet of waxed paper. Cover and refrigerate up to 1 day or freeze up to 1 month before serving.

Makes about 1 dozen crêpes

Salmon en Papillote

⅔ cup FRENCH'S® Dijon Mustard
½ cup (1 stick) butter or margarine, melted
3 cloves garlic, minced
¼ cup minced fresh dill weed *or* 1 tablespoon dried dill weed
4 pieces (2 pounds) salmon fillet, cut into 4×3×1½-inch portions
Salt
Ground black pepper
2 cups julienne vegetable strips, such as bell peppers, carrots, leek, celery or fennel bulb
2 tablespoons capers, drained

Combine mustard, butter, garlic and dill weed in medium microwave-safe bowl. Cover loosely with vented plastic wrap. Microwave on HIGH 1 minute. Whisk sauce until smooth; set aside.

Sprinkle salmon with salt and black pepper. Cut 4 (12-inch) circles of heavy-duty foil. Coat 1 side of foil with vegetable cooking spray. Place 1 piece salmon in center of each foil square. Spoon about 2 tablespoons mustard sauce over each piece of fish. Reserve remaining sauce. Top fish evenly with vegetables and capers. Fold foil in half over salmon and vegetables. Seal edges securely with tight double folds.

Place packets on grid. Grill over hot coals 15 to 20 minutes until fish flakes easily when tested with fork (open foil packets carefully). Serve with reserved mustard sauce.

Makes 4 servings

Diavolo Seafood Loaves

1 to 1½ pounds shrimp*
1 bunch fresh cilantro
3 cloves garlic, divided
2 green onions
4 round loaves sourdough bread, each about 5 inches in diameter
  Olive oil or butter
1 cup white wine
1 red bell pepper, diced
1 yellow bell pepper, diced
1 green bell pepper, diced
1 (26-ounce) jar NEWMAN'S OWN® Diavolo Spicy Simmer Sauce
  Softened butter
  Tomato and orange slices for garnish

*Substitute 1½ pounds other fresh shellfish or red snapper if shrimp is unavailable.

1. Peel and devein shrimp. Chop cilantro to make about 1 cup, reserving a few sprigs for garnish. Chop 2 cloves garlic and green onions. Prepare bread by horizontally slicing top off of each loaf. Hollow out loaves to within 1 inch of sides and bottoms; reserve removed bread in separate bowl.

2. Heat 3 tablespoons oil in skillet. Add chopped garlic and green onions; cook and stir 3 to 5 minutes until tender. Add wine; boil mixture until reduced by half. Add shrimp and bell peppers; cook and stir just until shrimp turn pink. *Do not overcook.* In large saucepan, heat Diavolo Spicy Simmer Sauce; add chopped cilantro.

3. Cut reserved bread into cubes; drizzle with small amount of olive oil. Chop remaining 1 clove garlic. Add half of chopped garlic to cubed bread mixture; stir well. Spread cubed bread mixture on ungreased baking sheet; bake in preheated 400°F oven 10 minutes or until golden brown.

4. Spread some softened butter on inside of each bread shell; sprinkle with remaining chopped garlic. Broil to brown lightly. Remove; set aside.

5. To serve, fill each bread shell with even amount of shrimp mixture; add heated Diavolo Sauce to within 1 inch of top of each filled bread shell. Garnish with bread cubes, reserved cilantro sprigs and tomato and orange slices.

Makes 4 servings

Shrimp Ravioli with Curry Sauce

½ cup finely chopped
   mushrooms
4 green onions, thinly
   sliced
2 tablespoons minced fresh
   ginger
3 cloves garlic, minced
8 ounces shrimp, finely
   chopped
32 wonton wrappers
   Curry Sauce (recipe
   follows)
2 tablespoons finely
   chopped fresh cilantro

1. Spray skillet with cooking spray; heat over medium heat until hot. Add mushrooms, green onions, ginger and garlic; cook and stir 2 to 3 minutes. Add shrimp; cook 3 to 5 minutes or until shrimp turn pink and opaque.

2. Place 1 rounded tablespoonful shrimp mixture in center of 1 wonton wrapper; brush edges with water. Top with second wonton wrapper; seal edges. Repeat with remaining shrimp mixture and wonton wrappers.

3. Bring 2 quarts water to a boil in medium saucepan; add 4 to 6 ravioli. Cook 3 to 4 minutes or until ravioli are tender. Remove and repeat with remaining ravioli. Serve with warm Curry Sauce; sprinkle with cilantro. Garnish as desired.

Makes 4 servings

Curry Sauce

¼ cup finely chopped onion
1 clove garlic, minced
1½ tablespoons all-purpose
   flour
1½ teaspoons curry powder
⅛ teaspoon ground cumin
1 cup fat-free reduced-
   sodium chicken broth
   Salt
   Black pepper

Spray saucepan with cooking spray; heat over medium heat until hot. Add onion and garlic; cook and stir 2 to 3 minutes. Stir in flour, curry powder and cumin; cook and stir 1 to 2 minutes. Add chicken broth; cook and stir 1 minute or until thickened. Season with salt and pepper to taste.

Shrimp Ravioli with Curry Sauce

Vegetable Adventures

Pinto Bean & Zucchini Burritos

6 flour tortillas (6 inches each)
¾ cup GUILTLESS GOURMET®
    Spicy Pinto Bean Dip
2 teaspoons water
1 teaspoon olive oil
1 medium zucchini, chopped
¼ cup chopped green onions
¼ cup GUILTLESS GOURMET®
    Green Tomatillo Salsa
1 cup GUILTLESS GOURMET®
    Medium Salsa, divided
1½ cups shredded lettuce
    Fresh cilantro leaves (optional)

Preheat oven to 300°F. Wrap tortillas in foil. Bake 10 minutes or until softened and heated through. Meanwhile, combine bean dip and water. Heat oil in large skillet over medium-high heat until hot. Add zucchini and onions. Cook and stir until zucchini is crisp-tender; stir in bean dip mixture and tomatillo salsa. Fill tortillas evenly with zucchini mixture. Roll up tortillas; place on 6 serving plates. Top with salsa. Serve hot with lettuce. Garnish with cilantro, if desired.

Makes 6 servings

50

Pinto Bean & Zucchini Burrito

Primavera Strudel

4½ teaspoons olive oil
1 small onion, chopped
2 cloves garlic, minced
8 ounces thin asparagus,
   cut diagonally into
   ¾-inch pieces
1 red bell pepper, cut into
   julienne strips
1 cup frozen peas, thawed
½ teaspoon salt
½ teaspoon black pepper
1 container (15 ounces)
   ricotta cheese
¾ cup grated Asiago
   cheese
⅓ cup chopped fresh basil
1 egg, lightly beaten
10 frozen phyllo dough
   sheets, thawed
½ cup butter, melted
6 tablespoons dry bread
   crumbs, divided

1. Heat oil in large skillet over medium heat. Add onion and garlic; cook and stir 5 minutes. Add asparagus and bell pepper; cook and stir 6 to 7 minutes or until crisp-tender. Stir in peas, salt and black pepper. Remove from heat; let cool to room temperature.

2. Preheat oven to 375°F. Combine ricotta, Asiago, basil and egg in large bowl; mix well. Stir in vegetable mixture.

3. Line 15×10-inch jelly-roll pan with foil; set aside.

4. Place 1 sheet phyllo on work surface. (Keep remaining phyllo covered with plastic wrap and damp towel to keep from drying out.) Lightly brush phyllo with butter. Top with second phyllo sheet. Lightly brush with butter and sprinkle with 1 tablespoon bread crumbs. Place third phyllo sheet over crumbs; lightly brush with butter; sprinkle with 1 tablespoon bread crumbs. Top with fourth phyllo sheet and 1 tablespoon bread crumbs. Place fifth phyllo sheet over bread crumbs and brush with butter.

5. Spoon ½ of ricotta mixture along 1 short side of phyllo in 3-inch-wide strip, beginning 1½ inches in from short side and leaving 2-inch border on long sides. Fold long sides in over filling; lightly brush folded edges with butter. Starting at filled side, gently roll up, jelly-roll style, forming strudel. Lightly brush strudel with butter. Transfer to prepared pan, seam side down.

6. Repeat process with remaining ingredients to make second strudel. Bake strudels 25 to 28 minutes or until golden brown. Cool 10 minutes before slicing. Serve warm.

Makes 8 servings

Primavera Strudel

Veggie Calzones

1½ cups BIRDS EYE® frozen
   Farm Fresh Mixtures
   Broccoli, Red Peppers,
   Onions & Mushrooms
½ cup ricotta cheese
½ cup shredded mozzarella
   cheese
¼ cup grated Parmesan
   cheese
1 teaspoon dried Italian
   seasoning
¼ teaspoon pepper
1 pound fresh pizza dough
   or thawed frozen bread
   dough
1 egg, beaten

• Preheat oven to 425°F. Rinse
vegetables under warm water
to thaw; drain well and pat
gently with paper towel.

• In medium bowl, combine
vegetables, cheeses, Italian
seasoning and pepper.

• Divide dough into 4 pieces.
Roll out each piece into 6-inch
circle. Spoon ¼ of vegetable
mixture over ½ of each circle,
leaving ½-inch border. Moisten
edge of dough with water; fold
dough over filling to form half
circle. Pinch edges well to seal.
Cut several slits in top of
dough; brush with egg.

• Place on greased baking
sheet and bake 12 to 14
minutes or until golden brown.
Makes 4 servings

Breakfast Burritos with Tomato-Basil Topping

1 large tomato, diced
2 teaspoons finely chopped
   basil (or ½ teaspoon
   dried basil leaves)
1 medium potato, peeled
   and shredded (about
   1 cup)
¼ cup chopped onion
2 teaspoons
   FLEISCHMANN'S®
   70% Corn Oil Spread
1 cup EGG BEATERS®
   Healthy Real Egg
   Substitute
⅛ teaspoon ground black
   pepper
4 (8-inch) flour tortillas,
   warmed
⅓ cup shredded reduced-
   fat Cheddar cheese

In small bowl, combine tomato
and basil; set aside. In large
nonstick skillet, over medium
heat, sauté potato and onion in
spread until tender. Pour Egg
Beaters® into skillet; sprinkle
with pepper. Cook, stirring
occasionally until mixture is set.

Divide egg mixture evenly
between tortillas; top with
cheese. Fold tortillas over egg
mixture. Top with tomato
mixture.   *Makes 4 servings*

Prep Time: 15 minutes
Cook Time: 25 minutes

Veggie Calzone

Potato Pierogi

4 medium potatoes (about
1½ pounds), peeled
and quartered
⅓ cup milk
2 tablespoons butter or
margarine
2 tablespoons chopped
green onion
1 teaspoon salt, divided
½ teaspoon ground white
pepper, divided
2¾ cups all-purpose flour
1 cup sour cream
1 egg
1 egg yolk
1 tablespoon vegetable oil
Melted butter, cooked
crumbled bacon or
sour cream (optional)
Fresh rue sprigs for
garnish

1. To prepare filling, place potatoes in medium saucepan; cover with water. Bring to a boil over high heat. Reduce heat to medium. Simmer, uncovered, 20 minutes or until tender. Drain; return potatoes to saucepan.

2. Mash potatoes with potato masher. Stir in milk, butter, green onion, ½ teaspoon salt and ¼ teaspoon pepper. (Potato mixture should be quite stiff.) Cool.

3. To prepare pierogi dough, combine flour, sour cream, egg, egg yolk, oil, and remaining ½ teaspoon salt and ¼ teaspoon pepper in medium bowl; mix well.

4. Turn out dough onto lightly floured surface. Knead dough 3 to 5 minutes or until soft and pliable, but not sticky. Let rest, covered, 10 minutes.

5. Divide dough in half. Roll out each half into 13-inch-diameter circle on lightly floured surface with lightly floured rolling pin. Cut out dough with 2½-inch-round cutter.

6. Place 1 rounded teaspoon potato filling in center of each dough circle. Moisten edges of circles with water and fold in half; press edges firmly to seal.

7. Bring 4 quarts lightly salted water in Dutch oven to a boil over high heat. Cook pierogi in batches 10 minutes. Remove with slotted spoon to serving dish.

8. Drizzle butter over pierogi, top with bacon or serve with sour cream, if desired. Garnish, if desired.

Makes about 5 dozen

Potato Pierogi

French Breakfast Crêpes

1 cup all-purpose flour
1 cup skim milk
⅔ cup EGG BEATERS®
   Healthy Real Egg
   Substitute
1 tablespoon
   FLEISCHMANN'S®
   70% Corn Oil Spread,
   melted

In medium bowl, combine flour, milk, Egg Beaters® and spread; let stand 30 minutes.

Heat lightly greased 8-inch nonstick skillet or crêpe pan over medium-high heat. Pour in scant ¼ cup batter, tilting pan to cover bottom. Cook for 1 to 2 minutes; turn and cook for 30 seconds to 1 minute more. Place on waxed paper. Stir batter and repeat to make 10 crêpes. Fill with desired fillings or use in recipes calling for prepared crêpes.

Makes 10 crêpes

Prep Time: 10 minutes
Cook Time: 40 minutes

Strawberry Yogurt Crêpes: *In medium bowl, combine 1 pint low fat vanilla yogurt and 2 tablespoons orange-flavored liqueur or orange juice; reserve ½ cup. Stir 2 cups sliced strawberries into remaining yogurt mixture. Spoon ¼ cup strawberry mixture down center of each prepared crêpe; roll up. Top with reserved yogurt mixture.*

Blueberry Crêpes: *In medium saucepan, combine 2 cups fresh or frozen blueberries, ⅓ cup water, 2 teaspoons lemon juice and 2 teaspoons cornstarch. Cook over medium-high heat, stirring frequently until mixture thickens and begins to boil. Reduce heat; simmer 1 minute. Chill. Spoon 2 tablespoons low fat vanilla yogurt down center of each prepared crêpe; roll up. Top with blueberry sauce.*

Strawberry Yogurt Crêpe

Spinach Phyllo Bundle

1 tablespoon vegetable oil
¼ cup finely chopped onion
1 package (10 ounces) frozen chopped spinach, thawed and well drained
1 package (10 ounces) frozen artichoke hearts, thawed and cut into quarters
1 cup small broccoli flowerets, steamed
2 red bell peppers, seeded, cut into cubes and roasted
1 cup (4 ounces) shredded Monterey Jack cheese
¾ cup grated Parmesan cheese
1 cup minced fresh cilantro
¼ teaspoon ground nutmeg
6 to 8 tablespoons butter or margarine, melted
12 sheets frozen phyllo dough, thawed
Fresh cilantro for garnish

1. Heat oil in large skillet over medium heat until hot. Add onion; cook and stir 3 minutes. Add spinach; cook 5 minutes or until spinach is dry.

2. Add artichoke hearts, broccoli and bell peppers to skillet; cook and stir 2 to 3 minutes or until heated through. Remove from heat; stir in cheeses, cilantro and nutmeg.

3. Preheat oven to 375°F. Brush 12-inch pizza pan with butter. Unroll phyllo dough. Cover with plastic wrap and damp, clean kitchen towel to prevent phyllo from drying out.

4. Lay 1 sheet phyllo dough on clean surface; brush with butter. Fold crosswise in half and place on pizza pan. Brush with butter.

5. Repeat with remaining phyllo dough sheets and butter, arranging phyllo in pinwheel fashion on pan.

6. Spoon spinach mixture onto phyllo, making a mound 8 inches in diameter. Bring up several phyllo dough sheets at a time over filling; repeat with remaining phyllo dough. Brush with butter.

7. Bake 40 to 45 minutes or until golden brown. Let stand 5 to 10 minutes; cut into wedges. Garnish with cilantro, if desired.
Makes 6 to 8 servings

Spinach Phyllo Bundle

Acknowledgments

The publishers would like to thank the companies and organizations listed below for the use of their recipes in this publication.

Alpine Lace Brands, Inc.

Birds Eye®

Bob Evans®

EGG BEATERS® Healthy Real Egg Substitute

GREY POUPON® Mustard

Guiltless Gourmet®

Lawry's® Foods Inc.

National Turkey Federation

Nestlé USA

Newman's Own, Inc.®

Reckitt & Colman Inc.

USA Rice Federation

Index

SPANISH

for

SCHOOL PERSONNEL

PATRICIA RUSH
Ventura College

PATRICIA HOUSTON
Pima Community College

CLIFF RODRIGUES
Education Consultant
Ventura County Superintendent of Schools Office
Ventura, California

Prentice
Hall

UPPER SADDLE RIVER, NEW JERSEY 07458

Library of Congress Cataloging-in-Publication Data

Rush, Patricia, 1948-
    Spanish for school personnel / Patricia Rush, Patricia Houston.—1st ed.
      p. cm—(Spanish at work series)
    ISBN 0-13-140134-3 (alk. paper)
    1. Spanish language—Conversation and phrase books (for school employees)
    I. Houston, Patricia, 1948- II. Title. III. Series.

PC4120.S34R87 2003
468.3'4'02407—dc22   2003020927

PUBLISHER: *Phil Miller*
SENIOR ACQUISITIONS EDITOR: *Bob Hemmer*
ASSISTANT DIRECTOR OF PRODUCTION: *Mary Rottino*
EDITORIAL/PRODUCTION SUPERVISION: *Nancy Stevenson*
EDITORIAL ASSISTANT: *Pete Ramsey*
PREPRESS AND MANUFACTURING MANAGER: *Nick Sklitsis*
PREPRESS AND MANUFACTURING BUYER: *Brian Mackey*
INTERIOR DESIGN: *Javier Amador-Peña*
FORMATTING AND ART MANAGER: *Guy Ruggiero*
COMPOSITION/FULL-SERVICE PROJECT MANAGEMENT:
  Natalie Hansen and Sue Katkus, PreMediaONE, A Black Dot Group Company
ILLUSTRATOR: *Steve Mannion*

Photo Acknowledgments appear on p. A-26, which constitute a continuation of the copyright page.

This book was set in 11/14 Bembo typeface by Black Dot and was printed and bound by Courier–Westford. The cover was printed by Coral Graphics.

© 2004 by Pearson Education, Inc.
Upper Saddle River, NJ 07458

Printed in the United States of America
10 9 8 7 6 5 4 3 2 1

ISBN 0-13-140134-3

Pearson Education LTD., *London*
Pearson Education Australia PTY, Limited, *Sydney*
Pearson Education Singapore, Pte. Ltd.
Pearson Education North Asia Ltd., *Hong Kong*
Pearson Education Canada, Ltd., *Toronto*
Pearson Educación de Mexico, S.A. de C.V.
Pearson Education—Japan, *Tokyo*
Pearson Education Malaysia, Pte. Ltd.
Pearson Education, *Upper Saddle River*, New Jersey

A Bud y a Bob: Maestros de aventuras…

—we LOVE you guys!

el presente - o to ue stemchanging			
poder	jugar	morir	costar
puedo	**juego**	devolver	volver
puedes	**juegas**	recordar	doler
puede	**juega**	dormir	llover
podemos	**jugamos**	encontrar	probar
podéis	**jugáis**	almorzar	morder
pueden	**juegan**	acordar	mover
		colgar	resolver

spanishspanish.com

Preface

Purpose

One of the fastest-growing markets for Spanish-language instruction through-out the country is the field of occupational or vocational courses either for contract training within organizations or for general student access as a regularly scheduled class. This series of materials, *Spanish at Work,* is designed to allow colleges to create and deliver pragmatic, "real-world" language and culture training programs so that students can master "need-to-know" language. It is designed for students without previous Spanish study, at the beginning level, but it also works well to reinforce background knowledge already in place for intermediate level students. *Spanish for School Personnel* is the third of this series, following *Spanish for Health Care* and *Spanish for Business.* Students, whether professionals already working in the field or career/goal-oriented students in an occupational training program, are presented key vocabulary in a comprehensible-input format, focusing on easily mastered core expressions. Art, realia, photographs and brief dialogues reinforce needed terms, supported by concise grammar explanations. In class, students will practice communicative survival using key vocabulary essential to each context to enable them to utilize their Spanish in the real world at work.

Highlights of the Program

Spanish for School Personnel has ten chapters plus a brief preliminary lesson and two review chapters. Each lesson has two modules, each with a vocabulary segment and a grammar segment using the context-appropriate vocabulary. The lessons end with the vocabulary list and synthesis activities combining listening, speaking, reading and writing. All exercises move from mechanical to production-oriented, following the logical progression of language acquisition. The final section, *Algo más,* features a culturally informative reading and sends the student out to the real world to look for material tied to the theme of the chapter.

Organization of the Text

- **Vocabulary presentation:** Each of the two modules presents key vocabulary by means of art, realia, photographs, and brief dialogues. The inclusion of two separate spreads in each module allows for manageable amounts of easily mastered, core expressions pertinent to each occupational area.

- **Grammar approach:** Grammar practice is embedded automatically in context, not called out as mastery exercises. In class, students will focus on communicative survival using basic vocabulary essential to the topic to enable them to utilize their Spanish in the real world of their job environment. Concise grammar explanations, two per module, are presented in "chunks."

- **Vocabulary summary:** Each module's vocabulary is listed by function—nouns, verbs, adjectives, and other expressions. The glossary at the end of the book lists the lesson in which the item was introduced, intended as a convenient reference, especially for preview/review.

- *Síntesis*: Skills and topics are interwoven at the end of each chapter into a series of skill-building and skill-chaining activities that bring together the chapter vocabulary, structures, and cultural content. In recognition of the increased interest in Applied Spanish courses across the country, each of the ten regular lessons concludes with a task-based module in which students use Spanish in a realistic, applied way. Modules focus on a variety of fields where students may be likely to seek their future or current careers. Art, articles, and other documents emphasize the usefulness and vitality of Spanish in today's world.

  A escuchar develops students' ability to understand spoken Spanish in a variety of authentic contexts.

  A conversar includes open-ended speaking activities based on naturally-occurring discourse situations. Students learn to express and discuss their own needs and interests.

  A leer introduces basic readings for students to become independent readers, able to understand the general meaning of a text as well as to extricate specific information from it.

  A escribir provides activities in which students learn to compose messages and memos, paragraphs and publicity announcements.

- *Algo más:* This section focuses on contemporary cultural issues related to the chapter theme. The *Ventana cultural* reading exposes the student to key information. A broad variety of contemporary topics is featured, appropriate to the lesson's context. *A buscar,* immediately following, then guides students to gather information to enhance their own connection to this topic.
  A conocer introduces students to prominent Hispanics succeeding in the occupational field and to in-depth cultural close-ups related to education.

Components

- Text

- Audio CD with available tapescript, including listening segments, dialogues, and vocabulary lists

- Instructor's Resource Manual, including tests

- Interactive, text-specific Website, including tests and links

For the student

Welcome! *Spanish at Work* has been designed for YOU to use in your daily work situation, improving your ability to interact with your students and their families. You'll find a user-friendly text, combining appropriate vocabulary and concise grammar explanations with realia from today's world to lead you into the real world of *Spanish for School Personnel.* We want you to be able to react to your daily job environment, meeting your needs with hands-on language and giving you enough to survive in the education area without loading you down with translation exercises. Our real-life context is intended to transfer directly to your daily "need-to-know" activities. We encourage you to jump right in and join us.

Acknowledgments

First, *gracias* to all who have helped us to bring ***Spanish for School Personnel*** into existence. While it is clear that core language courses continue to be the foundation of our profession, the demand for pragmatic, rapid-acquisition courses is exploding. We want to acknowledge our colleagues and our students who have shown us beyond a doubt the unquestionable need for this series. Their insight, support, and collaboration have been a powerful force in the creation of these texts.

We are grateful to the members of the Spanish teaching community for their invaluable comments and suggestions on everything from the sequence of material to the final versions of the lessons: Enrica J. Ardemagni, *Indiana University—Purdue University Indianapolis;* Roberto Bravo, *Texas Tech University;* Teresa H. Johnson, *Saint Louis University;* Dimitrios H. Karayiannis, *Southern Illinois University;* Patricia M. Lestrade, *Mississippi State University;* Krystyna P. Musik, *University of Delaware;* Julia Villaseñor, *Malone College.*

Our Prentice Hall partners enabled the vision to become reality and we are grateful. We offer special thanks to Phil Miller, Publisher; Bob Hemmer, Senior Acquisitions Editor; Nancy Stevenson, Production Editor; Pete Ramsey, Editorial Assistant; and Eileen Moran, Marketing Manager. Our appreciation extends to Natalie Hansen, Editorial Project Manager, and Sue Katkus, Project Manager, at PreMediaONE, A Black Dot Group Company.

Our developmental editor, Mariam Rohlfing, deserves more thanks than we can ever say. Her vision, language skill, organization, and attention to detail keep us focused on our task—she should be listed as a co-author!

We appreciate the expert input provided by Cliff Rodrigues, who read our manuscript to be sure we provided accurate information. A special thank you goes to Dr. Bettye Mashack and to Patricia McElroy for their guidance and to Peace Builders® for their enthusiastic participation.

We owe *besos y abrazos* to our families and friends for enduring our long hours, especially to Bud and Bob. An occasional dialogue is based on reality, so if you recognize yourself in any situation, we hope you like your portrait!

¡Por aquí, por favor!

Los saludos y las despedidas

El abecedario/el alfabeto

Los números

El calendario:
- los días de la semana
- los meses del año
- la fecha

Consejera

Los pronombres personales

Expresiones de cortesía

¡Bienvenidos! welcome

Buenos días, if you are reading this in the morning.

Buenas tardes, if you are reading this in the afternoon.

Buenas noches, if you are reading this after dark.

As a professional working in one of the many areas of education, you have recognized the growing need for basic Spanish on the job. This book will help you build a language bridge to your Spanish-speaking students, parents, and colleagues. Be aware that, because this text is geared to the use of Spanish in the workplace, we will emphasize language that reflects formal, professional relationships more than personal and familiar ones, unless we are focusing on children. The formality or informality of address is an extremely important aspect of the Spanish language and the variety of cultures it represents.

In this preliminary chapter, we will show you such basic—and critical—Spanish points as:

- Greetings, courtesies, and amenities,
- Pronunciation and listening strategies,
- Using *cog*nates (words that you can re*cog*nize from one language to the other),
- The important cultural courtesies implied in polite or formal address and informal address,
- And enough about days, months, and numbers so that you can *immediately* begin to make appointments, provide telephone numbers, and offer other basic services.

In addition, we will offer you some strategies to take the stress out of learning a new language and to make your study time efficient, productive—and even fun! The key to your success will be your willingness to practice and speak out loud without worrying about feeling silly and making mistakes. Mistakes are a very normal and natural part of learning a language. The more mistakes you allow yourself to make, the faster you will learn.

Ready? ¿Listos? ¡Vamos!

Los saludos y las despedidas

RECEPCIONISTA:	Buenas tardes. Me llamo Ángela. ¿Cómo se llama usted?
CLIENTE:	Me llamo Pablo Fernández.
RECEPCIONISTA:	Mucho gusto, señor Fernández.
CLIENTE:	Igualmente.

SECRETARIO:	Buenos días, señora. Soy Alejandro, el secretario del Sr. Vallejo. A sus órdenes.
MADRE:	Mucho gusto. Soy Claudia Móntez, madre de Cecilia y Marco.
SECRETARIO:	Es un placer.

RECEPCIONISTA:	Hola, Alejandro. ¿Cómo estás hoy?
SECRETARIO:	Regular. ¿Y tú, Ángela?
RECEPCIONISTA:	Muy bien, gracias. Nos vemos.
SECRETARIO:	Hasta luego.

- Use **Buenos días** usually before noon to say *Good morning,* before lunchtime in some regions; **Buenas tardes** until dark to say *Good afternoon,* and **Buenas noches** after dark to say *Good evening* or *Good night.*

- Both **usted** and **tú** mean *you.* In business settings, especially, it is important to show respect by using **usted**, unless addressing very close friends or children. Children show respect to adults by using the **usted** form.

- **Yo soy** followed by a name means *I am.* **Me llamo** followed by a name means *My name is …* (literally: *I call myself …*). Both are proper in making introductions.

- **Mucho gusto** *(it's a pleasure)* and **igualmente** *(likewise)* are courtesies, usually accompanied by the gesture of a handshake.

Para practicar

La fiesta de cóctel.　There are so many receptions and parties where you don't know anyone! Lift your imaginary martini glass or Perrier in the air and walk around the room, meeting as many of your colleagues (classmates) as possible. Follow the above dialogues for guidance, and don't forget the three steps:

1. the salutation, depending on the time of day
2. the exchange of names
3. the courtesy replies and handshake

When you sit down again, write down as many of the names as you can remember.

El abecedario/el alfabeto

Spanish forms words around vowel sounds, while English forms them around consonants. Mastering these five sounds will enable you to pronounce nearly any word. The vowel sounds in Spanish are short, precise, and clear, not drawn out as in English.

Las vocales		
A	(ah)	Open your mouth and say "**Ah**."
E	(eh)	P**e**t the dog.
I	(ee)	We have another m**ee**ting at thr**ee**.
O	(oh)	**Oh**, no, not another meeting!
U	(oo)	B**oo**, scared ya!

watch out!

¡OJO!

As in English, some letters change pronunciation in certain combinations. Note the following list:

C ca, co, cu, or c preceding consonant sound like (k). ce, ci sound like (s).

G ga, go, gu, or g preceding consonant sound like (g). *[g]* ge, gi sound like the Spanish **j**. *[h]*

R rolled or trilled when it is the first letter of a word, just like **RR**.

rr = erre

El abecedario

Letra	Nombre		Ejemplo
A	a		administradór
B	be		bicicléta
C	ce *[c]*		clase, cerveza
D	de *ge*		decisión
E	e *əqe*		educación
F	efe *[he]*		familia
G	ge *[he]*		gáto, génte *[hente]*
H	hache *[atʃe]*	*always silent*	humór
I	i *u*		idea
J	jota *[hɔta]*	*like English "h"*	julio
K	ka		kilo
L	ele *əʋe*		lección
M	eme		memoria
N	ene		número
Ñ	eñe	*"ny" sound*	señores
O	o		oficina
P	pe		profesor
Q	cu		quince *[v]*
R	ere, erre *əpe, əppe*		copiadora, radio, currículum
S	ese		servicios
T	te		tecnología
U	u	*small*	uniforme
V	ve (ve chica)	*"b" sound*	vacaciones
W	doble ve *əkure*		windsurf
X	equis *əkure*		excelente
Y	y griega *greek* *cema*		yate
Z	zeta	*"s" sound*	zoológico

- **Cognados:** As you read down the list of Spanish words on the right of the alphabet list, see how many you can recognize. Cognates are great tools to help you understand spoken and written Spanish.

Para practicar

A. Favor de contestar. Provide the appropriate information.

1. Which letter is always silent? *h*
2. Pronounce the difference between **n** and **ñ**. *n nj*
3. Which five letters form the basis for Spanish pronunciation? *vowels a, e, i, o, u*
4. Pronounce the five Spanish vowels.
5. What do you call words that you can recognize in two languages? *cognates*

B. Entre amigos. *between friends* Spell your name in Spanish, letter by letter, as a classmate writes it down. Check to see if it is correct. When it is, you write as your classmate spells his/her name. Note that it is extremely rare for Spanish speakers to "spell" words or names, as nearly everything is pronounced exactly as it is written!

MODELO: Jaime
    Jota-a-i-eme-e

C. Personas famosas. *famous* Continue taking turns spelling out the names of famous people to each other—in Spanish! See how many you can get right.

Los números

Is there anything in our lives that doesn't require numbers? Well, yes, but not that much. By learning a few basic numbers now, you will have the foundation for many lessons in Spanish. With just a few numbers, you can give and take telephone numbers or messages and work with math. Add a few days and months and you can plan your calendar. Two or three more words and you are telling time!

Here we go with numbers 1–15! As you read through these, remember to use the five Spanish vowel sounds as a pronunciation guide.

0	cero	4	cuatro	8	ocho *[ɔcho]*	12	doce
1	uno	5	cinco	9	nueve	13	trece
2	dos	6	seis	10	diez	14	catorce
3	tres	7	siete	11	once	15	quince

[kinse]

qu [k]
cu [kw]

Para practicar *count*

A. A contar. It's naptime in the kindergarten class and, as the teacher, you like to combine a little bit of number practice with the "siesta" to help the students relax. Have your students visualize counting sheep in the following patterns.

1. Count from 1 to 10 in Spanish.
2. Count from 1 to 10 by 2s (2, 4, 6, etc.).
3. Count backwards from 10 to 1.
4. Count from 1 to 15.
5. Count backwards from 15 to 1.
6. Count by 3s from 1 to 15 (3, 6, 9, etc.).

with a friend

B. Con un amigo. Time for some arithmetic! Now, you can practice some basic addition. One of you will make up a simple arithmetic problem and await a response. Then switch roles—five times. Be careful not to add numbers above 15 yet!

> **MODELO:** E1: *5 y (and) 5 (cinco y cinco)*
> E2: *10 (diez)*

more

Más números

After 15, numbers in Spanish are formed by addition. For example, 16 is the sum of **diez y seis,** and often it is written just that way. Also common is the one-word alternative for numbers from 16 to 29. There is no one-word alternative after 30.

modern way

16	diez y seis	o	dieciséis
17	diez y siete	o	diecisiete
18	diez y ocho	o	dieciocho
19	diez y nueve	o	diecinueve
20	veinte		
21	veinte y uno	o	veintiuno
22	veinte y dos	o	veintidós
23	veinte y tres	o	veintitrés
24	veinte y cuatro	o	veinticuatro
25	veinte y cinco	o	veinticinco
26	veinte y seis	o	veintiséis
27	veinte y siete	o	veintisiete
28	veinte y ocho	o	veintiocho
29	veinte y nueve	o	veintinueve
30	treinta		
31	treinta y uno		

When counting things or objects in Spanish, the word hay (sounds like "eye", not "hey") can be used to indicate "there is" or "there are." Both questions "is there?" and "are there?" are simply stated with ¿Hay...? For example:

Hay siete días en una semana.   *There are seven days in a week.*
Hay una clase aquí.   *There is a class here.*
¿**Hay** una clase por aquí?   *Is there a class around here?*
¿**Hay** clases por aquí?   *Are there classes around here?*

Para practicar

A. ¡A contar!   Count these patterns to help relax during rest hour.

I. Count from 11 to 30.
2. Count backwards from 30 to 20.
3. Count from 1 to 30 by 5s.
4. Count from 1 to 30 by 2s.
5. Count the number of people in the room with you right now.

B. ¿Cuántos? *— How many?*   Oops! A first-grader accidentally hit an older student in the head with a kickball on the playground. Check to see if the student is alert and can answer the following questions—in Spanish.

MODELO: E1: *How many hours are there in a day?*
            E2: *Hay veinticuatro.*

I. How many days are there in a week?
2. How many minutes are there in a half hour?
3. How many days are there in September?
4. How many days are there in February (usually)?
5. How many female students are in your Spanish class?
6. How many male students are in your Spanish class?

¡Y más números!

Learning more numbers may *seem* difficult, but they are really easy. Pretend you need them for math lessons. The bigger the better!

Los números 40–100

40	cuarenta	70	setenta
41	cuarenta y uno	80	ochenta
42	cuarenta y dos, etc.	90	noventa
50	cincuenta	100	cien
60	sesenta		

Remember, there is no one-word spelling alternative for numbers after 29.

Para practicar count

A. ¡A contar! You are teaching your students about bank accounts. Read the following amounts you have in a savings account and ask students to give the balance that is $5.00 dollars more.

MODELO: $30.

¿Treinta? No, ¡treinta y cinco!

100 cien

1.	25	**4.**	50	**7.**	80
2.	30	**5.**	60	**8.**	90
3.	40	**6.**	70	**9.**	95

B. ¡Menos! LESS You're having a "guess-how-many-buttons-are-in-the-bottle" game with your class. For each number that you suggest, a student yells out a number that is five less.

MODELO: 100

¿Cien? No, ¡noventa y cinco!

1.	95	**5.**	73	**8.**	24
2.	80	**6.**	34	**9.**	17
3.	66	**7.**	59	**10.**	83
4.	41				

El calendario: Los días de la semana

d
[d] – in initial
[ð] between vowels

There are seven days in the week #1 on

Hay siete días en la semana:

el lunes	*Monday*	**el viernes**	*Friday*
el martes	*Tuesday*	**el sábado**	*Saturday*
el miércoles	*Wednesday*	**el domingo**	*Sunday*
el jueves	*Thursday*		

- Hispanic calendars often use Monday as the first day of the week.
- To say *on* a day, use **el** or **los.**

No hay clase **el** lunes.   *There is no class on Monday.*
No hay clase **los** lunes.   *There is no class on Mondays.*

- Days of the week are not capitalized in Spanish unless they begin a sentence or stand alone as distinct words.
- To ask what day it is, use **¿Qué día es hoy?**
- To answer, use **Hoy es (martes).**

[handwritten: Wed Th]

lunes	martes	miércoles	jueves	viernes	sábado	domingo
						1
2	3	4	5	6 *[trabajo]*	7	8
9	10	11	12	13	14	15
16	17	18	19	20	21	22
23	24	25	26	27	28	29
30	31					

[handwritten: viernes ↓ more like b or v?]

Para practicar

A. Los días.   Evenings and weekends you and another teacher volunteer on the local **homework hotline**. For the next month you are responsible for Wednesdays through Sundays. Use this calendar to say if you work—**Trabajo**—or don't work—**No trabajo**—on the following days.

MODELO: el dos
[handwritten: on 2 is]
El dos es lunes. No trabajo.

1. el quince   **3.** el cinco   **5.** el diecisiete
2. el veintiuno   **4.** el treinta   **6.** el seis

B. Números.   Here's a list of the days you have to work on the hotline. Use the calendar to say and write the numbers of the dates in Spanish.

1. El *cuatro*, el _once_, el _dieciocho_, el _vienticinco_ y el _____ son miércoles.   *[Wed]*

2. El _siete_, el _catorce_, el _vientiuno_ y el _vientinueve_ son sábados.   *[Sat]*

3. El _seis_, el _trece_, el _viento_ y el _vientisiete_ son viernes.   *[friday]*

4. El _cinco_, el _doce_, el _diecinueve_ *[vientiseis]* y el _____ son jueves.   *[Th.]*

[handwritten: → couples]
C. En parejas.   You are both in charge of making sure the hotline is covered next week Monday through Saturday. Decide which one of you will work which days and then make a list of the dates you are on and off. Use a current calendar for help.

MODELO: E1: *No trabajo el lunes.*
            E2: *Sí trabajo el lunes.*

Los meses del año

Most of the months are cognates. As with days of the week, only use capital letters with the months if they begin a sentence.

Hay doce meses en el año: *There are twelve months in the year*

enero	*January*	**mayo**	*May*	**septiembre**	*September*
febrero	*February*	**junio**	*June*	**octubre**	*October*
marzo	*March*	**julio**	*July*	**noviembre**	*November*
abril	*April*	**agosto**	*August*	**diciembre**	*December*

for practice

Para practicar

Festival days

A. Los días festivos. As a receptionist in a "year-round" elementary school, you like to keep the office appropriately decorated for major events and holidays. Write in the month—or months—when you would use the following decorating themes.

1. Santa Claus   *diciembre*
2. graduations   *junio*
3. the Great Pumpkin   *octubre*
4. fireworks and flags   *julio*
5. New Year's   *enero*
6. valentines and cupids   *febrero*

Birthdays

B. Fiesta de cumpleaños. ¡Feliz cumpleaños! Circulate among your classmates and find out who else was born in the same month as you. Get them to sign next to the month. Then, report back to the class how many students you found.

MODELO: *¿Febrero? Firma, por favor.* — *signature* *Hay cinco estudiantes con cumpleaños en febrero.*

enero	
febrero	
marzo	
abril	
mayo	
junio	
julio	
agosto	
septiembre	
octubre	
noviembre	
diciembre	

(handwritten margin notes: in initial position [b] / in transition from b v / after a vowel – brushed / in initial position d [d] / between vowels [ð])

La fecha

To ask what the date is, use: **¿Cuál es la fecha de hoy?** or **¿Qué fecha es hoy?**

Use the following format to answer: **Hoy es** (día), **el** (número) **de** (mes).

Hoy es lunes, el 24 de julio. *Today is Monday, the 24th of July.*

While ordinal number **primero** is used for the first of the month in many places, some regions will use **uno**. All other dates are given in cardinal numbers.

El primero de enero/el uno de enero   *January 1ˢᵗ*
El dos de enero   *January 2ⁿᵈ*

Para practicar

A. Días feriados. Your district superintendent's office has asked you to block the following days on the calendar because all regular and after-hours offices will be closed. Write a memo to your co-workers telling them exactly what days they will have off. Use a current calendar to see what day each date falls on.

MODELO: 1/1
       Sábado, el primero de enero

1. 15/1
2. 12/2
3. 27/3
4. 4/7
5. 2/9
6. 31/10

B. Más cumpleaños. Find again the people in your class who were born in the same month as you were. Then find out the rest of the date to see if any of them matches yours exactly. If no one was born in the same month as you, use a family member's birthday.

MODELO: E1: *¿Cuál es la fecha de su cumpleaños?*
           E2: *El 14 de febrero.*

¡OJO!

Unlike English, Spanish retains the format of day first, then month when writing the date in digits:

el dos de enero de 2004 ⇒ **2/1/04** in Spanish, not *1/2/04* as in English.

Los pronombres personales

Use a subject pronoun to tell who or what is doing an action. Subject pronouns can also express the familiarity or formality of relationships. Professional relationships in Spanish-speaking cultures require the courtesy of the formal term of address (**usted** and **ustedes**) to say *you*, while relationships among friends and family use the informal terms of address (**tú** for the singular form and, in Spain, **vosotros/as** for the plural form). In the professional context of education, our focus will be on using the more formal forms, unless we are focusing on communication with children.

The subject pronouns are:

Singular (one person)		Plural (more than one person)	
yo	*I*	**nosotros/as**	*we*
tú	*you (informal)*	**(vosotros/as)**	*you—plural (informal, Spain)*
usted (Ud./Vd.)	*you (formal)*	**ustedes (Uds./Vds.)**	*you—plural*
él	*he*	**ellos**	*they*
ella	*she*	**ellas**	*they (fem.)*

- Use nosotr**as** *(we)* if referring to an all-female group. In Spanish, if the group is all male or mixed male and female, the masculine form is used, in this case, nosotr**os.**
- Use **tú** *(informal),* **usted** *(formal),* or **ustedes** *(plural)* to mean *you* when talking *to* people.
- Use **él** *(he),* **ella** *(she),* **ellos** *(they, all masculine, or mixed),* or **ellas** *(they, feminine)* when talking *about* people.
- Subject pronouns are not necessary in Spanish as the verb form indicates the subject. You will find them used in the early lessons of this book, and then omitted unless included for emphasis or clarity.

Para practicar

A. ¿Recuerda usted? Answer the following questions about subject pronouns.

1. What information does the subject pronoun supply?
2. In a professional relationship, would you be more likely to express the subject *you* with **tú** or **usted?**
3. What subject pronoun would you use to address more than one person as *you* in most regions, whether the relationship is formal or informal?

B. ¿Quiénes? *Who* Which subject pronoun from the list above would you use in the following situations?

MODELO: You are talking about two students (two possibilities)
ellos or *ellas*

1. You are talking *about* yourself.
2. You are talking *to* an older man.
3. You are talking *about* a co-worker's daughter.
4. You are talking *about* two school board members (two possibilities).
5. You are talking *to* two school board members.
6. You are talking *about* yourself and a friend.
7. You are talking *about* the President of the United States.
8. You are talking *to* a 7-year-old student.

C. ¡Ahora en español! *Now in Spanish* Change the following subjects to subject pronouns.

MODELO: *Usted y su amigo son inteligentes.*
Ustedes son inteligentes.

1. *Elena y María son cómicas.*
2. *Susana y yo somos secretarios.* — male nosotros
3. *El director y su secretaria son dinámicos.* ellos
4. *El asistente es perfeccionista.* perfectionist él
5. *El muchacho es rebelde.*
6. *Usted y sus amigos son inteligentes.* ustedes

Expresiones de cortesía

Expression of courtesy.

Use these expressions of courtesy to help establish good relations with Spanish-speaking colleagues.

A sus órdenes.	*At your service; may I help you?*
Por favor.	*Please.*
Gracias.	*Thank you.*
De nada.	*You're welcome.*
No hay de qué.	*You're welcome.*
Con permiso.	*Excuse me.* (cut in the line, breaking in front of) May I?
Perdón.	*Pardon me.* (stepped on a person's foot)

- **Con permiso** is primarily used *before* an action—leaving a room, making your way through a crowd, getting up from a table, or interrupting a conversation.
- **Perdón** is usually used *after* the action is complete—if you have accidentally bumped or jostled someone. des culpa

Para practicar
for practice *what do you say?*

A. ¿Qué dice usted?   As a receptionist in a busy school office, you interact with people all day long. Give the expression of courtesy that you would use in each of the following situations.

MODELO: a parent comes to your desk
A sus órdenes.

1. A co-worker brings you a home-grown rose.
2. You ask a new student to fill out papers.
3. You bump into another colleague behind the crowded desk.
4. You must interrupt the principal's meeting for an urgent phone call.
5. A parent thanks you for your time and help.
6. You have to leave a meeting early to attend to a student who is waiting.

con permiso

Vocabulario — *Greetings*

Saludos y contestaciones — *replies*

bien	*well*	**¿Cómo está Ud.?**	*How are you? (formal)*
bienvenidos	*welcome*	**¿Cómo estás?**	*How are you? (familiar)*
buenas noches	*good evening, good night*	**hola**	*hello, hi*
buenas tardes	*good afternoon*	**mal**	*not well*
buenos días	*good morning*	**regular**	*so-so*

Presentaciones — *presentation*

¿Cómo se llama Ud.?	*What is your name? (formal)*	**igualmente**	*likewise*
¿Cómo te llamas?	*What is your name? (familiar)*	**Me llamo …**	*My name is …*
es un placer	*it's a pleasure*	**mucho gusto**	*pleased/nice to meet you*

Despedidas — *farewells*

adiós	*good-bye*	**hasta luego**	*see you later*

Expresiones de cortesía

a sus órdenes	*at your service; may I help you?*	**gracias**	*thank you*
con permiso	*excuse me*	**no hay de qué**	*you're welcome*
de nada	*you're welcome*	**perdón**	*pardon me*
		por favor	*please*

can we reply equalmente to both

es un placer
mucho gusto

stress?

Los pronombres de sujeto

él	*he*	tú	*you (familiar)*
ella	*she*	usted	*you (formal)*
ellos/as	*they*	ustedes	*you (plural)*
nosotros/as	*we*	yo	*I*

[handwritten grid: yo | nosotros/as ; tú/usted | ustedes ; él/ella | ellos/as]

Los días de la semana

¿Qué día es hoy?	*What day is today?*	miércoles	*Wednesday*
domingo	*Sunday*	jueves	*Thursday*
lunes	*Monday*	viernes	*Friday*
martes	*Tuesday*	sábado	*Saturday*

[handwritten: lunes, martes, miércoles, jueves, viernes, sábado, domingo]

[handwritten French: LUNDI, MARDI, MERCREDI, JEUDI, VENDREDI, SAMDI, DIMANCHE]

Los meses del año

el calendario	*calendar*	mayo	*May*
¿Cuál es la fecha de hoy?	*What's today's date?*	junio	*June*
		julio	*July*
¿Qué fecha es hoy?	*What's today's date?*	agosto	*August*
		septiembre	*September*
enero	*January*	octubre	*October*
febrero	*February*	noviembre	*November*
marzo	*March*	diciembre	*December*
abril	*April*		

[handwritten: Which; ¿? ; 7 8 9 10]

Personas

el/la amigo/a	*friend*
el/la asistente	*assistant*
la clase	*class*
la madre	*mother*
el/la muchacho/a	*boy/girl*
el/la secretario/a	*secretary*

Otras expresiones

cómico/a	*comical*
muy	*very*
soy	*I am*

[handwritten: Yo soy]

¡OJO! Don't forget to study **los números 0–100** and **el abecedario!**

[handwritten: femme, homme]

LECCIÓN 1

Let's go to school

Vamos a la escuela

Módulo 1
- La inscripción
- Telling time: *La hora*
- Los maestros y las clases
- Introducing and describing yourself and others: *Ser* + *adjetivos*

Módulo 2
- Para conocernos
- Asking for information: *Las preguntas*
- En la clase
- Descriptions: *Los artículos: género y número*

Síntesis
- A escuchar
- A conversar
- A leer
- A escribir

Consejera

counselor

Algo más — *enrichment section*
- Ventana cultural: Si usted no habla español...
- A buscar
- A conocer: Bilingual education vs. English-only immersion programs

Módulo I

La inscripción *(registration)*

¡Feliz año (escolar) nuevo! Bienvenidos a la escuela Menlo Park

OFICINA DE LA DIRECTORA
Patricia McCant

la recepcionista

Formulario de inscripción
Distrito Escolar Sesabe

Fecha de hoy <u>21 enero</u>   Escuela primaria _____   Grado <u>2, 3</u>

Nombre del estudiante: <u>Yáñez Durán</u>   <u>Elena</u>   <u>María</u>
                               Apellidos   Nombre   Inicial

Domicilio <u>1449 E. Fresno</u>   <u>Sesabe</u>   <u>AZ</u>   <u>85745</u>
               Número y calle   Ciudad   Estado   Código postal

Teléfono del domicilio <u>501-325-3020</u>

Sexo ☐ 1. Hombre   **Fecha de nacimiento** <u>8/17/98</u>   **Edad** <u>5 años</u>
    ☒ 2. Mujer   Mes Día Año

Lugar de nacimiento <u>Puebla</u>   <u>México</u>
                           Estado   País

Preferencia de grupo:

☐ Blanco (no de origen hispano)   ☐ Negro (no de origen hispano)
☒ Hispano   ☐ Nativo Americano   Tribu _____
☐ Asiático

Idioma materno del estudiante

☐ Inglés   ☒ Español   ☐ Otro

(Handwritten annotations:)
escuela
estudiante
(they can't say school → eschool
steve → esteve

office of the principal

Registration
(Name.
tradition - Father last - Mother last)

read in pairs
Masculino y also
Feminino
Mil novicientos noventa y ocho
den
lenguage
[lengwahe]
20 Thousand verds in 20 minutes - Kynumb

Dirección
Número y calle — yhuya
de casa
Age
Place
X
(etnicidad)
language — mother tongue
Tribe (for Nat. Am)
Dad's — Mom's maiden
State

univercidad
actividad -ity

[handwritten: How do you say?]

A. ¿Cómo se dice? Look back at the form and tell what question the following information answers.

MODELO: Yáñez Durán   *apellidos*

1. (501) 325–3020
2. 1449 E. Fresno Ave.
3. Tucson, Arizona 85747
4. Hispano
5. 9/17/1998
6. 5 años

B. Entrevista. One of you is the receptionist in the school office; the other is the parent of a new student. Complete the following interview, then switch roles.

1. ¿Apellido(s)? *[handwritten: last name]*
2. ¿Nombre(s)? *[handwritten: first]*
3. ¿Dirección? *[handwritten: adress]*
4. ¿Teléfono del domicilio?
5. ¿Grupo étnico?
6. ¿Su fecha de nacimiento? *[handwritten: birthday]*

En la oficina de la nueva escuela

La recepcionista de la oficina habla con la madre de una estudiante nueva, Elena.

RECEPCIONISTA:	Buenas tardes. A sus órdenes.
MADRE:	Buenas tardes. Necesito matricular a mi hija, Elena, en la escuela y tengo cita con la directora. *[handwritten: registrar = inscribir]*
RECEPCIONISTA:	Elena, bienvenida a tu nueva escuela. Señora, ¿cuál es su nombre?
MADRE:	Mis apellidos son Durán de Yáñez y mi nombre es Margarita. *[handwritten: of]*
RECEPCIONISTA:	¿A qué hora es su cita? *[handwritten: hour / husband]*
MADRE:	En diez minutos, a la una.
RECEPCIONISTA:	Excelente. Aquí está el formulario para llenar con la información personal de Elena.
MADRE:	¿Qué más necesitamos? *[handwritten: what is necessary]*
RECEPCIONISTA:	Tres documentos: el acta de nacimiento de Elena, el certificado de inmunizaciones y un documento con la dirección de su domicilio aquí. (A Elena) Elena, ¿celebramos tu primera visita a la escuela con un chocolate?

[handwritten margin note: What time is your appointment]

C. ¿Comprende usted? Give the following information based on the dialogue.

1. Los apellidos de la madre: _____.

2. El nombre de la estudiante: _____.

3. La recepcionista necesita 3 documentos: 1. _____,

2. _____ y 3. _____.

4. La recepcionista quiere dar _____ a Elena para celebrar.

D. En caso de emergencia. You have offered to be the emergency contact for a friend whose children are in elementary school. First, fill out the student's information based on a child that you know—if you don't know one, make up an imaginary one! Then fill in the emergency contact information with your personal (or made-up) information.

Tarjeta de emergencia

Apellidos del estudiante _____ Nombre _____

Fecha de nacimiento ____ Teléfono del domicilio _____

Domicilio _____ N° de apartamento ____ Código postal _____

Nombre completo del padre _____ Compañía _____

Nombre completo de la madre _____ Compañía _____

Nombre completo del tutor legal _____ Compañía _____

Persona responsable en caso de emergencia _____

Teléfono durante el día o celular _____ Relación _____

Preferencias de:

1. Médico a. Nombre _____ b. Número de teléfono _____

2. Dentista a. Nombre _____ b. Número de teléfono _____

3. Seguro médico (insurance) _____

En caso de enfermedad o accidente serio, doy mi consentimiento para proporcionarle atención médica a _____

Firma _____

the hour (tiempo = a time period)

Estructuras   *Telling time: La hora*

- To ask *What time is it?* use **¿Qué hora es?**
- Answer with: **Es la…** when saying one o'clock, or **Son las…** + the hour for all other hours.

  Es la una.   *It's one o'clock.*   **Son las** dos.   *It's two o'clock.*

- To tell how many minutes past the hour it is, add **y** + the number of minutes.

  Son las tres **y diez.**   *It's 3:10.*   Es la una **y cinco.**   *It's 1:05.*

- To tell how many minutes before the hour it is, use the next hour **menos** the number of minutes.

  Son las **tres menos cinco.**   *It's 2:55.*   Es la **una menos veinte.**   *It's 12:40.*

- For the half hour, use **y media** or **treinta.**

  Son las tres **y media** *or* Son las tres **y treinta.**   *It's 3:30.*

- For quarter hours, **cuarto** and **quince** are interchangeable.

  Son las tres menos **cuarto**   *It's a quarter to three (2:45).*
  or Son las tres menos **quince.**

(3:15) → Son las tres y cuarto
→ Son las tres y quince

- Other useful time-telling phrases are: **en punto** for *on the dot* or *sharp;* **de la mañana** for A.M., **de la tarde** for P.M. until dark, and **de la noche** for P.M. after dark. Use **el mediodía** for noon and **la medianoche** for midnight.

  La reunión es a las diez **en punto.**   *The meeting is at ten o'clock sharp.*
  Son las cuatro **de la tarde.**   *It's four P.M.*
  Es **el mediodía.**   *It's noon.*

de la madrugada (wee hour)

- To tell the time *at* which an event will take place, use **a las** or **a la** + the hour.

  ¿A qué hora es la cita? *at*   *At what time is the appointment?*
  La cita con el director es **a las once.**   *The appointment with the principal is at eleven.*

  Llego a la oficina **a la una.**   *I arrive at the office at one o'clock.*

- Official documents in Spanish—as at times in English—will often use a 24-hour clock (military time).

  1:00 A.M.   Es la **una** de la mañana.   *It is one A.M.*
  1:00 P.M.   Son **las trece** horas.   *It is thirteen hundred hours.*

Para practicar

A. ¿Qué hora es?   Tell what time it is now, according to the following digital clocks. If there is more than one way, give both.

MODELO: 6:30 A.M.

Son las seis y media de la mañana. Son las seis y treinta de la mañana.

1. 2:20 P.M.　　**3.** 12:00 A.M.　　**5.** 10:30 A.M.　　**7.** 12:45 P.M.

2. 8:55 P.M.　　**4.** 6:15 A.M.　　**6.** 1:20 P.M.　　**8.** 11:09 A.M.

B. Citas.　La señora Yáñez has called for an appointment to meet with the principal and fill out an application. Read to her the available appointment times listed below.

MODELO: 4:30 P.M.

Hay una cita a las cuatro y media de la tarde.

1. 10:15 A.M.　　**3.** 1:10 P.M.　　**5.** 9:00 A.M. sharp　　**7.** 12:00 P.M.

2. 2:40 P.M.　　**4.** 5:45 P.M.　　**6.** 12:30 P.M.　　**8.** 1:10 P.M.

C. ¿A qué hora?　*— At what time?*　The school principal also leads a busy life. Look at her agenda for today and tell at what time she will be in the following places.

MODELO:　En la fiesta de la Sra. Miller

Al mediodía. or *A las doce.*

6:00	
7:00	Ejercicio en el gimnasio　　*es a la*
8:10	Cafetería de la escuela — desayuno (breakfast) con los nuevos estudiantes
8:45	Reunión con el superintendente del distrito　*es a las nueve menos cuarto de la mañana*
12:00	Fiesta en la clase de la Sra. Miller　*es al mediodía*
1:15	Cita con el dentista　*es a la una y cuarto de la tarde*
2:25	Reunión de maestros en la cafetería
4:55	Conferencia telefónica con el personal médico del distrito
7:35	Teatro San Ramón con Miguel
10:00	Reservación en el restaurante Mosaico　*es a las diez de la noche*
11:30	Las noticias del día — televisión

1.　En la reunión con el superintendente

2.　En el consultorio del dentista

3.　En la cafetería con los estudiantes

4.　En el teatro San Ramón

5.　En el gimnasio de la escuela

6.　En la cafetería con los maestros

7.　En la clase de la Sra. Miller

8.　En una conferencia telefónica con el personal médico

Handwritten notes (right margin):

① Son las dos y treinta de la tarde

② Son las nueve menos cinco de la noche

③ de la doce en punto la medianoche

④ Son las seis y cuarto de la mañana

Módulo I

Los maestros y las clases

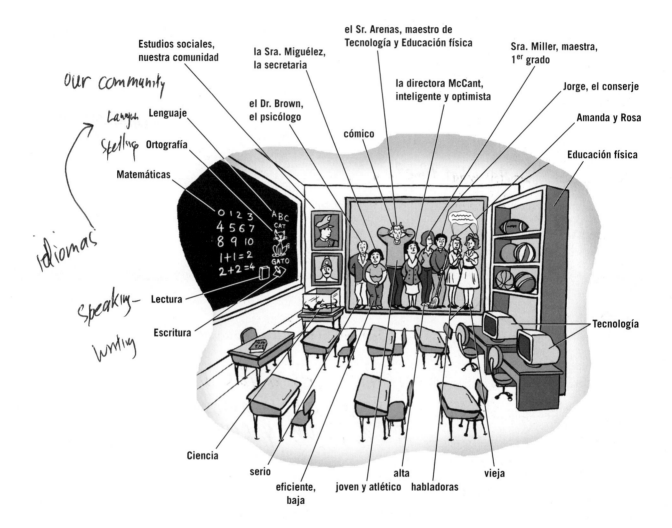

Estudios sociales, nuestra comunidad

la Sra. Miguélez, la secretaria

el Sr. Arenas, maestro de Tecnología y Educación física

Sra. Miller, maestra, 1er grado

la directora McCant, inteligente y optimista

Jorge, el conserje

Amanda y Rosa

el Dr. Brown, el psicólogo

cómico

Educación física

our community

Languu

Lenguaje

spelling

Ortografía

Matemáticas

idiomas

speaking—

Lectura

writing

Escritura

Tecnología

Ciencia

serio

eficiente, baja

joven y atlético

habladoras

alta

vieja

A. ¿Cómo se dice? Using the illustration, your imagination, and common sense, can you find the word in column **B** that has the opposite meaning of the word in column **A**?

A

1. dedicado
2. hablador
3. simpático
4. tímido

B

a. antipático
b. irresponsable, negligente
c. extrovertido
d. silencioso

OPPOSITES

B. ¿Qué profesión? Can you find a logical match for the school personnel from column **A** with something indicative of their jobs from column **B**?

A

1. _b_ un maestro de Lenguaje
2. _d_ un maestro de Estudios sociales
3. _a_ el administrador de una escuela
4. _c_ un instructor de deportes: béisbol, básquetbol

B

a. el director
b. el abecedario (el alfabeto)
c. maestro de Educación física
d. los presidentes

Los maestros y las clases

Elena's mother meets with the principal to talk about Elena's first grade teacher. Surprise! Elena may not be the only one starting school.

DIRECTORA: Buenas tardes, señora. Soy Patricia McCant, directora de la escuela. Por aquí, por favor.

MADRE: ¿Usted habla español?

DIRECTORA: Sí, aquí muchos de nosotros somos bilingües.

MADRE: ¡Qué maravilla! Nosotros somos de México. Elena no habla inglés muy bien y necesita una maestra especial.

DIRECTORA: ¿Cómo es Elena?

MADRE: Es una niña activa. Normalmente es muy habladora. Pero en inglés, es muy tímida.

DIRECTORA: Entonces, la Sra. Miller es la maestra perfecta. Es bilingüe y muy paciente. Ella es la maestra de Matemáticas, Lenguaje, Ciencias y Estudios sociales. Para las clases de Tecnología y Educación física, el maestro es el Sr. Arenas. Es muy cómico.

MADRE: ¡Qué bien! Imagínese. Mi hija—estudiante bilingüe. Yo también quiero ser estudiante aquí para aprender inglés.

DIRECTORA: Estudiante, no. Pero, siempre necesitamos voluntarios aquí. Bienvenida a la familia de Menlo Park.

C. ¿Comprende usted? Decide if each of the statements is **Cierto (C)** or **Falso (F)**. If the statement is incorrect, provide the correct information.

F 1. La directora no es bilingüe.
F 2. Elena no habla español.
F 3. La Sra. Miller es la maestra de Tecnología.
C 4. La madre quiere ser estudiante.

D. ¿Quién es? ¿Qué es? ¿Cómo es? For each of the participants in the following list, tell *what s/he does* in the school **(¿Qué es?)** and *what s/he is like* **(¿Cómo es?)**. Use the picture on page 22 as a guide.

MODELO: ¿Quién es?   ¿Qué es?   ¿Cómo es?
            Jorge   *Es portero.* *Es popular.*

1. Amanda y Rosa   *son viejas, son habladoras y viejas*
2. David Arenas   *es maestro Tecnología, es cómico, joven*
3. la Sra. Miguélez *es secretaria es eficiente y baja y atlético*
4. el Dr. Brown

E. Excelencia en el trabajo. For each of the following professions, find at least one typical characteristic from the new vocabulary.

MODELO: un profesor de español
            Es inteligente. or *Es hablador.*

1. un maestro de niños
2. un secretario
3. un estudiante de español
4. un jugador *(player)* de básquetbol

E. Una carta del director. You are an assistant in the school principal's office and have been asked to summarize the information he has sent home to parents in this letter. Read the letter and then finish the summary sentences with the information you have read.

ABCDEFGHIJKLMNOPQRS

Del escritorio de John Cassidy, Director

3 de septiembre

Estimada familia:
¡Bienvenidos a la escuela primaria de Corona Avenue! Damos la bienvenida a nuestros 400 estudiantes desde Kinder hasta el quinto grado, a sus padres y familiares, y también a nuestros cinco maestros nuevos. Gracias a ellos, este año las clases tienen menos estudiantes.

Los maestros
Ahora, hay más de un maestro para cada clase. El maestro principal es responsable de enseñar Matemáticas, Lenguaje (Lectura, Escritura, Ortografía), Ciencias y Estudios sociales. También hay otros maestros que enseñan clases de Computadoras y Tecnología, Educación física y Salud (health). Este año, somos muy afortunados al tener con nosotros a un maestro de Arte y a un maestro de Música una vez por semana.

La tarea *(homework)* **para casa**
La tarea en casa es muy importante para desarrollar la autodisciplina, la independencia, la responsabilidad y los buenos hábitos de estudio en los niños. La cooperación de la familia es esencial.

Las visitas a la escuela
¡Están invitados! Queremos que los padres participen en todas las actividades que tenemos. Si usted decide participar en la clase de su estudiante como voluntario o como miembro de nuestra Asociación de Padres (PTA), usted participará de una manera muy importante en el futuro de esta escuela—y de su estudiante. Espero saludar a cada uno de ustedes personalmente muy pronto.

Atentamente,
John Cassidy
John Cassidy,
Director

ABCDEFGHIJKLMNOPQ

1. Este año hay 400 estudiantes en los grados _Kinder hasta el quinto_

2. Hay cinco maestros nuevos y ahora las clases tienen _menos estudiantes_

3. La tarea para la casa es importante para _desarrollar la_

4. El director quiere que los padres participen en _PTA_.

F. Entrevista. One of you is the principal and the other the parent of a new student who wants to find out what the teacher is like. Use these guidelines for your interview and then switch roles.

Principal: Greet the parent, find out his or her name, find out the student's name, and who the teacher is. Then give two characteristics that might be important to the parent.

Parent: Answer the principal's questions, and then ask for information about the teacher.

MODELO:
E1: *Buenos días. ¿Cómo se llama Ud.?*
E2: *Soy* ___Susana___
E1: *¿Cómo se llama su estudiante?*
E2: *Se llama* ___Jorge___
E1: *¿Cómo se llama el maestro de* _____?
E2: *Se llama* _____. *¿Cómo es él/ella?*
E1: *El maestro (La maestra)* _____ *es muy* ___interesante y dificil___

Estructuras   *Introducing and describing yourself and others: Ser + adjetivos*

The verb **ser** is one of the Spanish equivalents to the verb *to be* in English. Use **ser** to tell who people are, what they do, what they are like, or where they are from. The forms of **ser** are:

[handwritten margin notes: personal physical Characteristics time date personality appearance]

ser to be			
yo **soy**	*I am*	nosotros/as **somos**	*we are*
tú **eres**	*you are (familiar)*	(Spain – vosotros/as)	(you all)(sois)
usted **es**	*you are (formal)*	ustedes **son**	*you are (plural)*
él **es**	*he is*	ellos **son**	*they are(m)*
ella **es**	*she is*	ellas **son**	*they are(f)*
—¿Quién **es** usted?		*Who are you?*	
—**Soy** Susana.		*I am Susana.*	
—¿**Son** ustedes secretarias?		*Are you secretaries?*	
—Yo **soy** secretaria y ella **es** recepcionista.		*I am a secretary and she is a receptionist.*	

[handwritten: "it" pointing to usted/él/ella; "those" pointing to ustedes/ellos/ellas]

- To describe what a person or thing is like, use **ser** with an adjective.

—¿Cómo **es** la directora?	*What is the principal like?*
—**Es** simpática.	*She is nice.*
—¿Cómo **es** usted?	*What are you like?*
—**Soy** tímido.	*I am timid (shy).*
—El problema **es** difícil.	*The problem is difficult.*

- Many adjectives end in **–o** when describing characteristics of men/boys and **-a** when describing characteristics of women/girls.

Masculine	**Feminine**	
tímid**o**	tímid**a**	*shy*
extrovertid**o**	extrovertid**a**	*outgoing*
simpátic**o**	simpátic**a**	*nice*
antipátic**o**	antipátic**a**	*unpleasant*
alt**o**	alt**a**	*tall*
baj**o**	baj**a**	*short*
ambicios**o**	ambicios**a**	*ambitious*

Most adjectives ending in a letter other than **–o** or **-a** use only one form for masculine or feminine. All nouns in Spanish have gender classification; that is, they are all designated as masculine or feminine, and their accompanying adjectives must agree in number and gender.

El secretari**o** es inteligent**e.**	*The (male) secretary is intelligent.*
La secretari**a** es inteligent**e.**	*The (female) secretary is intelligent.*
La situación es grav**e.**	*The situation is serious.*
El estudiante es difíci**l.**	*The student is difficult.*

- Nouns and adjectives ending in **–dor** or **–tor** will add an **-a** to the end when referring to females.

El directo**r** es trabajado**r.**	*The (male) principal is hard-working.*
La directo**ra** es trabajado**ra.**	*The (female) principal is hard-working.*

- To pluralize nouns and adjectives ending in **–o, –a,** or **–e,** simply add an **–s.** (*VOWELS)*

La ejecutiv**a** es interesant**e.**   La**s** ejecutiva**s** son interesante**s.**

- To pluralize nouns and adjectives ending in consonants, add **–es.**   *(CONSONANTS)*

Es instructo**r.**	*He is an instructor.*
Son instructo**res.**	*They are instructors.*
La instructo**ra** es jove**n.**	*The (female) instructor is young.*
Las instructo**ras** son jóve**nes.**	*The female instructors are young.*

Natural emphasis on second to last syllable in the word — to preserve original sound add accent mark también = also, too

o/a

estadounidense) USA

- Use **ser** with adjectives to talk about nationality and country of origin. In Spanish nationalities are not capitalized, but countries are.

Yo **soy mexicana.**	*I am Mexican.*
Yo **soy de** México.	*I am from Mexico.*
El maestro **es puertorriqueño.**	*The teacher is Puerto Rican.*
El maestro **es de** Puerto Rico.	*The teacher is from Puerto Rico.*

- Use **ser** with **de** to tell what something is made of or to whom it belongs.

El portafolios **es de** cuero.	*The briefcase is made of leather.*
El portafolios **es de** la señora Rosa.	*The briefcase is Mrs. Rosa's.*

Para practicar

A. ¿Quiénes?   To whom might the following sentences refer? Insert names of people you know or people who are famous.

MODELO: Es presidente.
George W. Bush es presidente de Estados Unidos y Vicente Fox es presidente de México.

1.	Son maestros famosos.	**4.**	Somos amigos.
2.	Es muy inteligente.	**5.**	Son de California.
3.	Es muy alto.	**6.**	Es de México.

B. ¿Cómo son?   You are sitting in the reception area of an elementary school, thinking about the people you see there and about the things you are experiencing. Use the correct form of the verb **ser** to describe them.

MODELO: (La secretaria) eficiente
La secretaria es eficiente.

1. (Los niños) altos y guapos   *Son*
2. (La recepcionista) simpática   *es*
3. (Las maestras jóvenes) mexicanas   *Son*
4. (Nosotros) optimistas   *Somos*
5. (Ustedes) paciente   *Son*
6. (Los estudiantes) interesantes   *Son*
7. (La música) suave   *es*
8. (El asistente de la directora) atractivo   *es*

C. **Otra fiesta de cóctel.** You are a school principal at a cocktail party and would like to get to know the person next to you—since he/she could be a great resource for Career Day. Find out everything you can about this interesting stranger: who s/he is, where s/he is from, what profession s/he is in and what s/he is like. Then, switch roles. When you are finished, describe your new friend to the class.

¿Cómo se llama?	¿De dónde es?	¿Cuál es su profesión?	¿Cómo es?

Irlandés (a)
Domicano/a
Guatemalateco/a
salvadoreño/a
hondureño/a
panameño/a
Alemán/a

Módulo 2

Para conocernos

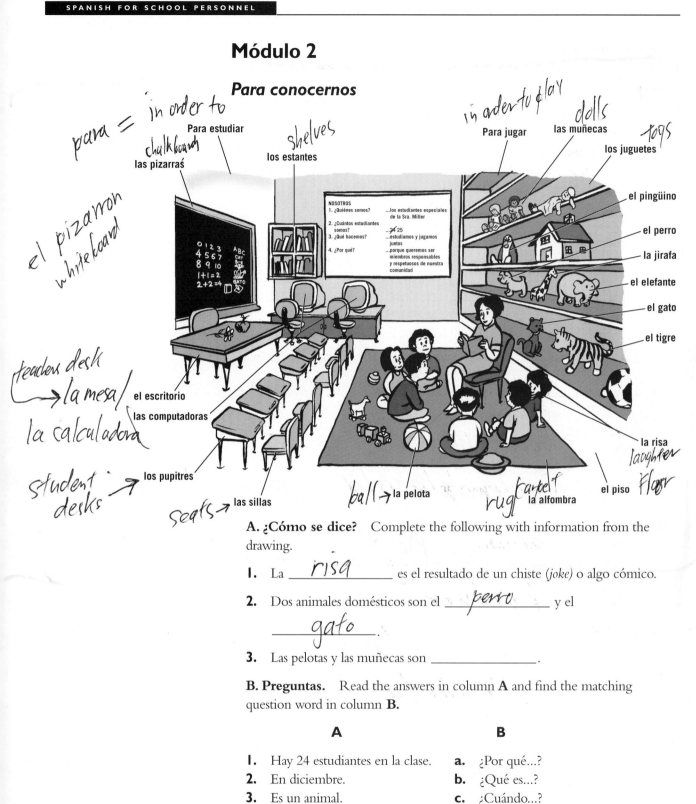

Handwritten annotations:
- para = in order to
- chalkboard
- el pizarron whiteboard
- teachers desk → la mesa
- la calculadora
- student desks →
- seats →
- shelves
- in order to play
- dolls
- toys
- ball → la pelota
- rug
- la risa laughter
- Floor

Labels in drawing:
Para estudiar
las pizarráś
los estantes
Para jugar
las muñecas
los juguetes
el pingüino
el perro
la jirafa
el elefante
el gato
el tigre
el escritorio
las computadoras
los pupitres
las sillas
la pelota
la alfombra
la risa
el piso

NOSOTROS
1. ¿Quiénes somos? ...los estudiantes especiales de la Sra. Miller
2. ¿Cuántos estudiantes somos? ...24 25
3. ¿Qué hacemos? ...estudiamos y jugamos juntos
4. ¿Por qué? ...porque queremos ser miembros responsables y respetuosos de nuestra comunidad

A. ¿Cómo se dice?   Complete the following with information from the drawing.

1. La _____risa_____ es el resultado de un chiste (*joke*) o algo cómico.

2. Dos animales domésticos son el _____perro_____ y el
   _____gato_____.

3. Las pelotas y las muñecas son _____.

B. Preguntas.   Read the answers in column **A** and find the matching question word in column **B**.

A	B
1. Hay 24 estudiantes en la clase.	a. ¿Por qué...?
2. En diciembre.	b. ¿Qué es...?
3. Es un animal.	c. ¿Cuándo...?
4. Porque somos inteligentes.	d. ¿Cuántos...?

Para conocernos

Today is the first day of school and Mrs. Miller's first grade class has already had a tour of the building, of the classroom, and of the playground. Now that they know the school and the rules, it's time to get to know each other—Mrs. Miller first. She's not shy!

SRA. MILLER: Y así es mi familia: tengo dos hijos, Ali y Greg. Ellos están fuera, en la universidad, pero nos visitan en diciembre y agosto. También tengo un gato, Tiburón, que es muy grande porque come mucho y un perro Tink, que es blanco. No tengo elefantes.

NIÑOS: (risa)

SRA. MILLER: Y ahora, niños, ustedes tienen mi biografía. ¿Qué es una biografía?

NIÑOS: (Silencio).

SRA. MILLER: Una biografía es la historia de una persona con mucha información interesante sobre sus experiencias. Cada estudiante va a contar su biografía a la clase. Pero primero, tengo una pregunta: ¿quiénes tienen buena memoria?

NIÑOS: ¡Yo! Maestra, ¡yo! ¡Yo!...

SRA. MILLER: A ver. Entonces, contesten ustedes estas preguntas: ¿quién soy yo?

NIÑOS: ¡La Sra. Miller!

SRA. MILLER: Excelente. ¿De dónde soy?

NIÑOS: De California.

SRA. MILLER: ¿Cuándo me visitan mis hijos?

NIÑOS: En diciembre y en agosto.

SRA. MILLER: ¿Cuántos animales tengo? ¿Y cómo son?

NIÑOS: Dos animales... un gato y un perro. El gato es gordo y el perro es blanco.

SRA. MILLER: ¿Por qué es gordo?

NIÑOS: Porque come mucho.

SRA. MILLER: Ustedes son muy inteligentes y tienen muy buena memoria. Una pregunta final. ¿Cómo es mi elefante?

NIÑOS: (risa) ¡Usted no tiene elefantes!

C. ¿Comprende usted? Answer the following questions based on the dialogue.

1. ¿Qué es una biografía?
2. ¿Cómo es Tiburón?
3. ¿Cuándo visitan los hijos?
4. ¿Cómo es su elefante?

D. Preguntas para la directora.   As the parent of a new first-grader, there is a great deal you need to know before the first day of school. Write four questions that you would like to ask the principal in order to be ready.

MODELO: *¿Cuándo es el primer día de clases?*

E. El programa de desayuno y almuerzo a precios reducidos.   After reading the informational brochure on the free or reduced price breakfast and lunch programs, answer the following questions. Don't worry about writing full sentences—this time!

El programa de desayuno y almuerzo a precios reducidos			
Comida	Hora	Precio normal	Precio reducido
Desayuno escolar	7:30–8:00	$1.00	$.30
Almuerzo escolar	11:00–12:15	$1.50	$.40
Almuerzo para adultos	11:00–12:15	$2.50	

La cafetería

La cafetería

La cafetería sirve el desayuno y el almuerzo todos los días que hay clases. Las comidas se pueden pagar por adelantado el primer día de la semana en la oficina o en el momento de comprar la comida en la cafetería. Si va a pagar con cheque, favor de escribirlo a nombre de: *Cafetería Corona Ave.*

Los estudiantes que participan en el plan para desayuno o almuerzo gratuito (*sin costo*) o a precio reducido necesitan rellenar el formulario de elegibilidad antes del 30 de septiembre. Las secretarias de la oficina no están autorizadas a prestar (*lend*) dinero a los estudiantes para comer en la cafetería. Recomendamos que los estudiantes no regresen a casa para almorzar porque no es posible determinar su seguridad (*safety*).

1. ¿Cuánto es el precio reducido del desayuno?
2. ¿Dónde pagan las comidas a la hora de la comida?
3. ¿Cuándo pagan las comidas por adelantado?
4. ¿Quiénes no están autorizadas a prestar dinero para comer?

Estructuras   *Asking for information: Las preguntas*

- To ask a question requiring a yes or no answer, change the intonation of a statement.
- The word *do*, used in English questions, is not translated into Spanish.
- The subject of the sentence usually comes after the verb in a question.

¿Tiene usted animales?	*Do you have animals?*
¿Está la directora?	*Is the director in?*

- The Spanish question **¿verdad?** or **¿no?** can be added to the end of a statement if your question is just confirming what you believe to be true. It is the equivalent of the English, *right?*

Usted es Marta, ¿verdad?	*You are Marta, right?*
La madre de Mario tiene una cita a las tres, ¿no?	*La madre de Mario has an appointment at three, doesn't she?*

- When your question requires new information to be provided, use the following question words:

¿Quién/es?	*Who?*	**¿Quién** es el señor?	*Who is that man?*
¿Qué?	*What?*	**¿Qué** es esto?	*What is this?*
¿Cuál/es?	*Which?*	**¿Cuál** de ellas es la maestra?	*Which one of them is the teacher?*
¿Dónde?	*Where?*	**¿Dónde** está la oficina?	*Where is the office?*
¿Cuándo?	*When?*	**¿Cuándo** es la cita?	*When is the appointment?*
¿Cómo?	*How?*	**¿Cómo** está usted?	*How are you?*
¿Cuánto/a?	*How much?*	**¿Cuánto** tiempo hay?	*How much time is there?*
¿Cuántos/as?	*How many?*	**¿Cuántos** libros hay?	*How many books are there?*
¿Por qué?	*¿Why?*	**¿Por qué** estudia?	*Why do you study?*

[handwritten margin notes: Question words — De dónde → from where? — Adónde → to where? — de qué → of what — de quién → of whom]

- Some question words have plural forms (**¿Cuál?** and **¿Quién?**) depending on whether the questioner is expecting a singular or plural response.

—**¿Quién es** la señora alta?	*Who is the tall woman?*
—**Es Mónica,** una amiga.	*She is Monica, a friend.*
—**¿Quiénes son** los señores altos?	*Who are the tall men?*
—**Son** unos amigos.	*They are some friends.*
—**¿Cuál es** la directora?	*Which woman is the principal?*
—**La señora alta** es la directora.	*The tall woman is the principal.*
—**¿Cuáles son** los formularios?	*Which are the forms?*
—**Son los papeles** azules.	*They are the blue papers.*

- **¿Cuánto?,** meaning *how much,* can become feminine, depending on the noun that follows.

¿Cuánt**o** tiemp**o** están en clase?	*How much time are they in class?*
¿Cuánt**a** informa**ción** hay?	*How much information is there?*

- **¿Cuántos?,** meaning *how many,* can also become feminine, depending on the noun that follows.

¿Cuánt**os** candidat**os** hay?	*How many candidates are there?*
¿Cuánt**as** cit**as** hay hoy?	*How many appointments are there today?*

- Use **¿Cuál?** or **¿Cuáles?** to indicate a selection—or selections—from a group. It is used instead of **¿Qué?** when asking for specific or personal information, rather than general definitions.

General definition:

¿Qué es un elefante?	*What is an elephant?*

Personal definition:

¿Cuál es su número de teléfono?	*What is your telephone number?*
¿Cuáles son sus números de teléfono?	*What are your telephone numbers?*

Para practicar

A. Una invitación. Read the following invitation and answer the questions.

> *¡El Distrito Escolar de Franklin celebra la apertura (opening) de su nueva escuela primaria, Jefferson Park, y Ud. y su familia están invitados a la celebración!*
>
>
>
> *La fiesta es el 15 de septiembre, desde las dos de la tarde hasta las cuatro, en la cafetería de la escuela, en la Calle Linden, número 24.*
>
>
>
> *Favor de confirmar su presencia llamando al número de teléfono: 630-2115 antes del diez de septiembre.*

1. ¿Cómo se llama la escuela?
2. ¿Quiénes celebran la fiesta? ¿Por qué?
3. ¿Cuándo y dónde es la celebración?
4. ¿Cuántas horas dura *(lasts)* la celebración?
5. ¿Cuál es el número de teléfono para confirmar su presencia?

B. ¡Jeopardy! The following statements are logical answers to specific questions. Provide a logical question for each.

MODELO: Son las ocho de la noche.
¿Qué hora es?

1. Estoy bien, gracias.
2. La escuela está en la calle Estonia.
3. La cita es a las tres.
4. Los estudiantes son inteligentes.
5. Yo soy Patricia y ella es Elena.
6. Hay 24 horas en un día.
7. Hay dos secretarias bilingües.
8. El número de teléfono es 555–1234.

C. Entre amigos. With a partner, make up five questions about your Spanish class. Then ask other students to answer them.

MODELO: ¿Quién es el profesor/la profesora?
El profesor es el señor Fernández.

Módulo 2

En la clase / escuela

la informa— health

la gaveta) locker
el casillero

el marcador marker

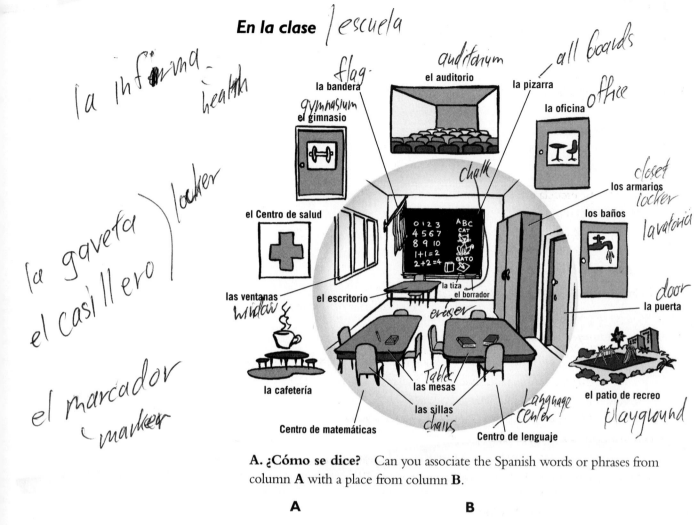

el auditorio

auditorium

all boards
la pizarra

flag
la bandera

gymnasium
el gimnasio

la oficina office

chalk

closet
los armarios
locker
los baños
lavatoria

el Centro de salud

la tiza
el borrador

las ventanas
window

el escritorio

eraser

door
la puerta

la cafetería

Table
las mesas

las sillas
chairs

Language
Center

el patio de recreo
playground

Centro de matemáticas

Centro de lenguaje

A. ¿Cómo se dice?   Can you associate the Spanish words or phrases from column **A** with a place from column **B**.

A	B
1. $2 + 2 = 4$	**a.** la oficina
2. un accidente	**b.** el patio de recreo
3. el fútbol	**c.** el centro de salud
4. una visita al director	**d.** el centro de matemáticas

B. Las actividades escolares.   Tell where you might send your students under the following circumstances.

1.   They have been seated doing quiet work all morning.

2.   A child has come in late without a note from home.

3.   It's lunchtime!

4.   The principal is giving a speech to the school.

La clase y la escuela

Mrs. Miller and her class have just finished their tour of the school and classroom. Her students may have learned much more than simple institutional geography! Let's listen.

SRA. MILLER:	La escuela es bonita, ¿verdad?
NIÑOS:	¡Y grande!
SRA. MILLER:	Es una escuela muy grande—y bonita. ¿Quién recuerda todos los sitios que visitamos?
ELENA:	La biblioteca.
SRA. MILLER:	Muchas personas usan los libros y las computadoras en la biblioteca para concentrarse en el trabajo o en la lectura. Y, ¿cómo hablamos en la biblioteca? Una demostración, por favor.
NIÑOS:	(silencio)
SRA. MILLER:	Muy bien. No hablamos en la biblioteca, o hablamos en voz baja. Por favor, una demostración de hablar en voz baja.
NIÑOS:	habla-bla-bla-bla-bla...
SRA. MILLER:	Muy bien. ¿Hay otro sitio donde no hablamos?
PAQUITO:	En el auditorio durante una presentación. Y en la clase en el centro de lectura.
SRA. MILLER:	Excelente. ¿Dónde hablamos en voz normal?
NIÑOS:	En la cafetería. En la clase. En el centro de grupos. En la oficina. En el centro de salud. En los baños.
SRA. MILLER:	Una demostración de hablar en voz normal, por favor.
NIÑOS:	Habla-bla-bla-bla-bla-bla-bla...
SRA. MILLER:	¡Así es! Juanito, ¿cuál fue *(was)* tu sitio favorito?
JUANITO:	Tengo dos: el gimnasio y el patio de recreo.
SRA. MILLER:	¡Ajá, el recreo y los deportes! Niños, ¿cómo hablamos en el gimnasio o durante el recreo? Demostración, por favor.
NIÑOS:	¡A gritos!
SRA. MILLER:	¿Cómo?
NIÑOS:	**¡A gritos!**
SRA. MILLER:	¿Cómo?
NIÑOS:	***¡¡A-A-A G-R-I-T-O-S!!*** *(mucha risa).*

C. ¿Comprende usted? Fill in the missing information based on the dialogue.

1. La escuela es _____ y _____.

2. Un lugar donde hay silencio es _____.

3. En la oficina o en el centro de salud, los niños hablan en

_____.

4. Durante el recreo o la clase de educación física, los niños hablan

_____.

D. La cronología. One of our writers has no sense of time. Please help out by putting the following sentences in the order of a typical school day.

A. _____ Los maestros necesitan una siesta.
B. _____ Los niños dicen "buenos días" a la maestra.
C. _____ Los niños buscan libros nuevos en la biblioteca.
D. _____ Los niños van al patio de recreo para esperar el autobús para ir a casa.

E. Los útiles escolares. Match the following school supplies with a famous brand name.

pencil sharpener — el saca puntos

tissue / kleenex

la caja de pañuelos de papel

los libros para practicar la lectura

la mochila — backpack

pencil — el lápiz

el cuaderno — notebook

folder — folleto — carpeta

el libro — el texto

glue — el pegamento

la regla — ruler / rule

las tijeras — scissors

los crayones — crayon

la pluma — pen
el bolígrafo
el lapicero

el papel — paper
una hoja de papel — a sheet of paper

a. Kleenex   **b.** Bic   **c.** Crayola   **d.** Fiskar   **e.** Elmer's   **f.** Jansport

1. ___C___ crayones

2. ___a___ pañuelos de papel

3. ___f___ la mochila

4. ___d___ las tijeras

5. ___b___ la pluma

6. ___e___ el pegamento

F. Una carta de apreciación.   The students want to write a thank you note. Since they are just learning how, they need help filling in the blanks with the correct words—and spelling. Help them, **por favor**, by reading the letter and supplying the missing items.

Estimados señores de Costco:
Muchas gracias por las _____ que dan a nuestra escuela con los útiles escolares. Usamos los _____ en el centro de matemáticas para escribir los números y calcular los totales. Los _____ son especialmente buenos para borrar nuestros errores. También en el centro de matemáticas, usamos las _____ para medir (measure) las cosas.
En el centro de lenguaje usamos los _____ para leer las historias y los cuentos. Practicamos la ortografía y la escritura en los _____ espirales. No usamos mucho las _____ para escribir porque no tienen borradores. Durante la clase de arte, dibujamos y coloreamos objetos con los _____. Entonces cortamos (cut) los dibujos con las _____ y los pegamos en los cuadernos con _____ Elmer's.

Muchas gracias por todo,
La clase de la Sra. Miller

Estructuras   *Descriptions: Los artículos: género y número*

You have already seen that all nouns in Spanish have *gender*, meaning they are classified as either masculine or feminine. Words associated with nouns—adjectives and articles—take on the same characteristics as the noun and will match the noun in number and gender.

- There are four ways to express *the* in Spanish. The one you use depends on the characteristics of the noun that follows it—whether it is masculine or feminine, singular or plural.

The definite article: *The*	Singular	Plural
Masculine	**el** teléfono	**los** teléfonos
Feminine	**la** casa	**las** casas

- Noun gender has little to do with being male or female, unless the noun refers to a sexed being:

el director   **los directores**
la directora   **las directoras**

- Nouns ending in **-e** generally have the same form for men and women. Only the article will change. It is important to note that in groups of mixed males and females, the masculine form is used. Nouns ending in **-ista** are both masculine and feminine.

el estudiant**e**   *the (male) student*
la estudiant**e**   *the (female) student*
los estudiant**es**   *the students (either all male or mixed male and female)*
el tur**ista**   *the (male) tourist*
la tur**ista**   *the (female) tourist*

- In general, nouns ending in **-a, -ción, -sión, -dad, -tad,** and **-tud** are feminine.

la op**ción**   las op**ciones**   la solici**tud**   las solici**tudes**
la universi**dad** las universi**dades** la facul**tad**   las facul**tades**

- Generally, nouns ending in **-o** or **-l** are masculine:

el formulari**o**   **los** formulari**os**
el pape**l**   **los** pape**les**

- There are many exceptions to the general rules of gender. Some of the most common are:

  la man**o (f)**   *the hand*
  el d**ía (m)**   *the day*
  el map**a (m)**   *the map*

- Additional exceptions include words ending in **–ma.** While there are **–ma** words that are feminine: **la mamá** (*the mama*) and **la pluma** (*the pen*), many **–ma** words are masculine.

  el proble**ma**   *the problem*   **el** trau**ma**   *the trauma*
  el dra**ma**   *the drama*   **el** idio**ma**   *the language*

Note: In a sentence, when the word **de** comes directly before **el,** they form the contraction **del.**

el libro **de + el** candidato ⇒ el libro **del** candidato   *the candidate's book*

del = of the

- To say *a, an,* or *some,* use the form of the indefinite article that matches the noun in number and gender. **Un** and **unos** are masculine indefinite articles and **una** and **unas** are feminine indefinite articles.

The indefinite article: *a, an, some*				
	Singular		**Plural**	
Masculine	**un** libro	*a book*	**unos** libros	*some books*
Feminine	**una** mesa	*a table*	**unas** mes**as**	*some tables*

Para practicar

A. En la escuela.   Use the correct form of the definite article (**el, la, los,** or **las**) to identify these things associated with schools. Be careful!

1. __El__ señor Rodríguez está en __la__ oficina.

2. __Los__ maestros están en __el__ auditorio.

3. __Los__ mapas están en __los__ clases.

4. __Las__ maestras están en __el__ patio.

5. __El__ problema está en __la__ cafetería.

6. __La__ solicitud está en __la__ computadora.

7. __La__ variedad en __la__ biblioteca es enorme.
   variety

8. __La__ educación es importante para todos   ?

application

B. El mundo académico.   Complete the following thoughts, first with a form of the indefinite article (**un, una, unos,** or **unas**), and then with the name of an appropriate person, place, or thing. When you are finished, compare your responses with those of a classmate.

MODELO: _____ maestro famoso es _____.
Un maestro famoso es Jaime Escalante.

1. _____ publicación para niños es _____.

2. _____ biblioteca famosa es _____.

3. _____ problema para los maestros es _____.

4. _____ autor importante es _____.

5. _____ programa excelente para niños es _____.

6. _____ universidad famosa es _____.

C. En la oficina. You and a partner have just been named to the renovation committee for your school office. As you look at the following list, decide what is good, what is bad, and what you will need new. Include any additional items that you think of.

MODELO: sillas horribles
Necesitamos (we need) unas sillas nuevas.
2 diccionarios modernos
Hay diccionarios buenos.

Inventario de la oficina:

1. 3 computadoras 386 (trescientos ochenta y seis)
2. 100 plumas *(pens)* viejas
3. 2 teléfonos celulares
4. 3 televisores en blanco y negro
5. recepcionistas excelentes
6. directorio telefónico del año 66 (sesenta y seis)
7. una copiadora "ditto"
8. unas revistas *(magazines)* de 1978

¡OJO!

Many vocabulary words are almost identical to English so they don't need to be translated. As you study your vocabulary words, look for tips to help you learn these parallel words. You'll note that double consonants, as in *aggressive* (**agresivo**) don't exist in Spanish, except for **cc, ll,** and **rr**, each of which has a different sound than if they were single consonants.

ción=*tion*	**educación**=*education*
dad=*ity*	**realidad**=*reality*
oso=*ous*	**ambicioso**=*ambitious*
ista=*ist/istic*	**pesimista**=*pessimistic*
mente=*ly*	**generalmente**=*generally*

Vocabulario Módulo 1

Sustantivos — Nouns

el acta (f.)		el inglés	English
de nacimiento	birth certificate	la inscripción	registration
la alfombra	rug, carpet	el juego	game
el apellido	last name	la lectura	reading
la calle	street	el lenguaje	language
la carta	letter	el lugar	place
la casa	house	el/la maestro/a	teacher
la ciencia	science	la matrícula	registration
la cita	appointment, date	la medianoche	midnight
la ciudad	city	el/la médico/a	doctor
el código	code	el mediodía	noon
el conserje	custodian	la mujer	woman
el consultorio	office (medical)	el nacimiento	birth
el desayuno	breakfast	el nombre	name
la dirección	address	las noticias	news
el domicilio	address	la ortografía	spelling
la edad	age	el padre	father
el ejercicio	exercise	el país	country
la enfermedad	illness	el personal	personnel
la entrevista	interview	el piso	floor
la escritura	writing	el portero	custodian, doorman
la escuela	school	la pregunta	question
el español	Spanish	el/la psicólogo/a	psychologist
el estado	state	la reunión	meeting
el/la estudiante	student	el seguro	insurance
los Estudios		el señor	sir, Mr.
sociales	Social Studies	la señora	ma'am, Mrs.
la fiesta	party	la solicitud	application
la firma	signature	el/la	
el formulario	form	superintendente	superintendent
el gimnasio	gymnasium	la tarea	homework, chore
el/la hijo/a	son/daughter	la tarjeta	card
el hombre	man	el teatro	theater
la hora	hour	el/la tutor/a	guardian, tutor
el idioma	language	la ventana	window

Verbos *Verbs*

buscar	to look for	llegar	to arrive
comprender	to understand	llenar	to fill
conocer (zc)	to know, be acquainted with	necesitar	to need
		practicar	to practice
escribir	to write	reconocer (zc)	to recognize
escuchar	to listen	rellenar	to fill out
hablar	to talk, to speak	ser	to be
leer	to read	ver	to see

Adjetivos *Adjectives*

actual	current	hablador/a	talkative
alto/a	tall	joven	young
americano/a	American	medio/a	half
antipático/a	unpleasant	mi	my
asiático/a	Asian	nuestro/a	our
bajo/a	short (height)	nuevo/a	new
bienvenido/a	welcome	otro/a	other, another
blanco/a	white	pequeño/a	small (size)
bueno/a	good	primer/o/a	first
cuarto/a	quarter, fourth	simpático/a	nice
escolar	school related	su	his, her, your, their
este/a	this	todo/a	all
feliz	happy	tu	your (familiar)
guapo/a	good-looking	viejo/a	old

Otras expresiones *Other expressions*

a	to	estoy	I am
¿A qué hora…?	At what time…?	más	more
ahora	now	pero	but
algo	something	¡Qué bueno!	That's great!
¿Cómo se dice?	How do you say?	¡Qué maravilla!	How wonderful!
con	with	si	if
de	of, from	siempre	always
durante	during	también	also, too
en caso de	in case of	tengo	I have
en punto	exactly, on the dot	vamos	we go, let's go
entonces	then	y	and

¡OJO!

From time to time you will see verbs followed by a series of letters in parentheses—e.g., **tener (ie)** or **demostrar (ue).** These are spelling hints that will help you to conjugate the verbs in later chapters.

Módulo 2

Sustantivos   *Nouns*

el almuerzo	*lunch*	**la mochila**	*backpack*
el armario	*closet*	**el mundo**	*world*
el autobús	*bus*	**la muñeca**	*doll*
la bandera	*flag*	**el/la niño/a**	*child*
el baño	*bathroom*	**el pañuelo**	*handkerchief*
la biblioteca	*library*	**el pegamento**	*glue*
el borrador	*eraser*	**la pelota**	*ball*
la caja	*box*	**el perro**	*dog*
la comida	*food, meal*	**la pizarra**	*chalkboard*
la computadora	*computer*	**la pluma**	*pen*
la copiadora	*copier*	**el precio**	*price*
la cosa	*thing*	**el programa**	*program*
el crayón	*crayon*	**la puerta**	*door*
el cuaderno	*notebook*	**el pupitre**	*student desk*
el cuento	*story*	**el recreo**	*recreation*
el deporte	*sport*	**la regla**	*ruler, rule*
el diccionario	*dictionary*	**el respeto**	*respect*
el dinero	*money*	**la risa**	*laughter*
el escritorio	*desk*	**el salón**	*room*
el estante	*shelf*	**la salud**	*health*
el gato	*cat*	**la señorita**	*miss, young lady*
el grito	*shout*	**la siesta**	*nap*
la historia	*history, story*	**la silla**	*chair*
la jirafa	*giraffe*	**el sitio**	*place*
el juguete	*toy*	**las tijeras**	*scissors*
el lápiz	*pencil*	**la tiza**	*chalk*
el libro	*book*	**el trabajo**	*work, job*
la mano	*hand*	**los útiles**	*supplies, tools*
el mapa	*map*	**la voz**	*voice*
la mesa	*table*		

Verbos   *verbs*

aprender	*to learn*	**estudiar**	*to study*
borrar	*to erase*	**jugar (ue)**	*to play games, sports*
comer	*to eat*		
comprar	*to buy*	**pagar**	*to pay*
contar (ue)	*to tell, to count*	**pegar**	*to glue*
contestar	*to answer*	**proteger**	*to protect*
demostrar (ue)	*to demonstrate*	**recomendar (ie)**	*to recommend*
dibujar	*to sketch, to draw*	**regresar**	*to return*
enseñar	*to teach*	**trabajar**	*to work*

Adjetivos

bonito/a	*pretty*	**junto/a**	*together*
gordo/a	*fat*	**respetuoso/a**	*respectful*
grande	*big*		

Otras expresiones

A ver	*Let's see*	**mucho/a**	*a lot*
¡Aja!	*Aha!*	**¿Por qué?**	*Why?*
así	*so, thus*	**porque**	*because*
¿Cuál/es?	*Which (one/s)?*	**que**	*that*
¿Cuándo?	*When?*	**¿Qué?**	*What?*
¿Cuánto/a?	*How much?*	**¿Quién/es?**	*Who?*
¿Cuántos/as?	*How many?*	**sólo**	*only*
¿Dónde?	*Where?*	**¿Verdad?**	*True? Right?*

Síntesis

A escuchar

Listen to the following conversation and tell if each of the following statements is **Cierto (C)** or **Falso (F).** If the statement is incorrect, provide the correct information.

1. _____ Carlos es recepcionista en la escuela Menlo Park.

2. _____ Carlos es de México.

3. _____ Carlos quiere establecer residencia en Arizona.

4. _____ Juanito es estudiante de primer año.

5. _____ Carlos acepta una cita con el director para el lunes a las 9:00.

A conversar

In groups of two or three, brainstorm everything you can think of that can be found in the following places.

a. una escuela   **b.** un salón de clase   **c.** una mochila

MODELO: *En una escuela hay clases, maestros, bibliotecas…*

A leer

Programa Bilingüe, Escuela Río Real

¿Por qué?
Hoy en día es muy importante hablar más de un idioma para poder trabajar en nuestra economía global. Los estudiantes que saben comunicarse con varias culturas tendrán una ventaja en el futuro. La Escuela Río Real tiene un programa bilingüe para los estudiantes que quieren aprender a leer, hablar y escribir en inglés y español.

¿Cómo?
Este programa ayuda a los estudiantes que hablan español como idioma materno, y a los estudiantes que hablan inglés como idioma materno en la misma clase.

- En Kindergarten se aprenden Estudios sociales, Lenguaje, Ciencia, Educación física y Arte—en español. Las Matemáticas se aprenden en inglés y todos los días hay una lección de inglés.

- Del primer al tercer grado, se aprenden Ciencia, Lenguaje, Educación física y Arte en español. Las Matemáticas se aprenden en inglés. También hay lecciones diarias en inglés.

- En los grados cuarto y quinto se enseñan Ciencias, Educación física y Arte en español. Las Matemáticas y los Estudios sociales se enseñan en inglés. También hay lecciones estructuradas sobre el uso de español e inglés.

¿Quiénes?
El éxito *(success)* académico de su estudiante no sólo es la responsabilidad de la escuela. La familia también tiene que ayudar al estudiante. Todos los sábados, el programa bilingüe ofrece clases para todas las familias.

¿Comprende usted?   After reading the notice on this bilingual program, answer the following questions.

1. ¿Cómo se llama la escuela con el programa bilingüe?
2. ¿Por qué es importante hablar dos idiomas?
3. En K-5, ¿en qué idioma estudian Artes y Educación física?
4. ¿Qué ofrece el programa bilingüe para las familias?

A escribir

You have a meeting with your child's principal to find out about the school's bilingual program. Write down the five questions you want to be sure to ask. Compare your notes with a classmate's.

MODELO: *¿Son bilingües todos los maestros?*

Algo más

The **Ventana cultural** is, as its name suggests, designed as a window so that we can get a glimpse of some of the contemporary cross-cultural issues that we will encounter as more and more Latinos arrive in the United States to work, to live, and to go to school. There is no doubt that our own everyday culture is changing as a result of the growing Latin influence. Can you see and identify some of the influences in your own community? In the **A conocer** section, we will also encourage you to become more aware of some of the key Latino figures and issues that are having an impact on different aspects of educational trends today.

Ventana cultural

Si usted no habla español...

Según el censo de 2000 (dos mil), hay más de 35.3 millones de hispanos en Estados Unidos y muchos de ellos hablan solamente español. El español es la segunda lengua de esta nación.

Para comunicarse con estudiantes, colegas o familias, hay que hablar español. Se ve el impacto del español en los negocios, trabajando con los inmigrantes o con un nuevo ejecutivo de Colombia. Es imposible escaparse de la cultura popular en español—del chihuahua que "quiere Taco Bell" o de "la vida loca" de Ricky Martin. Las películas de Antonio Banderas y Jennifer López, así como la música de Marc Anthony, son las puertas a un mundo en español.

En las tiendas, las clínicas médicas y las escuelas se oye español por todas partes. Ahora es la lengua materna de 332 (trescientos treinta y dos) millones de personas. El español es tan importante que puede ayudarnos a obtener un trabajo—y muchas veces a recibir un salario más alto.

¿Ud. no está convencido todavía? Considere estos datos:

- Más de 3.3 millones de estudiantes en las escuelas secundarias estudian español.
- En empresas de California a Nueva York, muchos patrones pagan la matrícula para los empleados que estudian español.
- Varias agencias públicas del gobierno (government), la policía y los hospitales requieren que sus empleados estudien español.

Con un poco de español se puede hacer mucho. ¡Nuestro Presidente habla español! Y usted está en esta clase porque comprende que el mundo actual es un mundo en el que ayuda mucho saber español. ¡Adelante con el español!

En mis propias palabras.   Do you believe that it is important for all students to learn at least two languages? Write three sentences in your own words about the importance of speaking Spanish in today's workplace according to the article above. Compare your ideas with a classmate's. If you disagree, say why!

A buscar

The Internet offers a wealth of information in Spanish to help you on the job. It is especially helpful to see what other schools and districts are doing to facilitate communication with non English-speaking families. Have you seen what some are putting on their websites in Spanish to help families understand the educational system? Using the keywords **escuelas primarias California** (or your own state!) and **educación** as the "Search" topic, see what you find of interest to you. Check specific school districts in your area to see if they have started putting information **en español** on their website. Go to www.prenhall.com/rush, category School districts/Distritos escolares for some links.

A conocer: Bilingual education vs. English-only immersion programs

Public education today is in the midst of a raging debate over the pros and cons of bilingual education vs. English-only immersion programs. Each side has valid points. Use the Internet to learn what each side is saying. Write at least three pros and cons for each. For this activity, you may use "English only!"

LECCIÓN 2

¡La vuelta al cole!

Módulo 1
- Una noche para los padres
- Naming and describing: *Más sobre los adjetivos*
- Actividades escolares
- Talking about present activities: *Los verbos que terminan en -ar*

Módulo 2
- A jugar
- Talking about present activities: *Los verbos que terminan en -er, -ir*
- Después de clase
- Physical conditions: *Expresiones con **tener** y **estar***

Síntesis
- A escuchar
- A conversar
- A leer
- A escribir

Algo más
- Ventana cultural: El impacto de la música latina
- A buscar
- A conocer: De colores

Módulo I

Una noche para los padres

Agenda
I. Bienvenida—Directora McElroy—5 minutos
II. Para conocernos: Presentación de la "Familia de Menlo Park"—5 minutos
III. Visión: Éxito académico para todos—10 minutos
IV. Responsabilidades y Tareas—10 minutos
      A. Estudiantes
      B. Maestros
      C. Padres
V. ¿Preguntas? ¡Respuestas!
VI. Tour de la escuela—15 minutos
VII. Visita a las clases y reunión con los maestros—30 minutos (salones de clase)
VIII. Celebración—30 minutos (cafetería)
Música: Coro y orquesta de Menlo Park: Estudiantes de 5to grado.
Servicio de Guardería desde las 6 hasta las 8: Babysitter's Club, (gimnasio)

Servicios familiares:
1. **Tarea Hotline**
2. **ESL para familias (gratis)**
3. **Noches de tecnología: los martes de 6 a 8**
4. **PTA—voluntarios**
5. **Kidco—servicio de guardería y recreo después
   de las clases**

screen
la pantalla

Éxito para todos/
Success for all

la bandera — flag
azul
blanco
rojo
Feliz año
(escolar) nuevo

el micrófono

los abuelos
grandparents

los padres
parents

los tíos
uncles/aunts

A. ¿Cómo se dice?   Complete the following with information from the drawing.

1. Un símbolo rojo, blanco y azul del patriotismo es la _____ .

2. Muchas escuelas ofrecen instrucción musical con coro y

_____ .

3. Para cuidar *(take care of)* a los niños después de la escuela necesitamos la

_____ .

4. Para cada pregunta hay una _____ .

B. Un desastre.   Whoever organized the Back to School Night program at your school did a terrible job. Please reorganize the evening by changing each of the following plans to make more sense.

1. La música es cortesía del <u>conserje.</u>
2. La pantalla está en <u>la oficina de la directora.</u>
3. Los miembros del "Babysitter's Club" ofrecen servicios de <u>tecnología.</u>
4. Los padres visitan a <u>las secretarias</u> en los salones de clase.

Tarea para todos

DIRECTORA: Ahora ustedes saben "quiénes somos" en la escuela. Comprenden por qué los uniformes—blancos y azules—son importantes. Y saben dónde están los sitios importantes de la escuela. Ahora, quiero presentar mi visión para el futuro de la escuela y nuestro plan llamado "éxito para todos los estudiantes". El secreto está en LA TAREA...

PADRE: ¡Excelente! Los estudiantes necesitan mucha tarea... (risa de todos)

DIRECTORA: Cuando hablo de tarea, hablo de la tarea de los padres y las familias...

PADRE: ¡TAREA para mí! Yo soy el padre. Yo no quiero tarea. No me gustan las Matemáticas—las fracciones.... (mucha risa)

DIRECTORA: ¡Esa es exactamente la reacción de los estudiantes! "No me gusta la tarea." "Hay un programa de televisión..." " "Estoy nervioso por la tarea..." "No puedo..."
La tarea es la prioridad número uno para toda la familia. Todos los días, todos los años... Es importante ser estudiante **con** su estudiante y participar en su vida escolar...

PADRE: Es verdad. Pero si es muy importante participar en la escuela con los niños y si somos también estudiantes dedicados con tarea diaria, ¡yo quiero mis galletas "Oreo" con leche, también!

DIRECTORA: (con risa). Excelente sentido del humor, señor... ¿Cómo se llama usted?

PADRE: Manuel Vargas.

DIRECTORA: Señor Vargas. Eso es precisamente lo que necesito para organizar a las familias. Vamos a hacer una cosa—yo busco las galletas "Oreos" y la leche y usted organiza a las familias—como nuestro nuevo Presidente de la PTA.

C. ¿Comprende usted? Answer the following questions based on the dialogue.

1. ¿Cuáles son los colores de los uniformes estudiantiles?
2. ¿Cuál es el elemento más importante para tener "éxito en las escuelas"?
3. Según *(according to)* el padre, ¿la tarea es buena o mala para los estudiantes?
4. ¿Qué necesita hacer el padre como nuevo Presidente de la PTA?

D. Los padres en la escuela. As a new PTA President, you have been asked to give a general overview of the role of the PTA in your school. Read the model that you found on the Internet for Corona School and use the guidelines to talk about the role of the PTA in your own words, with your partner.

¿Qué es la PTA de Corona?

La PTA de Corona es una asociación de padres y maestros que desean participar activamente en la educación de los niños. Nuestra misión incluye tres objetivos:

o Apoyar las actividades educativas en la escuela al recaudar fondos para ayudar a los maestros a comprar libros y útiles escolares, pagar los costos de las excursiones de los niños y contribuir al uso de la tecnología en la escuela.

o Promover la comunicación entre los alumnos, los padres, el personal de la escuela y el sistema educativo.

o Influenciar a la Junta Escolar para que se tomen decisiones que respondan a los intereses de la Escuela Corona.

¿Cómo puedo participar en la PTA de Corona?

Todos los padres y maestros de la ciudad están invitados a hacerse miembros de la PTA pagando una módica cuota de $5.00 por persona. Favor de mandar su cuota en el sobre adjunto.

La primera reunión del año de la PTA es el martes, 12 de septiembre, a las 7:00 p.m. durante la Noche de Regreso a la Escuela. Si usted no habla inglés, puede participar en el Comité Latino de Padres de la PTA que se reúne también todos los meses; las reuniones son en español.

---

1. La PTA de mi escuela tiene tres objetivos :
   a. Proveer dinero para...
   b. Promover la comunicación de...
   c. Influenciar...

2. El costo de hacerse miembro de la PTA es de $_____ por año.

3. La primera reunión es el...

4. Si usted no habla inglés puede...

E. La noche de regreso a la escuela. You and your co-president of the PTA must plan an agenda for the first meeting of the year. What three topics do you think are the most important to stress to the family members?

MODELO: *I. Los maestros necesitan voluntarios en las clases.*

Estructuras   *Naming and describing: Más sobre los adjetivos*

■ Some of the most useful adjectives in any public setting define physical characteristics of people or things. Because the adjective becomes part of the identity of the noun it describes, it assumes the same characteristics as its noun: masculine, feminine, singular, or plural. If you are unsure if a noun is masculine or feminine, you can tell by looking at the article **(el, la, los, las, un, una, unos, unas).** Remember: If the adjective ends in a letter other than **–o** or **-a**, it becomes plural or singular, but not masculine or feminine.

Colors:

blanco/a	*white*	**la** camis**a blanca**	*the white shirt*
negro/a	*black*	**los** libr**os negros**	*the black books*
rojo/a	*red*	**la** tinta **roja**	*the red ink*
amarillo/a	*yellow*	**las** copi**as amarillas**	*the yellow copies*
azul	*blue*	**los** ojos **azules**	*the blue eyes*
verde	*green*	**la** plant**a verde**	*the green plant*

anaranjado - orange
dorado - golden
platiado - silver
morado - berry
purpúreo - purple
violeto - violet

■ For hair and eyes, the following colors are often used:

Hair:

castaño	*brown*	**moreno**	*black or dark brown*
rubio	*blond*	**pelirrojo**	*red*

calvo = bald   cañoso = gray

Eyes:

(de color) cafés *brown*   **azules** *blue*   **verdes** *green*

Physical or mental characteristics:

alto/a	*tall/high*	**las** señor**as altas**	*the tall women*
bajo/a	*short/low*	**los** niñ**os bajos**	*the short children*
joven	*young*	**el** director **joven**	*the young director*
viejo/a	*old*	**la** coleg**a vieja**	*the old colleague (f.)*
gordo/a	*fat*	**el** gat**o gordo**	*the fat cat*
delgado/a	*thin*	**la** secretari**a delgada**	*the thin secretary*
fuerte	*strong*	**el** conserje **fuerte**	*the strong custodian*
débil	*weak*	**el** estudiante **débil**	*the weak student*
optimista	*optimistic*	**los** maestr**os optimistas**	*the optimistic teachers*

la flaca
skinny

¡**OJO!** Nouns and adjectives ending in **–ista** only become singular or plural.

Other

grande	*large*	**una** clase **grande**	*a large class*
pequeño/a	*small*	**un** grup**o** **pequeño**	*a small group*

Note: **chico/a** is another way of saying *small*.

- When **grande** is placed before the noun, the meaning changes from *large* to *great,* and the ending **–de** is omitted in the singular.

un gran maestro	*a great teacher*
unos grandes maestros	*some great teachers*
una gran trabajadora	*a great worker*
unas grandes trabajadoras	*some great workers*

- **Bueno** and **malo** are adjectives meaning *good* and *bad*. When placed after the noun they modify, they become masculine, feminine, singular, and plural.

bueno/a	*good*	**el** conserje **bueno**	*the good custodian*
malo/a	*bad*	**las** noticias **malas**	*the bad news*

- When **bueno** or **malo** is placed before a masculine singular noun, omit the **–o.**

un bue**n** amig**o**	*a good friend*
unos buen**os** amig**os**	*some good friends*
un ma**l** cas**o**	*a bad case*
unos mal**os** cas**os**	*some bad cases*

Rule re.
When to
place adjective
before OR after
noun

¡OJO!

Although the most convenient English translations of **me gusta** and **le gusta** are *I like* and *you, he/she like(s)*, they literally mean *it is pleasing to me* and *it is pleasing to you/to him/to her.*

Me gusta el plan.	*I like the plan. (The plan is pleasing to me.)*
Le gusta el plan.	*You/he/she like(s) the plan. (The plan is pleasing to you/to him/to her.)*

If more than one thing is pleasing, use **gustan.**

Me gust**an los planes.**	*I like the plans. (The plans are pleasing to me.)*
Le gust**an los planes.**	*You/he/she like(s) the plans. (The plans are pleasing to you/to him/to her.)*

You will learn more about this verb in **Lección 7.**

Para practicar

A. Asociaciones.   What color or colors do you associate with the following items? Rewrite the phrase to include the description. Don't forget a verb that matches the subject! Then, tell whether or not you like them.

MODELO: los zapatos *(shoes)* de tenis
              *Los zapatos de tenis **son blancos.***
              Me gustan los zapatos de tenis.

1. las bananas
2. las plantas de la oficina
3. los dólares
4. el papel para la copiadora
5. una pizarra (¡3 posibilidades!)
6. la bandera *(flag)* americana
7. una nota *(grade)* "F"
8. el café
9. la bandera mexicana

B. Más asociaciones.   When you see the following names, what characteristics do you immediately associate?

MODELO: Michael Jordan
              Michael Jordan es alto.

1. Whoopi Goldberg
2. Danny DeVito
3. Albert Einstein
4. Popeye con espinacas *(spinach)*
5. Donald Trump y Bill Gates
6. Popeye sin espinacas

C. ¿Problema o beneficio?   Make sure the following adjectives match their nouns and then tell a classmate if these economic issues are a benefit **(beneficio)** or a problem **(problema)** for the school.

MODELO: clases/pequeño
              Las clases pequeñas son un beneficio.

1. formularios/complicado
2. conserje/vigoroso
3. directores/visionario
4. empleado/deshonesto
5. padres/interesado
6. escuelas/viejo y malo

Módulo I

Actividades escolares

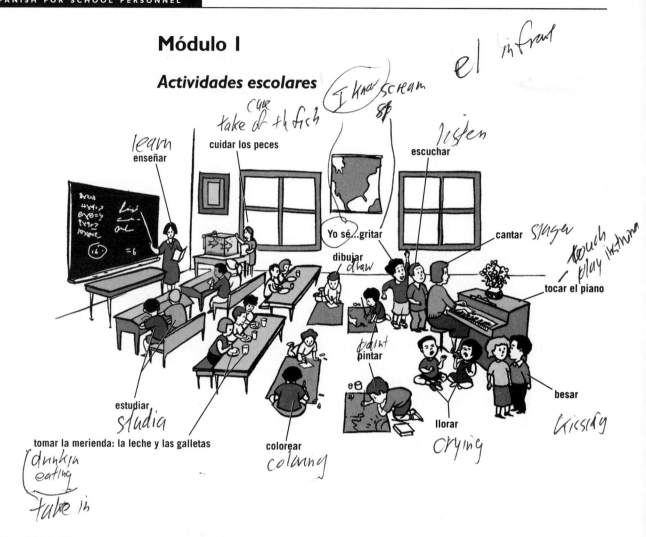

enseñar *(learn)*

cuidar los peces *(take car of th fish)*

Yo sé...gritar *(I knw scream)*

escuchar *(listen)*

dibujar *(draw)*

cantar *(singer)*

tocar el piano *(touch play instrum)*

pintar *(paint)*

besar *(kissing)*

llorar *(crying)*

estudiar *(studia)*

tomar la merienda: la leche y las galletas *(drinkin eating take in)*

colorear *(coloring)*

el in fronl

A. ¿Cómo se dice?   Find the activity in column **B** that the students would do during the following class periods in column **A**.

A		**B**
1. Música	**a.**	practicar vóleibol o fútbol
2. Arte	**b.**	tomar leche y galletas
3. Educación física	**d.**	colorear y pintar
4. Merienda	**e.**	cantar y escuchar

B. ¿Usted o los estudiantes? You are a first grade teacher with many responsibilities. Tell if you **(Yo)** or the students **(Ellos)** would be most likely to do the following things.

MODELO: explicar las matemáticas
Yo

1. llorar por su mamá

2. enseñar canciones nuevas

3. practicar las letras

4. estudiar los números

Elena y su abuela

Elena's grandmother is visiting from South America and wants to know all about Elena's adventures in her new school. How does she spend her time? What are her favorite subjects? And what are the other kids like?

ABUELA: Ahora, Elenita, háblame de tu escuela. ¿Te gusta la maestra?

ELENA: Sí, abuela, es muy buena y muy simpática. Pero tengo dos maestros: la Sra. Miller enseña Ciencias, Lenguaje y Matemáticas y el Sr. Arenas enseña Educación física y Estudios sociales. Los dos enseñan Arte y Música

ABUELA: ¿Qué hacen ustedes en la clase de Música?

ELENA: Cantamos muchas canciones divertidas: "De colores", "Bingo", "El conejito Fru-Fru"...

ABUELA: ¿Cantan en español o en inglés?

ELENA: Con la Sra. Miller hablamos y cantamos en inglés y en español. El Sr. Arenas sólo habla inglés. Con él hablamos y cantamos en inglés. Por eso, a él le gusta el Arte. Nos expresamos sin lenguaje cuando pintamos y dibujamos. A mí me gusta también.

ABUELA: Interesante, Elena. Y ¿cómo son los otros niños? ¿Tienes amigos?

ELENA: Sí, abuela. Paso mucho tiempo con Amalia y Lucía. Coloreamos juntas, trabajamos juntas y tomamos la merienda juntas. Son muy simpáticas.

ABUELA: ¿Y los muchachos?

ELENA: No me gustan los muchachos. Carlitos y Paquito siempre lloran porque quieren regresar a casa. Marco grita las respuestas a las preguntas de los maestros y Juanito besa a todas las muchachas. ¡Qué tontos!

C. ¿Comprende usted?   Answer the following questions based on the dialogue.

1. ¿Qué enseña la Sra. Miller?
2. ¿Qué enseña el Sr. Arenas?
3. ¿Qué enseñan los dos, la Sra. Miller y el Sr. Arenas?
4. ¿Cómo son los muchachos según Elena?

D. Las noticias de la clase de Kinder.   Here's a clever teacher who understands the importance of communication with families. Bet they have some fun in this class!

Queridos padres, abuelos y familiares,

Esta semana es una de las semanas culturales del año escolar. Ahora estudiamos acerca de Japón, su cultura y sus costumbres. Para la sección de geografía, miramos el mapa del mundo. Preparamos meriendas orientales y practicamos el uso de los palillos (*chopsticks*) para hablar de las diferencias entre las varias culturas. La familia de Yosei, uno de nuestros estudiantes japoneses, explica cómo es la vida en Japón. Ellos nos enseñan canciones infantiles japonesas y también escuchamos los instrumentos japoneses. Miramos un kimono de la madre de Yosei y en la televisión miramos unos dibujos animados (*cartoons*) de "Anime", una nueva forma artística de Japón. Expresamos nuestras impresiones de las actividades haciendo dibujos. En el dibujo de David hay un niño con un kimono con palillos. ¡El niño llora porque no puede tomar la merienda con palillos!

También pasamos tiempo con las mascotas de la clase, King y Kong, nuestros conejillos de Indias (*guinea pigs*). Los niños los cuidan bien y estudian su lenguaje. Escuchamos los "chi-chi-chi" que hacen para ver si comprendemos la comunicación de los animales. Los peces tropicales son coloridos y bonitos. Después de hacer muchas actividades en el patio de recreo, miramos los peces nadar en el agua en el acuario y todos estamos más tranquilos.

E. Muchas lecciones en un día.   This teacher is accomplishing more than one lesson with each of these activities. Tell which activities have involved the students in the following subjects:

1. Ciencias
2. Geografía
3. Arte
4. Música
5. Estudios sociales
6. Lenguaje

F. Más lecciones.   Oh, no! We forgot to include math lessons in these activities. Can you go back to the newsletter and find things to do within the activities to get these children working with numbers? The verbs **sumar** *(to add)* and **restar** *(to subtract)* might be helpful. When you are finished, compare your answers with those of other students.

Estructuras   *Talking about present activities: Los verbos que terminan en -ar*

- An infinitive is the basic form of the verb that is not yet matched to fit a specific person or subject. In English, an infinitive always starts with *to: to play, to speak, to run*.

- In Spanish, infinitives are single words that end in -**ar,** -**er,** or -**ir.**

  habl**ar**   *to speak*   com**er**   *to eat*   viv**ir**   *to live*

- The stem is the portion of the verb that tells the action and the ending tells who or what the subject is.

  habl**o**   *I speak*   **habl** is the stem   and   **o** tells that the subject is **yo.**

- In order to indicate the different subjects of a verb, use different endings. This is called *conjugating a verb.* To conjugate **-ar** verbs, drop the final **-ar** and add these endings:

hablar *to talk, to speak*			
yo habl**o**	*I speak*	**nosotros/as** habl**amos**	*we speak*
tú habl**as**	*you (familiar) speak*		
usted habl**a**	*you (formal) speak*	**ustedes** habl**an**	*you (plural) speak*
él/ella habl**a**	*he/she speaks*	**ellos/as** habl**an**	*they speak*

- Some additional **-ar** verbs that follow this pattern are:

ayudar	*to help*	**llamar**	*to call* / phone or verbal
buscar	*to look for*	**mirar**	*to look at* / watch
calcular	*to calculate*	**necesitar**	*to need*
caminar	*to walk*	**observar**	*to observe*
descansar	*to rest*	**pintar**	*to paint*
dibujar	*to draw*	**preparar**	*to prepare*
enseñar	*to teach*	**regresar**	*to return*
escuchar	*to listen*	**restar**	*to subtract*
examinar	*to examine*	**sumar**	*to add*
explicar	*to explain*	**tomar**	*to take*
limpiar	*to clean*	**trabajar**	*to work*

Les
a – people of favorite
pets

manejar
to drive

- When the subject of the verb is clear from the ending and the context, the subject pronoun may be omitted.

    (Yo) hablo con el maestro.   *I speak with the teacher.*

¡OJO! In a sentence where two verbs come together, the first verb is conjugated and the second verb stays in the infinitive form.

Necesito **hablar** con el maestro.   *I need to speak with the teacher.*
Voy a **llamar** a la oficina.   *I am going to call the office.*

Para practicar

A. ¿Quién habla?   Provide the subject pronoun (or pronouns) that would match the following verbs.

MODELO: Trabaja en una oficina.
    Él, ella or *usted trabaja en una oficina.*

1. Miramos los dibujos.
2. Tomo la merienda.
3. Hablo mucho.
4. Evaluamos los problemas.
5. Pintamos los dibujos.
6. Ayudan a los estudiantes.
7. Necesito papel.
8. Compras el libro.
9. Invitas al maestro.

B. Una cita con el superintendente. By matching the verbs in parentheses to the subjects given, you can follow the steps through institutional phone systems and talk to a real person—someday!

1. Yo _____ (llamar) al Distrito Escolar y _____ (hablar) con una recepcionista.

2. La recepcionista _____ (mirar) el libro de citas y me _____ (preguntar) mi nombre.

3. Yo _____ (esperar) en la línea y _____ (escuchar) la música por mucho tiempo.

4. Después, escucho: "Gracias. Nosotros _____ (ayudar) a otras personas."

5. Por fin, la voz _____ (regresar) a la línea:—Hay una cita con el superintendente en dos meses. ¿_____ (necesitar) usted la cita por la mañana o por la tarde?

6. ¿Dos meses? Bueno. Yo _____ (tomar) la cita por la mañana.

Módulo 2

A jugar

A. ¿Cómo se dice?   Many successful people showed a very early interest in their professional fields. Imagine the following celebrities and tell which **club** they might have joined.

MODELO: Milton Bradley
El Club de juegos

1.   Yao Ming   **2.**   Donald Trump   **3.**   Emeril   **4.**   Jennifer López

B. Actividades del club.   Tell what clubs these activities belong to.

1.   escribir música o poesía   **3.**   asistir a una ópera
2.   explorar la ciudad   **4.**   aprender ciencias en la cocina

¡Vengan al club!

Like many schools worried about children going home to empty houses after school, Menlo Park offers an after-school program to keep students safe, active, and learning.

¡Bienvenidos, niños y familiares, a las **Horas de aventuras!** Cada estudiante que participa automáticamente se convierte en miembro de nuestro club. Hay un club para todos.

Club de tarea.   Inmediatamente después de las clases, tenemos tutores y maestros voluntarios en la cafetería para ayudar con la tarea. Los estudiantes que no tienen tarea leen o escriben poesía o cuentos, y trabajan en el laboratorio de computadoras.

Club de cocina.   Una vez a la semana, todos los niños aprenden mucho sobre Matemáticas y Ciencias cuando transformamos la cocina de la cafetería en un laboratorio científico. Al terminar los experimentos, comemos los resultados—¡deliciosos!

Club de aventureros.   Una vez al mes tenemos una aventura fuera de la escuela. Exploramos un lugar de interés de la ciudad. Vemos el arte en el Museo del Niño o los animales en el zoo. Asistimos a una presentación de ópera o de teatro.

Club de música, drama y danza.   Escuchamos música, leemos o escribimos dramas y bailamos. Presentamos nuestras obras durante "Las noches de regreso a la escuela".

Club del jardinería.   Preparamos la tierra, plantamos flores y vegetales, cultivamos nuestro jardín y estudiamos el ciclo de la vida.

Club de juegos.   Tenemos una sala de juegos como Monopoly, Scrabble— en inglés y español. Los niños aprenden los números y se familiarizan con las finanzas cuando compran y venden propiedades... y mucho más.

Club de misterios.   En el Club de misterios siempre hay un invitado especial que visita nuestra ciudad o vive aquí—para hablar de su profesión—¿es autor? ¿futbolista? ¿astronauta? ¡Es un misterio!

C. ¿Comprende usted?   Decide if each of these statements is **Cierto (C)** or **Falso (F).** If the statement is incorrect, provide the correct information.

1. Los estudiantes reciben ayuda con los estudios académicos en el Club de misterios.
2. Es posible observar las conexiones entre las Ciencias y la comida en el Club de cocina.
3. El Club de juegos tiene muchos invitados misteriosos.
4. Los niños ven los animales en el zoo cuando están en el Club de jardinería.

D. Programas para antes y después de la escuela. After reading the informational brochure on before and after-school programs for child care, answer the following questions.

Elija el mejor cuidado para su niño

Visite los programas antes de inscribir a su hijo. Nuestro programa ofrece:

- Autorización por el Estado de Nevada
- Un centro seguro, limpio y sin peligros para la salud del niño
- Lugar para jugar adentro y afuera
- Variedad de actividades apropiadas para la edad de los niños
- Personas alegres, inteligentes y amistosas para cuidar a los niños
- Personal con entrenamiento y experiencia

- Suficientes empleados para supervisar a los niños

Usted y su hijo se van a sentir cómodos y contentos con este programa.

Para obtener más información, visite nuestro sitio web en: www.ccpn.org

Asistencia gratis y recomendaciones para cualquier persona en busca de guarderías autorizadas. El Programa de Pago Alternativo cubre el costo del cuidado del niño para familias con ingresos bajos.

1. ¿Los padres pueden visitar el centro para ver los programas?
2. ¿Cuáles son tres necesidades del centro para ofrecer un buen programa?
3. ¿Cómo deben sentirse usted y su hijo?
4. ¿Qué es el Programa de Pago Alternativo?

E. El cuidado para mi hijo. Jot down the five items that you would consider crucial in selecting a child-care facility for your own son/daughter. No kids? Use your imagination to describe what you'd find most important. Cleanliness of the facility? Quality of staff? Variety of activities? Compare your list with that of a classmate.

MODELO: *Ayuda con la tarea.*

Estructuras   *Talking about present activities: Los verbos que terminan en -er, -ir*

- Verbs ending in **-er** and **-ir** follow a pattern similar to the **-ar** ending verbs.
- Use the same endings for both **-er** and **-ir** verbs for all subjects except **nosotros/as.**

	comer *to eat*	**vivir** *to live*
yo	como	vivo
tú	comes	vives
él, ella, usted	come	vive
nosotros/as	comemos	vivimos
ellos, ellas, ustedes	comen	viven

- Additional **-er** and **-ir** verbs that will be useful include:

-er

aprender	to learn
beber	to drink
comprender	to understand
correr	to run
creer	to believe
deber ✳	to owe or ought to/should
leer	to read
prometer	to promise
vender	to sell
ver (yo **veo**)	to see

-ir

admitir	to admit
decidir	to decide
discutir	to argue
escribir	to write
existir	to exist
insistir en ✳	to insist on
recibir	to receive
sufrir	to suffer

[handwritten: followed by an infinitive verb]

[handwritten: MUST be with another verb]

Para practicar

A. ¿Correr o leer?   You have always been an avid people watcher and the children and grown-ups in your school's extended day program offer you a great variety of people to watch. You always seem to be able to predict which people choose which activities when given a choice. Today's choices are: **el Club deportivo o el Club literario.** Tell if you think the following people will decide to **correr** o **leer.** ¡OJO! Don't forget to match the subject to the verb.

MODELO: el niño intelectual
El niño intelectual lee...

1. el entrenador de fútbol
2. las niñas atléticas
3. la niña que quiere ser autora
4. la tutora de inglés
5. tu amigo intelectual
6. yo

B. Actividades en el trabajo. By choosing the correct form of the verb in parentheses, you can describe some of the activities in a school.

1. Un representante de la compañía le _____ (vender) una copiadora a la directora.

2. La clase de Mr. Art _____ (ver) un vídeo en el auditorio.

3. La maestra de Juan _____ (creer) que _____ (comprender) su problema.

4. Las recepcionistas _____ (recibir) las llamadas telefónicas de los padres.

5. Los estudiantes _____ (comer) pastel para celebrar el cumpleaños de Gregorio.

6. Dos niños _____ (recibir) una detención porque

_____ (correr) por el pasillo.

C. En la escuela. On a sheet of paper, write the following headings:

La oficina   El salón de clase   El patio de recreo

With a classmate, brainstorm as many activity verbs as possible for each place. Next, from your list of verbs, write sentences telling what people are doing in those places. Extra credit if you can do the same thing with the kitchen, cafeteria, and auditorium in the school!

MODELO: la oficina
escribir   La recepcionista escribe los números de teléfono.

Módulo 2

Después de clase

expressions with "to have" (tener)

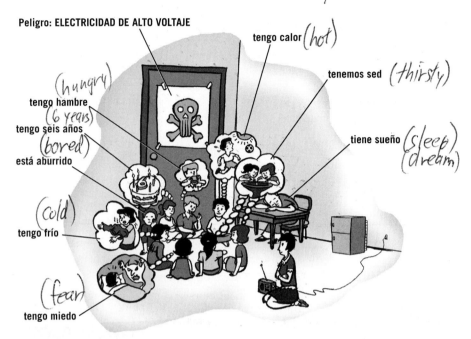

Peligro: ELECTRICIDAD DE ALTO VOLTAJE

tengo calor (hot)

tenemos sed (thirsty)

tengo hambre (hungry)

tengo seis años (6 years)

está aburrido (bored)

tiene sueño (sleep) (dream)

tengo frío (cold)

tengo miedo (fear)

A. ¿Cómo se dice? Complete the following with information from the drawing.

1. Una cosa que puede causar problemas serios es un _____.

2. Si tengo _____ yo necesito aire acondicionado.

3. Paquito no tiene nada que hacer. Está _____.

4. Cuando tengo _____, mi mamá pone la calefacción *(heater)* en la casa.

B. Remedios.   Can you offer a verb and a brand-name product to remedy the following situations?

MODELO: tener sed
beber Pepsi

1.   tener hambre   **3.**   estar muy nervioso/a o preocupado/a
2.   tener sueño   **4.**   estar aburrido/a

El Club de ciencias

Today's adventure for the youngest students in the Science Club has to do with electricity. Is it friend or foe? Here's how one group leader dispels fear, instills respect, and produces magic.

LÍDER: Ahora, niños, hoy vamos a explorar la electricidad.

PAQUITO: ¡Ay, no! Tengo miedo. Mi mamá dice que es peligrosa.

LÍDER: ¿Tienes miedo, Paquito? La electricidad es peligrosa si no tenemos cuidado. Pero también es mágica. Silencio, niños. (He turns on the radio). Donde hay silencio, tenemos música—gracias a la magia de la electricidad. En diciembre, cuando tienen frío, si no tenemos electricidad, no tenemos calefacción para la escuela. Y cuando están sucios, ¿prefieren tomar un baño con agua fría o caliente?

NIÑOS: ¡Con agua caliente!

LÍDER: Pues, si no tenemos electricidad, no tenemos agua caliente. Para mirar la tele o un vídeo o para usar la computadora cuando están aburridos, para tener aire acondicionado cuando tienen calor durante el verano, y para que el refrigerador funcione—necesitamos electricidad. ¿No son ustedes los que dicen diez veces al día: "Mamá, tengo sed. Quiero un refresco o leche o jugo de frutas"? No hay refrigeradores si no hay electricidad.

MARISA: Y cuando tengo sueño por la noche pero tengo miedo de dormir sola necesito electricidad para mi lámpara de noche, ¿verdad?

LÍDER: Así es, Marisa. Y Paquito, cuando tienes hambre y quieres algo para comer, ¿qué hace tu mamá?

PAQUITO: ¡Nos lleva a McDonald's!

C. ¿Comprende usted?   Answer the following questions based on the dialogue.

1.   ¿Por qué tiene Paquito miedo de la electricidad?
2.   Si los niños están aburridos, ¿qué pueden usar, gracias a la electricidad?
3.   ¿Qué necesitan durante el verano cuando tienen calor?
4.   ¿Qué necesita Marisa si tiene miedo durante la noche?

D. El juego correcto. It's important to select age-appropriate software programs and video games for your children. After reading the informational brochure, complete the following statements.

Guía del sistema de clasificación de juegos Cómo tomar las decisiones correctas para usted y su familia

En esta era tecnológica, usted, como padre o madre, toma decisiones sobre los programas que sus hijos usan en sus computadoras o sistemas de vídeo. Esta guía es un consejo independiente que ha desarrollado un sistema de clasificación estándar para todos los juegos interactivos.

¿Qué debe buscar?

La guía provee una representación visual que, con sólo mirarla, le informa exactamente de qué clasificación tiene su selección.

Símbolos de clasificación

PEQUEÑOS

Para los pequeños: Contenido apropiado para mayores de 3 años

TODOS

Para todos: ▲ Contenido apropiado para mayores de 6 años

ADOLESCENTES

Para ▲ **adolescentes:** Contenido apropiado para mayores de 13 años

Sólo adultos: ► Contenido apropiado sólo para adultos

SÓLO ADULTOS

CONTENIDO EXPLÍCITO

◄ **De contenido explícito:** Contenido apropiado para mayores de 17 años

Asistencia al cliente en español o inglés Número gratuito 1-800-751-6688 y una página de Internet (http://www.juegos.org)

1. Esta guía ayuda a los padres a comprar programas para _____.

2. La clasificación *Adolescente* indica que el juego de vídeo o programa es para

   _____.

3. La clasificación *Contenido explícito* es para _____.

4. Para recibir asistencia al cliente hay que llamar al número

   _____ o visitar el sitio en Internet en _____.

E. Usted tiene que decidir. Your six-year-old daughter heard about the latest craze in video games—**Mi vida loca**—and she wants it for her birthday. You read the review and find these comments. Which rating would you give this game and why? Discuss your rating with that of a classmate to see if you both agree.

> Mi vida loca contiene material provocativo, incluyendo representaciones fotográficas o animadas del cuerpo humano y el uso de palabras vulgares. El producto contiene imágenes en donde el uso de cigarros, alcohol y drogas se acepta y se glorifica. También hay representaciones realistas de situaciones violentas.

Estructuras   *Physical conditions: Expresiones con tener y estar*

- **Estar** *(to be)* and **tener** *(to have)* are two very useful verbs to describe certain temporary physical conditions.
- Use **estar** with an *adjective* to indicate *variable* physical or emotional circumstances. (Like **ser,** the English equivalent is *to be.* Remember that **ser** is used to describe long-term or identifying characteristics, while **estar** is used to indicate that a characteristic is more subject to change and circumstance). Use these forms of **estar:**

estar	to be				
yo	estoy	*I am*	**nosotros/as**	estamos	*we are*
tú	estás	*you are*		*estáis*	
Ud., él, ella	está	*you are, s/he is*	**Uds., ellos, ellas**	están	*you/they are*

—¿Cómo **están** ustedes? *How are you?*
—**Estamos** ocupados. *We are busy.*

The following descriptive words are commonly used with **estar** to describe how people are feeling.

aburrido/a	*bored*	**mal**	*bad, ill*
bien	*well*	**nervioso/a**	*nervous*
cansado/a	*tired*	**ocupado/a**	*busy*
confundido/a	*confused*	**preocupado/a**	*worried*
contento/a	*content, happy*	**regular**	*so-so*
interesado/a	*interested*	**triste**	*sad*

Los maestr**os** **están** preocupad**os** por los niños que están ausentes.   *The teachers are worried about the absent students.*
La secretari**a** **está** muy cansad**a**.   *The secretary is very tired.*

■ Use **estar** to indicate where something is located.

La escuela **está** en un barrio muy bonito. *The school is in a lovely neighborhood.*
Los libros **están** en la biblioteca.   *The books are in the library.*

■ The verb **tener** usually means *to have.* Use these forms:

tener	to have				
yo	**tengo**	*I have*	**nosotros/as**	**tenemos**	*we have*
tú	**tienes**	*you have*		*tenéis*	
Ud., él, ella	**tiene**	*you have, s/he has*	**Uds., ellos, ellas**	**tienen**	*you/they have*

Tengo cita con el director. *I have an appointment with the principal.*
El laboratorio **tiene** un equipo moderno.   *The lab has modern equipment.*

■ Used in the following idiomatic phrases with nouns, the English equivalent of **tener** is also *to be. Very* is expressed by **mucho (calor, frío, miedo, sueño)** or **mucha (hambre, sed, prisa, razón).**

tener... años	*to be ... years old*	**tener prisa**	*to be in a hurry*
tener calor	*to be hot*	**tener razón**	*to be right*
tener frío	*to be cold*	**tener sed**	*to be thirsty*
tener ganas de + infinitive	*to feel like*	**tener sueño**	*to be sleepy /dreamy*
tener hambre	*to be hungry*	**tener que** + infinitive	*to have to ...*
tener miedo	*to be scared*	*enojado/a*	*angry*

Para practicar

A. ¿Cómo están?   Use the correct form of **estar** to describe how the following people feel. Don't forget to make the adjective match the subject.

MODELO: Los niños (aburrido) en la clase de matemáticas
Los niños están aburridos en la clase de matemáticas.

1.   La familia (contento) con su nueva escuela
2.   Los niños (confundido) con la fonética
3.   Todos nosotros (nervioso) antes de los exámenes del estado
4.   Cuando los niños (en la clase), los maestros (ocupado)
5.   Yo (contento) cuando los estudiantes (interesado)
6.   La directora y yo (preocupado) cuando un estudiante no (en la escuela)
7.   Alejandro, ¿tú (bien)?
8.   Cuando usted y los amigos (en el auditorio), (contento)

B. ¿Qué tienen?   It is very late at night at the teacher's house. Use one of the **tener** phrases to give logical information about the following situations.

MODELO: El aire acondicionado está muy fuerte. Necesito un suéter.
Tengo frío.

1.   Son las tres de la mañana. La maestra y su esposo están cansados de preparar los materiales para mañana. Ellos...
2.   Paquito necesita un vaso de agua. Él...
3.   Juan está en la cocina. Busca algo para comer. Él...
4.   Hoy es el cumpleaños de Paquito. Ahora él... seis años.
5.   María ve un monstruo en su dormitorio. Ella...
6.   Un estudiante escribe que 2 + 2 son 5. Él *no*...

C. En la clase de español.   Make a list of five things you are feeling right now in your Spanish class. Then, look around you and see if you can guess who else might be feeling the same way.

MODELO: Tengo hambre. Estoy contento.
Helen y Roberto también tienen hambre.
El /La profesora está contento/a.

Vocabulario Módulo I

Sustantivos

el/la abuelo/a	grandfather/ mother	el mapa	map
la camisa	shirt	la merienda	snack (afternoon)
el cole(gio)	school	el mundo	world
el conejillo de Indias	guinea pig	el ojo	eye
		la orquesta	orchestra
el coro	choir	la pantalla	screen
la cortesía	courtesy	el pelo	hair
la costumbre	custom	el pez	fish
la cuota	fee	la pregunta	question
el desastre	disaster	el regreso	return
la galleta	cookie, cracker	la respuesta	answer, response
la geografía	geography	el sentido	sense
la guardería	child care	la tinta	ink
el kinder(garten)	kindergarten	la vida	life
la leche	milk	la vuelta	return
la letra	letter (alphabet)	el zapato	shoe

Verbos

apoyar	to support	mirar	to look at
besar	to kiss	nadar	to swim
caminar	to walk	pasar	to pass, to spend
cantar	to sing	pintar	to paint
cuidar	to take care of	restar	to subtract
descansar	to rest	sumar	to add
estar	to be	tocar	to play (music)
limpiar	to clean	tomar	to take, to drink
llamar	to call	vivir	to live
llorar	to cry		

Adjetivos

amarillo/a	yellow	moreno/a	brown (skin)
azul	blue	negro/a	black
café	brown	pelirrojo/a	redheaded
castaño/a	brown (hair/eyes)	quinto/a	fifth
chico/a	small (size)	rojo/a	red
débil	weak	rubio/a	blond
estudiantil	student	sano/a	healthy
fuerte	strong	tonto/a	silly, stupid
japonés/esa	Japanese	verde	green

Otras expresiones

entre	*between*	pero	*but*
le gusta	*he, she, you (formal) like(s)*	por eso	*that's why*
		por fin	*finally*
me gusta	*I like*	precisamente	*precisely*
te gusta	*you (fam.) like*	¡Qué emoción!	*How exciting!*
hay	*there is, are*	sin	*without*
para	*for, in order to*	sobre	*about, on*

Módulo 2

Sustantivos

la actitud	*attitude*	el/la director/a	*principal, director*
el agua (f.)	*water*	el disco compacto	*compact disc*
el aire		el dormitorio	*bedroom*
acondicionado	*air conditioning*	el/la entrenador/a	*trainer, coach*
la asignatura	*subject*	el entrenamiento	*training*
el autobús	*bus*	el equipo	*equipment, team*
el/la autor/a	*author*	el esfuerzo	*effort*
el/la aventurero/a	*adventurer*	el/la esposo/a	*spouse*
la ayuda	*help*	el examen	*test*
el/la ayudante	*helper*	la flor	*flower*
el baño	*bath, bathroom*	la fonética	*phonetics*
el barrio	*neighborhood*	el frío	*cold*
los bienes raíces	*real estate*	el/la futbolista	*soccer player*
el boletín	*bulletin*	la gana	*desire, urge*
el boxeo	*boxing*	el hambre (f.)	*hunger*
la calefacción	*heating*	el/la invitado/a	*guest*
la calidad	*quality*	el jardín	*garden*
el calor	*heat*	el juego	*game*
la canción	*song*	el jugo	*juice*
el/la chico/a	*boy, girl*	la lámpara	*lamp*
el ciclo	*cycle*	el/la líder	*leader*
la ciudad	*city*	el miedo	*fear*
el/la cocinero/a	*cook*	el misterio	*mystery*
el comportamiento	*behavior*	la moda	*fashion*
la confianza	*confidence*	la obra	*work*
el conocimiento	*knowledge*	la palabra	*word*
el/la consejero/a	*counselor*	el papel	*role*
el consejo	*advice*	el pasillo	*hallway*
el cuidado	*care*	el pastel	*cake, pastry*
el cumpleaños	*birthday*	el peligro	*danger*
el desarrollo	*development*	la poesía	*poetry*

el premio	prize	la sed	thirst
la prisa	haste	la sorpresa	surprise
la propiedad	property	el sueño	sleep, dream
la razón	reason	el teatro	theater
el refresco	refreshment, soda	la tierra	land
el resultado	result	el vaso	glass
la ropa	clothing	el vegetal	vegetable
la sala	room, living room	el verano	summer
el salón	room		

Verbos

aprender	to learn	lograr	to succeed
asistir	to attend	luchar	to fight, to struggle
bailar	to dance		
beber	to drink	mejorar	to improve
comer	to eat	pensar (ie)	to think
correr	to run	preferir (ie)	to prefer
creer	to believe	prometer	to promise
deber	to ought to, should	recibir	to receive
		recordar (ue)	to remember
decir (i) (g)	to say, to tell	sentirse (ie)	to feel
desarrollar	to develop	subir	to go up, to climb
discutir	to argue	sufrir	to suffer
dormir (ue)	to sleep	vender	to sell
ganar	to win, to earn	venir (ie) (g)	to come
llevar	to take (along), to carry		

Adjetivos

aburrido/a	bored	deportivo/a	sports-related
alto/a	high	limpio/a	clean
amistoso/a	friendly	mayor	older
ausente	absent	peligroso/a	dangerous
caliente	hot	próximo/a	next
cansado/a	tired	seguro/a	sure
cómodo/a	comfortable	sucio/a	dirty
confundido/a	confused	triste	sad
conjunto/a	joint		

Otras expresiones

adentro	inside	nada	nothing
afuera	outside	nadie	nobody
cada	each	nos gusta(n)	we like
después	after	sino	but
fuera	outside		

Síntesis

A escuchar

Each of the four children you are about to hear has a different problem. Complete the problems by matching the letter of the missing word to the correct child.

1. ____   **a.** sueño
2. ____   **b.** miedo
3. ____   **c.** hambre
4. ____   **d.** calor

A conversar

In groups of four, discuss the advantages of parent participation in a child's education. You may speak from the point of view of a teacher or as a parent.

MODELO: *Los padres necesitan ver el comportamiento de su hijo.*

A leer

Es necesario participar en la educación de su hijo/a

Los niños se benefician más cuando los padres toman parte en su educación.

- Disfrutan más de aprender y de la vida escolar
- Ganan más conocimientos y mejoran sus actitudes
- Tienen confianza y están más preparados

¡Los padres también se benefician!

- Usted se siente contento/a al ayudar a su hijo/a a tener éxito

Usted debe:

- Conocer a los profesores, las asignaturas y las normas generales de la escuela
- Participar en las actividades escolares
- Ayudar a su hijo/a a aprovechar los estudios al máximo
- Demostrar que <u>usted</u> aprecia la educación
- Mantenerse en contacto con el director, los consejeros y otros miembros del personal
- Servir como ayudante voluntario
- Visitar el salón de clase
- Apoyar los eventos con fines de recaudación de fondos
- Ayudar a hacer un boletín informativo
- Sugerir otras actividades

¡La escuela también es suya! Recuerde que todos luchamos por lograr el mismo objetivo. ¡Una educación de calidad requiere su participación!

¿Comprende usted?   Decide if each of the statements following the reading is **Cierto (C)** or **Falso (F)**. If the statement is incorrect, provide the correct information.

1. ____ Los hijos no se benefician si sus padres participan en la vida escolar.

2. ____ Hacer la tarea de su hijo es una buena manera de ayudar.

3. ____ Los padres deben expresar el valor *(value)* positivo de la educación.

4. ____ Es mala idea conocer al director, a los consejeros y a los profesores.

A escribir

Pretend you're an eight-year-old. What would you like YOUR parents to do to become involved at school? List at least three activities; then compare your ideas with those of a classmate.

MODELO: Mi mamá es buena cocinera *(cook)* y puede preparar galletas para una fiesta.

Algo más

Ventana cultural

EL IMPACTO DE LA MÚSICA LATINA

Si usted busca una lección bilingüe perfecta, considere esto: ¡la música de Shakira! Esta mujer colombiana canta en español y en inglés. Para los niños es muy importante la música popular—y la moda. Piense en la popularidad de Britney Spears con los chicos de todas las edades, y en su impacto no sólo en el mundo de música sino también en la moda. La verdad es que Britney es una industria—vende discos compactos, vídeos, ropa y mucho más.

Bueno, Shakira es la mujer del momento—popular entre los jóvenes de ambos sexos—por su talento y su belleza. Su primer disco en inglés, *Laundry Service*, es un éxito completo. Recibió premios Grammy, Premios MTV; y ahora la vemos en comerciales de Pepsi. Escribió su primera canción en español a los ocho años. Habla tres idiomas y es una perfeccionista que pasa horas en el estudio. Su compatriota, el autor Gabriel García Márquez escribió: "La música de Shakira tiene un sello personal que no parece de nadie más y que nadie puede cantar y bailar como ella". Shakira es una de las compositoras poéticas de su generación y está considerada como la mejor compositora en Latinoamérica.

Bueno, para su próxima lección hay más posibilidades: Ricky Martin, Jennifer López, Marc Anthony, Gloria Estefan, Enrique Iglesias…

En mis propias palabras. Do you feel it's important to study other cultures? Should we try to teach students about differences in customs? Does "different" mean "bad"? Write three things you would like to include in a lesson plan to help children learn about the diversity we find in today's schools.

A buscar

This is your lucky day—lesson plans for a month of music class can be found at this website. Listen to the songs, pick your favorite, and prepare a lesson plan for a single class session. Remember you can download the words to the song and print them on overhead transparencies to teach them to students. Of course, if you're musically inclined and can play an instrument too, your class-mates will really enjoy the activity. Their bookstore offers music CDs for purchase.

http://www.hevanet.com/dshivers/juegos/juegos.html

A conocer: De colores

"De colores" is one of the most well-known songs in Spanish, with many variations of verse. Here are the words to two of the most popular stanzas. Using the music from the above website, have a class sing-along.

¿De colores,
de colores se visten los campos
en la primavera.
De Colores,
de colores son los pajaritos que vienen de
afuera.
De colores,
de colores es el arco iris que vemos lucir.
Y por eso los grandes amores
de muchos colores me gustan
a mí.
Y por eso los grandes amores
de muchos colores me gustan
a mí.

Canta el gallo,
canta el gallo con el kiri, kiri, kiri, kiri, kiri.
La gallina,
la gallina con el cara, cara, cara, cara, cara.
Los pollitos,
los pollitos con el pío, pío, pío, pío, pí.
Y por eso los grandes amores
de muchos colores me gustan
a mí.
Y por eso los grandes amores
de muchos colores me gustan
a mí.

LECCIÓN 3

La oficina de salud

Módulo 1
- ¿Qué está pasando?
- Activities in progress: *El presente progresivo*
- ¿Dónde está mi familia?
- Ways of being: **Ser** y **estar**

Módulo 2
- ¿Qué vamos a hacer?
- Telling what you're going to do: *El verbo **ir** y el futuro inmediato*
- Salgo enseguida
- More present activities: *Verbos irregulares en el presente*

Síntesis
- A escuchar
- A conversar
- A leer
- A escribir

Algo más
- Ventana cultural: Los piojos en la escuela
- A buscar
- A conocer: Richard Carmona, U.S. Surgeon General

Módulo I

¿Qué está pasando?

What's going on? (handwritten)

- los paramédicos
- el tobogán/el resbalador
- los columpios *(swings)* (handwritten)
- correr *(run to)* (handwritten)
- el fútbol
- los juegos
- el gimnasio
- *nurse* (handwritten) la enfermera
- el radio
- el pito
- *whistle* (handwritten)
- el monitor
- se cayó
- la cabeza — *head* (handwritten)
- los ojos — *eyes* (handwritten)
- la boca, los dientes
- el brazo — *arm* (handwritten)
- llora — *cry* (handwritten)
- la mano — *hand* (handwritten)
- los pies — *feet* (handwritten)
- el sube y baja
- la nariz
- las piernas
- los tobillos — *ankles* (handwritten)
- *legs* (handwritten)
- saltar a la cuerda
- *hopscotch* (handwritten)
- la rayuela
- la caja de arena — *sandbox* (handwritten)
- *the ups and downs* (handwritten)

A. ¿Cómo se dice?   Complete the following sentences with information from the drawing.

1. La ___*enfermera*___ de la escuela es una profesional de medicina, pero no es doctora.

2. Tres equipos del patio de recreo son ___*los columpios*___, ___*el sube y baja*___ (handwritten) y ___*la caja de arena*___.

3. Tres juegos del patio de recreo son ___*saltar a la cuerda*___, ___*el fútbol*___ y ___*la rayuela*___.

4. Un ___*monitor*___ del patio de recreo es la persona que cuida a los niños.

B. Acciones. Give the verb that the following actions describe. If you cannot remember, check these drawings or drawings from earlier lessons for help.

1. Moverse rápidamente con los pies:_____

2. Tener agua en los ojos por tristeza o dolor *(sadness or pain)*:

_____

3. _____ a la cuerda.

4. Hablar en voz muy ALTA:_____

¿Qué está pasando?

What's all the commotion on the playground? While the principal is away from school, poor little Raúl has fallen from the jungle gym and landed head first on the ground. The school secretary calls on the cell phone with a blow-by-blow description of the action.

DIRECTORA:	Estoy regresando a la escuela en este momento. ¿Está consciente Raúl?
SECRETARIA:	Sí. Está gritando mucho y está llorando por su mamá.
DIRECTORA:	¡Pobrecito! ¿Quién está con él?
SECRETARIA:	Julia, la enfermera, está hablando con él para determinar cómo está y si necesita llamar al 911. Hay una posible fractura y concusión y la enfermera le está dando los primeros auxilios.
DIRECTORA:	¿Dónde están los monitores? ¿Y sus maestros?
SECRETARIA:	Los monitores están ayudando a los otros niños. Juanito y Elena tienen mucho miedo y también están llorando. La Sra. Miller está buscando a su familia, pero dice Raúl que sus padres están trabajando a estas horas.
DIRECTORA:	(corriendo hacia el niño) No llores, corazón. Estoy aquí…

C. ¿Comprende usted? Conteste las preguntas según la información del diálogo.

1. ¿Dónde está la directora en el momento en que Raúl tiene el accidente?
2. ¿Quién llama a la directora?
3. ¿Está consciente Raúl?
4. ¿Qué está haciendo la enfermera?

D. En caso de emergencia. Here's a wonderful place for children in need of emergency medical care. Read the following web page for Miami Children's Hospital's Kidsville services and then complete the activity.

En los centros pediátricos Kidsville - tratamos a los niños como niños

Miami Children's Hospital

Kidsville
Pediatric
Care

¿Qué es un centro pediátrico Kidsville?

En el centro pediátrico Kidsville los niños reciben rápida atención médica de urgencia. El ambiente es agradable y la decoración tiene colores brillantes. Cuenta con salones de juego equipados con juguetes para disminuir la ansiedad de los niños. Para los niños que necesitan atención ambulatoria después de las horas laborables, atención de emergencia o rutinaria, los centros pediátricos Kidsville están a la disposición de la población pediátrica del Sur de Florida. Estos centros sirven para demostrar que los hospitales y las consultas médicas pueden ser lugares agradables.

Los centros pediátricos Kidsville son especiales por muchas razones.

In your own words, describe the following parts of Kidsville.

1. El ambiente y la decoración
2. Los salones de juego
3. Los centros Kidsville

E. El accidente. After Raul's accident, the school principal has decided to see what the school needs to do to make the playground safer. Work with a partner and use these verbs to make a list of things that the school has to do to promote playground safety.

1.	explicar	5.	visitar
2.	enseñar	6.	aprender
3.	mirar	7.	escribir
4.	ver	8.	asistir

MODELO: *1. Visitar otras escuelas para ver sus patios de recreo.*

Estructuras
Activities in progress:
El presente progresivo

- To tell what someone is in the process of doing at a specific moment, use the present progressive.
- ¡OJO! The present progressive tense in English can refer both to an action currently in progress *or* to an action in the future: *I am having lunch with the principal right now* works as well as saying *I am having lunch with the principal next week.* The Spanish present progressive can *only* be used to indicate an action currently in progress, right now!

En este momento, estoy hablando con el maestro.   *I am speaking to the teacher right now.*

- The present progressive is formed by a combination of the verb **estar** (indicating a short-term activity) and the present participle *(-ing)* of the verb expressing what activity is in progress.
- To form the present participle of **–ar** verbs, take off the **–ar** ending and add **–ando.**

hablar > habl + ando = hablando   *speaking*
preparar > prepar + ando = preparando   *preparing*

- To form the present participle of most **–er** and **–ir** verbs, take off the **–er** or **–ir** ending and add **–iendo.**

comer > com + iendo = comiendo   *eating*
escribir > escrib + iendo = escribiendo   *writing*

- To form the present progressive tense, use a conjugated form of **estar** to indicate the person doing the action, and then the present participle.

Estoy comiendo.   *I am eating.*
Estamos esperando   *We are waiting.*
Están escribiendo.   *They are writing.*

- The following verbs have irregular present participles:

dormir *(to sleep)* **durmiendo**   **morir** *(to die)* **muriendo**

- ¡OJO! Spelling rule: Any time an unaccented **–i** falls between two vowels, it automatically changes to **–y.**

leer   *(to read)* > l**e** + **ie**ndo
        > le**y**endo   **Estoy leyendo.**   *I am reading.*

traer   *(to bring)* > tra + **ie**ndo
        > tra**y**endo   **Está trayendo el libro.**   *He is bringing the book.*

Para practicar

A. Actividades. By changing the following verbs to the present progressive tense, you should be able to tell what these people are doing right now.

MODELO: La enfermera examina al niño.
La enfermera está examinando al niño.

1. Las recepcionistas *contestan* los teléfonos.
2. La secretaria *hace* citas con los padres.
3. El estudiante *estudia* el mapa.
4. Dos monitores *trabajan* en el patio de recreo.
5. Unos estudiantes *esperan* en la sala de espera.
6. Dos maestros *escriben* la nueva lección de historia.
7. Los maestros *preparan* las lecciones para mañana.
8. Muchos estudiantes *comen* en la cafetería.

B. La agenda. Tell whom you are with and what you are probably doing at the following times.

MODELO: Son las tres de la mañana y...
Son las tres de la mañana y Patty y yo estamos escribiendo la lección tres.

1. Es mediodía...
2. Son las nueve de la noche y...
3. Son las seis de la mañana y...
4. Son las seis de la tarde y...
5. Es medianoche y...
6. Son las tres y media de la tarde y...

C. Mis compañeros de clase. Look around the room and describe ten things that your classmates or teacher are doing now.

MODELO: *Laura está escribiendo su tarea.*

Módulo I

¿Dónde está mi familia?

los padres (la madre/el padre) *parents*

los abuelos (la abuela/el abuelo) *grandparents*

la concusión *(concussion)*

el hijo *son*

el nieto *grandson*

el corte *(cut)*

la sangre *blood*

la hinchazón *swelling*

el tobillo torcido *twisted / sprained ankle*

la mascota *pet*

los hermanos *siblings*

A. ¿Cómo se dice?   From the illustration above, find a word that matches the following descriptions of injuries.

1. La presión en el cerebro que resulta de un golpe *(blow)* a la cabeza:

  la concución

2. Una lesión en la piel *(skin)* que resulta en la pérdida *(loss)* de sangre:

  el corte

3. Cuando una parte del cuerpo se pone más grande de lo normal:

  la hinchazón

4. Cuando el tobillo no tiene una fractura, pero presenta problemas después de

  un accidente, probablemente está _el tobillo torcido_.

B. La familia. Read the following definitions of family members and supply the correct one!

1. La madre de mi madre es mi _____.

2. El otro hijo de mis padres es mi _____.

3. La esposa de mi papá es mi _____.

4. Los hijos de mis hijos son mis _____.

Pobre Raúl

Poor Raúl. He's hurt and dazed. All he wants is his family.

ENFERMERA:	¿Cómo estás, Raúl? ¿Me escuchas?
RAÚL:	Sí. Yo quiero a mi mamá.
ENFERMERA:	(a la directora) Por lo menos está consciente. (A Raúl) ¿Quién eres? ¿Sabes tu nombre?
RAÚL:	Soy Raúl Torres.
ENFERMERA:	¿Dónde estás?
RAÚL:	Estoy en el patio de recreo.
ENFERMERA:	¿De dónde eres?
RAÚL:	Soy de Chihuahua, México. ¿Dónde está mi hermano, Gabriel?
ENFERMERA:	Él está corriendo hacia la cafetería para buscar hielo para tu hinchazón. El pobre está preocupado y quiere ayudar. Estamos buscando a tus padres o a tus abuelos. ¿Sabes dónde están?
RAÚL:	Mis padres están trabajando y mis abuelos están en México. Creo que mi tía Elena está en mi casa con mis hermanos.
ENFERMERA:	¿Quién es tu tía Elena?
RAÚL:	Es la hermana de mi mamá.

C. ¿Comprende usted? Answer the following questions with information from the dialogue.

1. ¿Por qué es evidente que Raúl está consciente?
2. ¿Qué tres preguntas le hace la enfermera a Raúl?
3. ¿Dónde está Gabriel?
4. ¿Dónde están los padres de Raúl? ¿Los abuelos?

D. Introducción a la Oficina de Salud de su escuela. The school nurse has sent this letter to all of the students and their families. Read the letter and then fill in the missing information in the sentences that follow.

Estimados Padres:

La Oficina de Salud del Distrito Escolar Número 1 tiene equipos de salud con una enfermera escolar certificada y un asistente de enfermería. Cada asistente de salud puede proporcionar resucitación cardiopulmonar y los primeros auxilios, además de ocuparse de la administración de la oficina de salud.

Inscripción:
- Inmunizaciones. La ley #15-872 declara: "todo estudiante debe estar al día con las inmunizaciones". Los padres tienen que presentar el archivo completo y al corriente de las inmunizaciones del niño.
- El formulario de la historia médica del niño.

Servicios de la Oficina de Salud:
- El equipo de la oficina de salud siempre está preparado para observar y evaluar las lastimaduras causadas por accidentes y las enfermedades típicas de los estudiantes. El equipo siempre notifica a los padres inmediatamente en caso de haber problemas.
- Cuando es necesario, la oficina de salud examina a los niños para determinar la presencia de piojos *(head lice)*.
- El equipo de salud es responsable de la administración diaria de medicinas recetadas por el médico.

Exámenes de la salud:
- **Evaluación de la salud dental.** Dos higienistas dentales ofrecen educación dental en todas las escuelas primarias y hacen exámenes dentales en varias escuelas durante todo el año escolar.
- **Evaluación de la vista.** La oficina de salud ofrece exámenes anuales de la vista en los grados: kindergarten, primero, cuarto y sexto.
- **Evaluación de la audición.** Nosotros examinamos la audición de los estudiantes cada año.

Si tiene alguna pregunta o preocupación relativa a los exámenes, por favor, comuníquese con la enfermera de salud.

---

1. Cada equipo de salud tiene dos personas: una _____ y un

_____.

2. Si la enfermera no está, el asistente puede proporcionar_____

y _____.

3. Para inscribir a un estudiante, es necesario presentar un _____

y un _____.

4. Dos exámenes de salud que ofrecen las escuelas son_____ y

_____.

E. Las cartas a las familias. You are in charge of sending letters out to families urging them to seek medical help for their children. As you read through the list of possible problems that each of the children has, decide if you will send a letter urging:

a. un examen de la vista   **b.** un examen dental

c. un examen auditivo   **d.** un examen general.

Then compare your answers with those of a colleague.

1. _____ Carlitos tiene problemas al leer.

2. _____ María siempre quiere que la maestra repita las instrucciones.

3. _____ Elena llora a veces cuando come.

4. _____ Juanito no ve la diferencia entre los colores.

5. _____ Alejandro no respira (*breathe*) bien durante los juegos.

6. _____ Susana siempre tiene sueño en la clase y no participa mucho en el recreo.

Estructuras   *Ways of being: Ser y estar*

- You have already seen that in Spanish, the English verb *to be* has two equivalents: **ser** and **estar.** Each of these Spanish verbs has its own meaning and usage. They are not interchangeable.

Use **estar** to indicate:

- where something or someone is located

El niño **está** en el gimnasio.   *The child is in the gym.*
El corte **está** en la cara.   *The cut is on the face.*

- physical or mental conditions

El niño **está** enfermo hoy.   *The child is sick today.*
Yo **estoy** nerviosa esperando al médico.   *I am nervous waiting for the doctor.*

- circumstances or variable conditions indicating a change from the normal condition

El tobillo torcido **está** hinchado.   *The sprained ankle is swollen.*
Los ojos del niño **están** cerrados.   *The child's eyes are closed.*

- an action in progress with a present participle

El niño **está llorando**. *The boy is crying.*
Estamos esperando la ambulancia. *We are waiting for the ambulance.*

Ser is used to:

- identify people or things

Yo **soy** Raúl Torres. *I am Raúl Torres.*
La Sra. López **es** enfermera. *Mrs. López is a nurse.*

- tell what someone or something is like, including personality and physical traits.

¿Cómo **es** la enfermera? *What is the nurse like?*
La enfermera **es** fuerte y simpática. *The nurse is strong and nice.*

- tell where someone or something is from

La señora **es de** México. *The woman is from Mexico.*
La ambulancia **es de un** hospital. *The ambulance is from a hospital.*

- to whom something belongs or what it is made of

El libro **es de la** enfermera. *The book belongs to the nurse.*
Las vendas **son de** algodón. *The bandages are made of cotton.*

- to indicate the time and place of an event

La cita **es** a las diez. *The appointment is at ten.*
La cita **es** en el hospital. *The appointment is at the hospital.*

- Some adjectives change meaning completely, depending on whether they are used with **ser** or **estar**

estar aburrido/a	*to be bored*	**ser** aburrido/a	*to be boring*
estar listo/a	*to be ready or prepared*	**ser** listo/a	*to be clever*
estar elegante	*to look elegant*	**ser** elegante	*to be elegant*

Para practicar

A. ¿Cómo son?   As a school nurse, you are a very keen observer of the children, adults, and events in the school. Describe what the following people or things are like by finding a logical description from the choices in column B and joining them with **ser.** Be sure to match the adjectives to the subject.

MODELO: El maestro de Educación física   atlético
El maestro de Educación física es atlético.

	A		**B**
1.	El maestro de español que tiene acento	**a.**	muy inteligente
2.	Las reuniones de empleados que duran tres horas	**b.**	alto
3.	El jugador de básquetbol	**c.**	de Colombia
4.	La señora con la sonrisa *(smile)* grande	**d.**	aburrido
5.	El conserje que trabaja 80 horas a la semana.	**e.**	dedicado
6.	Mis compañeros de clase y yo	**f.**	simpático
7.	El señor importante	**g.**	a las diez
8.	La cita	**h.**	director de la escuela

B. ¿Cómo están?   Now guess what the following people are feeling in these situations.

MODELO: Yo, en el examen de la clase de español
Estoy preocupado/a.

1.   La madre de la niña en el accidente
2.   La enfermera que salva la vida *(saves the life)* de un niño
3.   Los niños que esperan sus inmunizaciones para la escuela
4.   Los niños en una fiesta
5.   Un estudiante que tiene una "F" en el examen
6.   El maestro que califica muchos exámenes

C. En la clínica de la escuela.   You are hard at work in the nurse's office on a busy afternoon. Use the proper form of **ser** or **estar** to describe what is happening. Be sure to match the adjectives to the subjects!

MODELO: La enfermera/cansado
La enfermera está cansada.

1.   El maestro de Educación física/preocupado
2.   Los padres del niño enfermo *(sick)*/joven
3.   La maestra/María Espinoza
4.   La familia de Carlitos/de Chile y no habla inglés

Módulo 2

¿Qué vamos a hacer?

What are we going to do? (handwritten)

el resfriado *(cold)* (handwritten)

el vómito

la náusea

la gripe *(flu)* (handwritten)

the pain (handwritten)
el dolor de
estómago/barriga

picar/rascar
Itch/sting/scratch (handwritten)

la erupción
eruption (handwritten)

levantar
to lift (handwritten)

A. ¿Cómo se dice? From the drawing above, give the word that matches the following definitions.

1. Temperatura elevada: _____ *levantar* (handwritten) _____

2. Área de color rosado en la piel—a veces síntoma de una enfermedad:
   — the skin (handwritten)
   _____ *la erupción* (handwritten) _____

3. Sensación en la piel, a veces por un mosquito—¡No la toque!:
   _____ *picar/rascar* (handwritten) _____

4. Otra palabra para estómago o abdomen: _____ *barriga* (handwritten) _____

B. Acciones. Give the verb that the following actions describe.

1. Informar a una persona de una noticia importante: _____

2. Usar las uñas *(fingernails)* para aliviar una comezón: _____

3. Elevar: _____

4. No estar contento—gotas *(drops)* salen de los ojos: _____

No me siento bien

Alicia Prisa, a third grader, goes to the school nurse, la señorita Julia.

ALICIA: Señorita Julia, estoy enferma. Mi maestra dice que debo venir aquí.

ENFERMERA: ¿Qué tienes, Alicia? ¡No llores! Estás pálida. Antes que nada, voy a tomarte la temperatura.

ALICIA: ¿Tengo fiebre?

ENFERMERA: Sí, Alicia. Voy a llamar a tus padres... No hay nadie en casa.

ALICIA: Mi madre está en Dallas en una conferencia. Mi padre está en su oficina. Me duele la cabeza. Necesito una aspirina.

ENFERMERA: Con una fiebre, la aspirina puede ser peligrosa. Tienes que ir al médico. Él va a recomendar los medicamentos que necesitas. ¿Por qué te rascas? ¿Tienes comezón?

ALICIA: ¡Ay, sí! Me pica la barriga.

ENFERMERA: A ver. Levanta la camiseta. Tienes erupción y unas ampollas. Es importante no rascarte. Voy a avisar a tu maestra de que te vas a casa. Tu papá sale inmediatamente de su oficina y va a estar aquí dentro de quince minutos.

C. ¿Comprende usted? Tell who would say the following things, **la enfermera (E)**, **Alicia (A)**, **el padre (P)** or **la maestra (M).** In some cases, there may be more than one logical answer.

1. _____ Estoy enferma.

2. _____ Alicia, debes ir a la oficina de salud.

3. _____ Voy a estar en media hora.

4. _____ Tienes fiebre.

5. _____ Alicia, ¿qué tienes?

6. _____ Espera aquí. Voy a llamar a tus padres.

D. Las vacunas necesarias. Complete the sentences correctly after reading the information on vaccinations for children against measles.

Desde el jardín de infantes hasta la universidad… sus hijos pueden necesitar una segunda vacuna contra el sarampión.

P: *¿Qué es el sarampión?*

R: El sarampión, una enfermedad viral y extremadamente contagiosa, se propaga por el aire por medio de pequeñas gotas de la nariz, la garganta y la boca de la persona infectada. Está siempre acompañado de fiebre y de tos seca y, a veces, de sensibilidad visual a la luz. La mayoría de los niños no debe ir a la escuela por una semana o 10 días.

Casi todos los niños se recuperan por completo del sarampión pero las complicaciones incluyen pulmonía, infección del oído y encefalitis (*inflamación del cerebro*). La encefalitis provocada por el sarampión puede causar un daño permanente al cerebro y en ocasiones puede causar la muerte.

P: *¿Cuándo se debe vacunar a los niños?*

R: Los niños deben recibir su primera vacuna contra el sarampión a los 15 meses de edad y una segunda vacuna contra el sarampión:
• cuando ingresan al jardín de infantes o al primer grado, o
• cuando ingresan a los dos últimos años de la primaria o a los dos primeros años de la secundaria.

P: *¿Pueden causar reacciones las vacunas?*

R: Ocasionalmente se han reportado reacciones leves tales como fiebre o hinchazón y enrojecimiento de la piel en el lugar de la vacuna. Cualquier reacción a la vacuna debe ser reportada a su médico.

1. El sarampión es una enfermedad_____ que es muy

_____ y que se propaga por_____.

2. Algunas complicaciones posibles del sarampión son:_____,

_____ y_____.

3. La encefalitis puede causar _____ permanente y aún

_____.

4. Los niños pueden usar una_____ contra el sarampión.

5. Los niños deben recibir la primera vacuna a _____.

6. Unas reacciones ocasionales de la vacuna son:_____,

_____.

E. En la primaria.   Remember when you went to the nurse's office in elementary school? With a partner, role play a scene in which one of you is a sick child (or one eager to be sent home) and the other is the school nurse.

MODELO: E1: *Estoy enfermo.*
E2: *¿Qué tienes?*

Estructuras *Telling what you're going to do: El verbo ir y el futuro inmediato*

■ Use these forms of the verb **ir** to indicate where someone is going.

ir	to go		
yo	voy	nosotros/as	vamos
tú	vas		
él, ella, Ud.	va	ustedes, ellos/as	van

—¿**Va** Ud. a la cafetería?   —*Are you going to the cafeteria?*
—No, **voy** a la oficina.   —*No, I am going to the office.*

■ A simple way to indicate what is going to happen in the future is to use **ir a +** an infinitive.

—¿**Van Uds. a trabajar** si están   —*Are you both going to work if you're ill?*
enfermos?
—No, **vamos a descansar** hoy.   —*No, we are going to rest today.*
—¿**Va a llamar** a mi madre?   —*Are you going to call my mother?*
—Sí, **voy a llamar** a tu madre.   —*Yes, I am going to call your mother.*

Para practicar

A. ¿Dónde? Tell where these people have to go in order to do what they need to do.

MODELO: El estudiante necesita ver a la enfermera de la escuela. (la oficina)
El estudiante va a la oficina de la enfermera.

1. El maestro necesita trabajar. (la clase)
2. Los padres necesitan comprar medicina. (la farmacia)
3. Necesitamos comer. (McDonald's)
4. Necesito ver a un amigo enfermo. (el hospital)
5. Usted y yo necesitamos estudiar. (mi casa)
6. Ellos necesitan ayudar a una víctima de un accidente. (la sala de emergencia)
7. Los maestros tienen que aprender nuevos métodos. (una reunión)
8. Yo tengo sueño. (la casa)

B. ¿Qué van a hacer? Here's the situation. Tell what can be done to help.

MODELO: Tenemos un examen de español.
Vamos a estudiar.

1. Ustedes tienen hambre.
2. Carmen tiene comezón.
3. Los niños están cansados después de correr por una hora.
4. Elena tiene un nuevo libro de la biblioteca.
5. Soy la maestra de una estudiante enferma.
6. Estoy en el auto y veo un accidente terrible.

C. ¿Y usted? Pick three places that you will go to today and tell three things you will do in each place. Compare answers with a classmate.

MODELO: Voy a mi casa.
Voy a estudiar, voy a preparar comida y a descansar.

Módulo 2

Salgo enseguida — *I'll be right out*

A. ¿Cómo se dice?   From the drawing above, give the word that matches the following definitions.

1. Dos enfermedades de niños—una pica mucho y la otra afecta a los ojos:

_____

2. Información que una persona ausente necesita—puede ser un número de

teléfono: _____

3. Parte de una erupción que está elevada y tiene pus: _____

4. Una crema que se usa para la comezón: _____

B. Acciones. Find a verb from the drawing that matches the description below.

1. tener cuidado *(be careful)*: _____

2. tener información sobre algo: _____

3. abandonar un sitio para ir a otro: _____

4. situar una cosa en otro lugar: _____

¿Cuál es la enfermedad?

Alicia's father, Paco, calls the doctor's office as soon as he gets the news. The receptionist, Maricarmen, has more bad news. Let's listen.

PADRE: Maricarmen, soy Paco Prisa, el padre de Alicia. Salgo en este instante para buscar a Alicia en la escuela. Sé que es tarde, pero necesito hacer una cita urgente para hoy.

MARICARMEN: Lo siento, señor Prisa. El Dr. López no está. ¿Cuál es el problema?

PADRE: Según la enfermera de la escuela, Alicia tiene fiebre, está muy débil y le está saliendo una erupción que pica mucho. La enfermera de su escuela cree que puede ser varicela o sarampión.

MARICARMEN: ¡La pobre! El Dr. López tiene una reunión hoy a las cuatro en la clínica. Sé que Alicia es una de sus pacientes favoritas y él necesita saber lo que pasa. ¿Por qué no van a casa para esperar su llamada? Yo llevo un mensaje a la clínica.

PADRE: ¿Qué hago mientras espero? ¿Pongo loción de calamina en la erupción? ¿Necesita algún medicamento? ¿Debe comer algo especial?

MARICARMEN: La loción es buena idea. Pero yo conozco bien a los niños con varicela. Si es varicela, Alicia no va a tener ganas de tomar nada. Si usted mira la boca, probablemente va a ver que sale la erupción en llagas en la garganta y las encías.

PADRE: Gracias, Maricarmen, conduzco con ella a casa inmediatamente y allí esperamos su llamada. Un momento por favor. ¡Ay! Me pica la barriga...

C. ¿Comprende Ud.? Try to answer the following questions based on the dialogue.

1. ¿Para cuándo necesita el padre la cita para Alicia?
2. ¿Por qué es imposible ver al médico inmediatamente?
3. ¿Qué cree la enfermera de la escuela que tiene Alicia?
4. ¿Dónde va a estar el médico a las cuatro?

D. Una carta de la enfermera.   It is definitely "sick" season and the school nurse has sent home a letter explaining the symptoms of some of the childhood diseases making the rounds of the school. Read the letter and then write down the symptoms for each of the diseases.

Estimada familia:

Hay evidencia de enfermedades muy contagiosas en nuestra escuela. A continuación hay una lista parcial de las enfermedades y los síntomas. Es importante que usted esté alerta para ver si su niño manifiesta algún síntoma. Si usted nota algo, el niño debe permanecer en casa y usted debe llamar al médico y a la escuela para reportarlo.

1. **La varicela *(chicken pox):*** La varicela se caracteriza por ampollas en la cabeza, la boca, el cuello y el abdomen. El enfermo tiene mucho sueño, temperatura elevada y poco apetito.

2. **El sarampión *(measles):*** Al iniciarse, se caracteriza por los síntomas de la gripe: tos, nariz congestionada y fiebre. Al tercer o cuarto día aparece una erupción en la piel. Es importante consultar a su médico porque esta enfermedad a veces tiene complicaciones serias.

3. **Paperas *(mumps):*** Ésta es una enfermedad de las glándulas de la cabeza. Más notable es la inflamación y el dolor debajo de la barbilla (chin). El niño tiene que esperar en casa unos 8–9 días antes de regresar a la escuela.

4. **Conjuntivitis *(pink eye):*** Ésta es una infección causada por un virus, bacteria o alergia y a veces se llama "el ojo rosado". Si no es una reacción alérgica, es una enfermedad sumamente contagiosa. Los síntomas son: ojos muy rojos, secreción amarilla y comezón de los ojos. Con un tratamiento de gotas antibióticas la conjuntivitis normalmente se cura en uno o dos días.

---

1. La varicela se caracteriza por _____.

2. Tres síntomas del sarampión son _____.

3. Si un niño tiene paperas, tiene dolor en _____.

4. La conjuntivitis es una inflamación de los _____.

E. ¿Cuál es la enfermedad?   You are taking over the phones in the school health office today. As each of the following parents describe their child's symptoms, make an educated guess as to which of the above diseases it may be. Write down your diagnosis for each and then compare your list with that of a classmate.

1.   "Mi hijo no puede abrir los ojos esta mañana. Están hinchados y muy rojos..."

Su hijo tiene _____.

2.   "Mi Ángela tiene ampollas por toda la piel, especialmente en el estómago, le pica mucho..."

Creo que Ángela tiene_____.

3.   "Mario tiene una erupción roja por todo el cuerpo. Está sin ganas de comer, tiene un problema con los ojos..."

Mario tiene_____.

Estructuras   *More present activities: Verbos irregulares en el presente*

■ In the present indicative tense, the following verbs are conjugated as regular **-er** and **-ir** verbs in all forms except the **yo** form.

hacer	*(to make or do)*	**hago,**	haces, hace, hacemos, hacen
poner	*(to put or place)*	**pongo,**	pones, pone, ponemos, ponen
salir	*(to go out or to leave, to appear suddenly as in a rash)*	**salgo,**	sales, sale, salimos, salen
traer	*(to bring)*	**traigo,**	traes, trae, traemos, traen
saber	*(to know—information, how to)*	**sé,**	sabes, sabe, sabemos, saben

■ The verb **oír** *(to hear)* follows a different pattern:

oigo, oyes, **oy**e, **oí**mos, **oy**en.

■ The verb **venir** *(to come)* follows the same pattern as tener:

ir = (to go)

vengo, vienes, viene, venimos, vienen

- Verbs ending in **–cer** and **–cir** add the letter **z** before the **c** in the **yo** form only:

parecer *(to seem)*	pare**zco,** pareces, parece, parecemos, parecen
conocer *(to be acquainted with, to personally know people or places)*	cono**zco,** conoces, conoce, conocemos, conocen
traducir *(to translate)*	tradu**zco,** traduces, traduce, traducimos, traducen
producir *(to produce)*	produ**zco,** produces, produce, producimos, producen
conducir *(to drive)*	condu**zco,** conduces, conduce, conducimos, conducen

Ways of knowing: saber y conocer

Both **saber** and **conocer** have equivalents in English: *to know.*

- Use **saber** to indicate that someone knows facts, information, or when followed by an infinitive, how to do something.

Sé el número de teléfono del consultorio.	*I know the medical office number.*
La enfermera **sabe dar** inyecciones.	*The nurse knows how to give injections.*

- Use **conocer** to indicate that somebody is personally familiar with a person or place.

Conozco a un médico excelente.	*I know an excellent doctor.*
No **conozco** este hospital.	*I am not familiar with this hospital.*

Para practicar

A. En la clase de español.   As you sit in your Spanish class, you notice what other students are doing. Tell if you do the same things.

MODELO: Antonio *trae* una novela para leer.
Yo no traigo una novela para leer.

1. Manuela es muy inteligente. *Sabe* todas las respuestas.
2. Aristeo *sale* de la clase para fumar.
3. Marco *pone* los pies en la silla.
4. Carolina *oye* música en su Walkman.
5. Gregorio *hace* muchas preguntas para comprender.
6. Ana *trae* Fritos para comer en la clase.
7. Elena *traduce* su tarea.
8. Carlos *da* su tarea a la maestra muy tarde.

B. En la oficina de salud. It's the middle of flu season and sick children are coming in at an alarming rate. Since other staff members are sick, too, you have to take care of everything except what the patient has to do. Tell if you **(Yo)** or the patient **(P)** will do the following tasks. If you both will do it, use the **nosotros/as** form.

MODELO: limpiar la clínica
Yo limpio la clínica.

1. Hacer las llamadas telefónicas a las familias
2. Traer un libro para leer mientras (*while*) esperan
3. Poner los instrumentos médicos en orden
4. Oír los síntomas de los pacientes
5. Hacer tarea mientras esperan
6. Salir de la oficina muy tarde

C. El primer día en la oficina de salud. You and your classmate are school health assistants in training. Today, you are going to the office for the first time. Take turns quizzing each other on the following problems that you might see today. Find out if your partner knows the symptoms and what to do. Take turns asking and answering.

MODELO: E1: *¿Sabes cuáles son los síntomas de un tobillo torcido?*
E2: *Sé que hay hinchazón y dolor.*

1. la gripe
2. la varicela
3. un resfrío

Vocabulario Módulo 1

Sustantivos

el ambiente	*environment*	**la enfermería**	*nursing*
la ansiedad	*anxiety*	**el/la enfermero/a**	*nurse*
el archivo	*file*	**el/la hermano/a**	*brother, sister*
la arena	*sand*	**el hielo**	*ice*
la audición	*hearing*	**la hinchazón**	*swelling*
la boca	*mouth*	**la lastimadura**	*injury*
el brazo	*arm*	**la ley**	*law*
la cabeza	*head*	**la mascota**	*pet*
el cerebro	*brain*	**la medicina**	*medicine*
los columpios	*swings*	**la medida**	*measure*
el corazón	*heart, sweetheart*	**el/la monitor/a**	*monitor*
el corte	*cut*	**la nariz**	*nose*
el diente	*tooth*	**el/la nieto/a**	*grandchild*

el pie	foot	la resucitación	
la pierna	leg	cardiopulmonar	CPR
los piojos	lice	la sangre	blood
el pito	whistle	el sube y baja	jungle gym
la población	population	el sur	south
los primeros		el tobillo	ankle
auxilios	first aid	el tobogán	slide
la rayuela	hopscotch	la venda	bandage
la receta	prescription, recipe	la vista	vision, view
el resbalador	slide		

Verbos

caerse (ig)	to fall down	morir (ue)	to die
contactar	to contact	moverse (ue)	to move
dar	to give	notificar	to notify
declarar	to declare	ocuparse	to take charge of
disminuir (y)	to reduce	oír (ig) (y)	to hear
evaluar	to evaluate	salir (g)	to leave
gritar	to shout	traer (ig)	to bring
invitar	to invite	tratar	to try
ir	to go		

Adjetivos

adecuado/a	adequate	gratis	free (of charge)
agradable	pleasant	listo/a	ready, clever
capaz	capable	rápido/a	fast
común	common	sexto/a	sixth
consciente	conscious	típico/a	typical
crítico/a	critical	torcido/a	twisted, sprained

Otras expresiones

además	besides	por	through, by, for
al corriente	current	por lo menos	at least
enseguida	at once	saltar a la cuerda	to jump rope
¡Pobrecito/a!	Poor thing!		

Módulo 2

Sustantivos

el aire	air	la barriga	belly, tummy
la alergia	allergy	la cama	bed
la ampolla	blister	la comezón	itch
el asma	asthma	el cuello	neck
el ataque	attack	el daño	damage
la bacteria	bacteria	el dedo	finger
la barbilla	chin	el dolor	pain

la encía	gum (mouth)	la muerte	death
el enrojecimiento	reddening	la náusea	nausea
la erupción	eruption	las paperas	mumps
el estómago	stomach	el pecho	chest
la evidencia	evidence	la piel	skin
la fiebre	fever	la pulmonía	pneumonia
la garganta	throat	el resfriado	cold
la gota	drop	el sarampión	measles
la gripe/gripa	flu	la sensibilidad	sensitivity
el huevo	egg	el síntoma	symptom
el humo	smoke	el sombrero	hat
el jabón	soap	la tos	cough
la lista	list	el tratamiento	treatment
la llaga	sore	la vacuna	vaccination
la luz	light	la varicela	chicken pox
la mayoría	majority	las vías	
el mensaje	message	respiratorias	respiratory tract
la mitad	half	el vómito	vomit

Verbos

aclarar	to clarify	ingresar	to enroll
aliviar	to relieve	levantar	to lift
avisar	to notify	manifestar (ie)	to show
caracterizar	to characterize	parecer (zc)	to seem
cerrar (ie)	to close	permanecer (zc)	to remain, stay
conducir (zc)	to drive	picar	to itch, sting
consultar	to consult	poner (g)	to put, place
curar	to cure	producir (zc)	to produce
doler (ue)	to hurt, cause pain	quitar	to remove
entrar	to enter	rascar	to scratch
evitar	to avoid	recuperarse	to recuperate
		traducir (zc)	to translate

Adjetivos

alérgico/a	allergic	estadounidense	American (U.S.)
alerto/a	alert	pálido/a	pale
algún/uno/a	some	rosado/a	pink
contagioso/a	contagious	seco/a	dry
desconocido/a	unknown	último/a	last

Otras expresiones

a continuación	following	contra	against
a veces	at times	debajo de	under
acerca de	about, concerning	por medio de	by means of
casi	almost	tal	such
cerca de	near		

Síntesis

A escuchar

Alicia está en casa muy enferma con la varicela. Su mejor amiga, Elena, llama para saber cómo está.

Read the following questions before listening to the dialogue. Then, write your answers.

1. ¿Qué cree la maestra que tiene Alicia?
2. ¿Dónde está la erupción?
3. ¿Por qué no debe ir Elena a la casa de Alicia?
4. ¿Qué cree la madre de Elena?
5. ¿Qué lleva Elena a la casa de Alicia?

A conversar

In groups of four, discuss common childhood medical situations, including colds, minor accidents, illnesses such as chicken pox, and common reasons to be sent home from school that are related to health problems.

MODELO: E1: *Un niño resfriado tiene que regresar a casa.*
E2: *Hay accidentes a veces cuando juegan afuera (outside).*

A leer

Read the following informational brochure on asthma and then complete the activity by writing **Sí** or **No** after each statement. Correct any incorrect information.

Lo que cada paciente necesita saber acerca del asma

¿Qué es el asma?

El asma es una enfermedad de los pulmones y las vías respiratorias caracterizada por problemas respiratorios recurrentes. Durante un "ataque" de asma, puede sentir que le falta el aire y tener mucha dificultad al respirar. Las vías respiratorias se inflaman causando una constricción, y durante un ataque de asma prolongado pueden bloquearse con secreciones mucosas. El flujo de aire que entra y sale de los pulmones está restringido y usted puede toser, resollar (*wheeze*) y sentir una sensación de tener el "pecho apretado (*tight*)".

El asma no es una enfermedad contagiosa. Su causa es desconocida, pero es más probable que uno tenga asma si sus familiares sufren de esta enfermedad también.

¿Qué causa un ataque de asma?

Las vías respiratorias de los pacientes asmáticos son muy sensibles a ciertas alergias o sustancias en el aire que causan los ataques de asma. Las sustancias y actividades más comunes que pueden causar ataques de asma son…

- humo (tanto de tabaco como de madera (*wood*))
- polvo (*dust*) (incluyendo partículas microscópicas en la casa)
- polen
- pelo de animales
- plumas (*feathers*)
- moho (*mold*)
- ejercicio

Otras sustancias y actividades menos comunes que también pueden causar ataques de asma incluyen olores fuertes (*strong smells*) y rocíos (*sprays*) como la laca para el pelo, alimentos (*foods*) como los huevos, medicinas como la aspirina, cambios de clima, emociones fuertes y ciertos insectos como las cucarachas.

1. _____ El asma es una enfermedad del corazón.
2. _____ Sólo el humo de tabaco es un problema para asmáticos.
3. _____ El asma no es contagiosa.
4. _____ Las emociones fuertes pueden causar un ataque de asma.
5. _____ La persona que sufre un ataque siente la falta de aire.
6. _____ Una persona con asma puede tener familiares con la misma enfermedad.

A escribir

Summarize the information on asthma from the article above in three sentences, selecting only the important highlights. Compare your summary with that of a classmate.

Algo más = Something more

Ventana cultural

Estimada familia:

Tenemos una visita no muy bienvenida: piojos. Sin embargo, con un poco de cuidado, pronto podremos decir "adiós" a los parásitos que usan la cabeza y el pelo como "hotel". Los piojos son una epidemia entre los estudiantes de primaria. Si su estudiante tiene comezón constante de la cabeza, es posible que tenga piojos. Es un problema muy contagioso como la gripe; así que es importante tomar estas medidas:

1. Se necesita un champú especial. Llame al médico o hable con el farmacéutico para que le den algunas sugerencias.

2. Siga las instrucciones del champú. Después de lavar el pelo, use una solución de vinagre y agua para crear un entorno hostil para los piojos.

3. Use los dedos o un peine (*comb*) especial para quitar los huevos (*eggs*) del pelo.

4. Es muy importante desinfectar todos los artículos que usan las personas infectadas: lave la ropa, los sombreros y los peines con agua caliente y jabón. Lave la ropa de la cama (*bedding*) también. Una limpieza completa de la casa también va a ayudar a cerrar las puertas a los piojos.

5. El estudiante no debe venir a la escuela durante el tratamiento por peligro de contagiar a otros estudiantes. La enfermera tiene que revisar a su estudiante antes de su regreso a la clase.

Gracias. Y si tiene alguna pregunta, llámenos.

Atentamente,

Julia Rey

Julia Rey
La enfermera escolar

En mis propias palabras.   As a community liaison for the school, you have to make follow-up phone calls to the families who have received the letters. In four sentences or less, using your own words, please summarize the steps the families should take.

A buscar

It is common in Hispanic countries for doctors to make house calls, and pharmacies have **practicantes**, pharmacists who can administer injections and prescribe medication. There are **guardias**, pharmacies that take turns staying open 24 hours a day, that are listed in the local newspaper. But, once again, technology is changing the world by virtual consultations. Look up at least two websites that offer online "ask the expert" service. Try the links at www.prenhall.com/rush in the category of Health/Salud. Plus find your own! Look up **el asma** or **los piojos** on one of the medical advice websites and bring their recommendations to class.

A conocer: Richard Carmona, U.S. Surgeon General

In July, 2002, Richard Carmona was unanimously confirmed as the U.S. Surgeon General. Long involved in community trauma and health issues, Carmona has proven his commitment to education—both professional and community—in his on-going roles as Professor at the University of Arizona and Director of Emergency Medical Technology at Pima Community College. In his support of Carmona's nomination, Arizona Senator John McCain said:

> "Dr. Carmona's inspiring story is the living embodiment of the American dream. A high school dropout, Richard Carmona first served our nation with the Special Forces in Vietnam, where he became a decorated Green Beret. Upon his return, he obtained his high school equivalency and became the first member of his family to graduate from college. He went on to become a nurse and later enrolled in medical school, specializing in trauma surgery."

Find out more about the country's second Latino Surgeon General and his continuing focus on education at www.surgeongeneral.org

LECCIÓN 4

El personal de la escuela

Módulo 1
- Evaluaciones
- Indicating relationships: *Los adjetivos posesivos*
- Una reunión
- Describing daily activities: *Los verbos con cambios de raíz*

Consejera

Módulo 2
- Más ayuda, menos problemas
- Comparing and contrasting: *Los comparativos*
- Los mejores
- Comparing and contrasting: *Los superlativos*

Síntesis
- A escuchar
- A conversar
- A leer
- A escribir

Algo más
- Ventana cultural: PECES
- A buscar
- A conocer: Yolanda Benítez

Módulo I

Evaluaciones *Evaluations*

Nombre:
Alejandro Braun Prieto

Maestro/a: Sra. Miller

Año: 2ᵈᵒ

reading test
Prueba de lectura: F

mathematics test
Prueba de matemáticas: F
12 + 10 = _____
12 + 10 = 31

spelling test
Prueba de ortografía: D
1. see
2. baot
3. sircus

Materias	Calificación
Matemáticas	C
Lenguaje	D
Educación física	C
Esfuerzo	S
Comportamiento	S
Comentarios:	

effort

la Boleta de calificaciones
the report card

mal comportamiento
bad behavior

desanimado
discouraged

A. ¿Recuerda Ud.?   Fill in the blank with the word or phrase described.

1. _____*e*_____ calificaciones
2. _____*d*_____ desanimado
3. _____*b*_____ comportamiento
4. _____*a*_____ comentarios

a. opiniones y recomendaciones
b. la manera de actuar en la clase o comunidad
d. frustrado
e. la notas que miden el progreso en el aprendizaje

[handwritten: the notes that measure progress in learning]

B. Acciones.   Many of the above nouns have recognizable verb forms. See if you can match the actions in column **A** with close equivalents in column **B**.

A	B
[encourage] 1. animar	a. evaluar *[evaluate]*
[qualify] 2. calificar	b. examinar *[examine]*
[try] 3. probar	c. opinar *[review]*
[comment] 4. comentar	d. motivar *[motivate]*

La boleta de calificaciones

It's report-card day and Alejandro is showing his grades to his mother. Oh, no! His grades are down for the second quarter in a row. Poor Alejandro! What will his parents say? Let's find out.

MAMÁ: Alejandro, mi hijo, ¿qué pasó? Otra vez tus notas son malas. Mira esta nota en matemáticas: una "C". Y tu nota en lectura es una "D". ¿No estás estudiando bastante?

ALEJANDRO: (llorando) No sé, mamá. Estudio mucho. Ya sabes que preparo mi tarea todos los días. En la escuela, en la hora de recreo, cuando mis amigos salen a jugar, yo no salgo. Me quedo en clase y practico las letras y la lectura con la maestra. Pero nada me sale bien. ¡No quiero volver a la escuela, no quiero, no quiero, no quiero...!

[handwritten: CRYING]
[handwritten: You are not studying enough when my friends go out to play I dont go out]
[handwritten: but nothing]

MAMÁ: Alejandro, no llores. En las secciones de esfuerzo y comportamiento tus notas son "satisfactorias". Voy a llamar a tu maestra...

[handwritten: I'm going to call your teacher]

ALEJANDRO: (llorando más) No, mamá. Por favor, no...

MAMÁ: Alejandro, ¿por qué?

ALEJANDRO: ¡Ay, mamá! Porque la semana pasada ella te mandó esta nota (crumpled paper) para hacer una cita... Tengo miedo, Mama.

[handwritten: to make an appointment - I'm scared]

MAMÁ: Alejandro, tu maestra te quiere mucho. Nosotros tenemos un problema. Ella es nuestra solución. Voy a llamar inmediatamente. (regresa). Alejandro, la Sra. Miller tiene muchas ideas sobre las causas de tus problemas. Yo creo que sus soluciones son excelentes. Nuestra cita con ella y con la consejera es el lunes a las cuatro. Ánimo, hijo. Tus días escolares y tus notas van a ser mucho mejores.

[handwritten: loves you very much]
[handwritten: returns]
[handwritten: She is our solution]
[handwritten: I think]
[handwritten: counselor]

C. ¿Comprende usted?   Decide if each of the statements is **Cierto (C)** or **Falso (F)** based on the dialogue. If the statement is incorrect, provide the correct information.

1. ____F____ Alejandro está llorando porque tiene una buena boleta de calificaciones.

2. ____C____ Normalmente no sale a jugar durante la hora del recreo.

3. ____F____ La maestra opina que Alejandro es un estudiante que se comporta mal en la clase.

4. ____C____ Alejandro tiene miedo porque la maestra quiere hablar con su mamá.

D. Una prueba.   Not all students are as motivated as Alejandro. He's not succeeding, but it is not for lack of effort. Read the following quiz to tell if "your child" is motivated; then answer the questions.

¿Está su hijo en el camino al éxito en la escuela?

Con frecuencia, el éxito o el fracaso académico dependen de la actitud del estudiante. Si su hijo está contento en la escuela y tiene confianza en sus habilidades, claro que va a estar más motivado hacia la excelencia. Piense en la actitud de su hijo hacia la escuela y conteste estas preguntas para saber si su hijo está en el camino al éxito.

1. Cuando regresa de la escuela, mi hijo está contento con su día escolar:
     ⊗ **SÍ**   ○ **NO**

2. Si recibe malas notas, mi hijo dice que es por culpa (*the fault of*) del maestro u otro factor y no acepta la responsabilidad:
     ○ **SÍ**   ⊗ **NO**

I always have to promise my son a gift to motivate him to get good grades
3. Yo siempre tengo que prometerle a mi hijo un regalo para motivarlo a sacar buenas notas:
     ○ **SÍ**   ⊗ **NO**

4. Con frecuencia, mi hijo se levanta por la mañana con dolor de cabeza o del estómago:
     ○ **SÍ**   ⊗ **NO**

On Mondays after several days without seeing his classmates, my son wants to go back to school
5. Los lunes, después de varios días sin ver a sus compañeros de clase, mi hijo quiere regresar a la escuela:
     ⊗ **SÍ**   ○ **NO**

My son cries and says "I can't / I am not able" the work is a little difficult
6. Mi hijo llora y dice, "no puedo" si la tarea es un poco difícil:
     ○ **SÍ**   ⊗ **NO**

1. ¿Cuáles son dos indicadores de que su hijo está motivado?

2. ¿Cuáles son dos indicadores de que su hijo *no* está motivado?

E. Conclusiones. Both of you are student-teachers getting ready to have a conference with a parent whose student—according to this quiz—is not very motivated. Together, go through the list point-by-point and make some suggestions to the parent to help motivate the child.

MODELO: *Su hijo no está muy motivado si no habla mucho sobre su día en la escuela. Usted debe hacer preguntas específicas, como "¿Qué estudian en matemáticas?"*

Estructuras

Indicating relationships: Los adjetivos posesivos

- Possessive adjectives describe relationships among people and their belongings.

Los adjetivos posesivos					
	Singular			**Plural**	
yo	**mi/s**	*my*	nosotros	**nuestro/a/os/as**	*our*
tú	**tu/s**	*your, (familiar)*			
usted	**su/s**	*your, (formal)*	ustedes	**su/s**	*your*
él	**su/s**	*his*	ellos	**su/s**	*their*
ella	**su/s**	*her*	ellas	**su/s**	*their*

- Possessive adjectives agree in number with the noun that *follows* them. Only **nuestro/a** has additional forms for masculine and feminine.

Mi hijo es inteligente.	*My son is intelligent.*
Mis hijos son inteligente**s**.	*My children are intelligent.*
Nuestra familia es inteligente.	*Our family is intelligent.*

- Since **su/s** can mean *his, her, your, their,* or *its,* the form **de + él, ella, usted, ellos, ellas,** or **ustedes** is frequently substituted to ensure clarity. The accented **él** meaning *he* does not contract to **del.** Only **de + el** (unaccented, meaning *the*) has that ability.

sus amigos	**=**	los amigos **de él**	*his friends*
		los amigos **de ella**	*her friends*
		los amigos de **Ud./Uds.**	*your friends*
		los amigos de **ellos/ellas**	*their friends*

El examen **de ella** está en la computadora.   *Her test is on the computer.*
Los exámenes **de él** están en el escritorio.   *His tests are on the desk.*

■ Note: there is **no** apostrophe *s* ('s) in Spanish to show possession. Use the **definite article + noun + de** to show possession.

la familia de María   *María's family*
los exámenes de Julio   *Julio's tests*

■ To find out to whom something belongs ask, **¿De quién es…?**

—**¿De quién es el libro?**   *Whose book is this?*
—**Es el libro del profesor Mateo.**   *It's Professor Mateo's book.*

Para practicar

A. Mi familia.   Tell which of my relatives are described here.

MODELO: El otro hijo de mis padres
                   Mi hermano

1.   Los hermanos de mi padre   _mis tíos_

2.   Los padres de mi madre   _mis abuelos_

3.   Las hijas de mi tía   _mis primas_

4.   El padre de mis primas   _mi tío_

B. Posesión.   Give the correct form of the possessive adjectives **mi/s, tu/s, su/s, nuestro/a/as/os.**

MODELO: Yo tengo un buen maestro. _____ maestro trabaja
                   en el Colegio San Juan.
                   Mi maestro trabaja en el Colegio San Juan.

1.   Tú tienes crayones. _____Tus_____ crayones están en la mochila.

2.   Ustedes tienen dinero. _____Su_____ dinero está en la mesa.

3.   Ella tiene malas notas. _____Sus_____ malas notas son en lectura y
     ciencias.

4.   Nosotros tenemos una pregunta. _____Nuestra_____ pregunta es para el
     director.

5.   Ellos tienen un problema. _____Su_____ problema es fácil de
     remediar.

6.   Ellos tienen problemas con la historia. _____Sus_____ problemas no
     son serios.

C. Sus experiencias académicas. What is your academic history like? Have you ever gotten an "F" in a class? Answer the following questions as if it were happening now. If you've *never* gotten a bad grade ever, use your imagination to describe what it might be like. Then compare your answers with a classmate's.

1. ¿En qué clase recibes malas notas?
2. ¿Cómo es el maestro o la maestra?
3. ¿Estás aburrido en la clase o motivado?
4. ¿Qué puedes hacer para sacar una nota más alta?

Módulo I

Una reunión

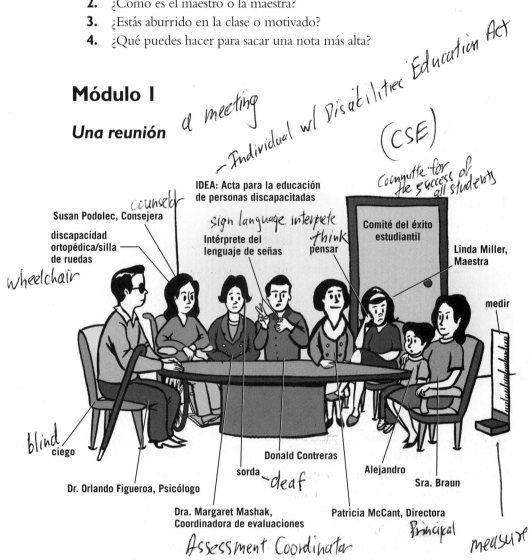

IDEA: Acta para la educación de personas discapacitadas

Susan Podolec, Consejera

discapacidad ortopédica/silla de ruedas

Intérprete del lenguaje de señas

pensar

Comité del éxito estudiantil

Linda Miller, Maestra

medir

ciego

Donald Contreras

sorda

Alejandro

Sra. Braun

Dr. Orlando Figueroa, Psicólogo

Dra. Margaret Mashak, Coordinadora de evaluaciones

Patricia McCant, Directora

A. ¿Cómo se dice? Use your imagination, the drawing, and your memory to match the words or concepts in column **A** with column **B**.

A

1. impedimento visual *B*
2. impedimento auditivo *C*
3. problemas específicos de aprendizaje *D*
4. lenguaje de signos *A*

B

a. communicación con las manos
b. ceguera *blindness*
c. sordera *deafness*
d. dislexia

B. ¿Recuerda usted? See if you can match the phrases in column **A** with close equivalents in column **B**.

A

1. Usar el cerebro y la imaginación *C*
2. Una evaluación es para _____ el progreso académico. *A*
3. Solicitar una cosa de otra persona *D*
4. Ofrecer soluciones *B*

B

a. medir *measure*
b. recomendar *recommend*
c. pensar *think*
d. pedir *ask*

La reunión *The meeting*

Today Alejandro and his mother are meeting with the team of resource specialists at his school to talk about his progress. There is good news. And more good news!

DIRECTORA: Bienvenida, señora. Alejandro, necesito un abrazo, por favor. Quiero presentarles a los miembros de nuestro Comité de éxito estudiantil: la Sra. Podolec, nuestra consejera, el Dr. Figueroa, el psicólogo estudiantil y la Dra. Mashak, jefa del Departamento de evaluaciones. Alejandro, ¿comprendes por qué estamos aquí?

ALEJANDRO: Sí. Porque no soy buen estudiante.

SRA. MILLER: Al contrario; eres muy inteligente... y muy aplicado. Hoy queremos hablar de las maneras en que podemos ayudarte a aprender las lecciones más fácil y rápidamente. ¿Quieres?

ALEJANDRO: ¿Y puedo salir al patio de recreo con mis amigos? ¡Claro que quiero!

PSICÓLOGO: Excelente. Señora, recomiendo un plan de tres pasos:
1. Una evaluación inicial con una batería de pruebas que miden el progreso y potencial de Alejandro para establecer su elegibilidad para servicios especiales.
2. La diagnosis e interpretación de los resultados.
3. El diseño de un IEP.

MADRE:	¿IEP? No comprendo.
PSICÓLOGO:	El programa individual de educación. Si Alejandro cualifica y usted pide nuestros servicios, nosotros junto con usted y Alejandro formulamos un plan detallado de su educación según sus necesidades. Y después, empezamos un proceso para vigilar su progreso y ajustar el plan.
MADRE:	Pienso que es una solución excelente. ¿Y tú, Alejandro? ¿Qué dices?
ALEJANDRO:	Si puedo ir al patio de recreo, y si puedo estar en la clase de la Sra. Miller, (una sonrisa grande) digo: ¡SÍ!

C. ¿Comprende usted?   Answer the following questions based on the dialogue.

1. ¿Quiénes forman el Comité del éxito estudiantil?
2. ¿Por qué cree Alejandro que necesitan una reunión?
3. ¿Qué hacen los evaluadores en la evaluación inicial?
4. ¿Qué es un IEP?

D. IDEA.   Read the following definitions of disabilities according to the federal Individuals with Disabilities Education Act. Then, in your own words, show your basic understanding of the indicated disabilities—in Spanish, of course!

MODELO: Sordera:
Es una discapacidad que afecta la habilidad de oír.

Definiciones de algunas "discapacidades" incluidas en IDEA que afectan adversamente el desempeño escolar

1. **Sordera:** Un impedimento auditivo tan severo que el niño se ve impedido al intentar procesar información lingüística a través del oído, con o sin amplificación.

2. **Retraso mental:** Un funcionamiento intelectual general bajo promedio, el cual coexiste con un déficit en la conducta adaptable, manifestándose durante el período del desarrollo.

3. **Otros impedimentos de la salud:** Una condición que se caracteriza por falta de energía, vitalidad o actividad, a causa de problemas de la salud crónicos o agudos, como una condición cardíaca, tuberculosis, fiebre reumática, nefritis, asma, anemia de hoz, hemofilia, epilepsia, envenenamiento con plomo, leucemia, diabetes o déficit de la atención.

4. **Problema específico del aprendizaje:** La presencia de algún trastorno en uno o más de los procedimientos psicológicos básicos necesarios para la comprensión o uso del lenguaje, hablado o escrito, que puede manifestarse como una habilidad imperfecta para escuchar, pensar, hablar, leer, escribir, comprender la ortografía o realizar cálculos matemáticos. El término incluye tales problemas como trastornos preceptuales, lesiones cerebrales, malfunción cerebral mínima, dislexia y afasia del desarrollo.

5. **Impedimentos visuales, incluyendo la ceguera:** Un impedimento visual, aún con corrección—incluye a los niños videntes-parciales y a los ciegos.

1. la ceguera
2. problemas del aprendizaje
3. déficit de la atención
4. retraso mental

Estructuras

Describing daily activities: Los verbos con cambios de raíz   *Verbs with root changes*

- You have already seen an example of a verb that has a spelling change in the stem (main part of the verb), as well as in the endings:

to have
tener > **tengo, tienes, tiene, tenemos, tienen**   *to have*

Note that the **nosotros/as** is the *only* form that is based on the spelling of the infinitive. That is what all stem-changing verbs have in common.

■ When stem-changing verbs are conjugated, the stressed **e** will become **ie** or **i,** and the stressed **o** will become **ue** in all forms except **nosotros/as.**

(can)

	recomendar (ie) *to recommend*	poder (ue) *to be able*	pedir (i) *to ask for*
yo	recom**ie**ndo	p**ue**do	p**i**do
tú	recom**ie**ndas	p**ue**des	p**i**des
Ud./él/ella	recom**ie**nda	p**ue**de	p**i**de
Nosotros/as	recomendamos	p**o**demos	pedimos
Uds./ellos/ellas	recom**ie**ndan	p**ue**den	p**i**den

*puede – can
(add to verb*

■ More stem-changing verbs are:

Use with other infinitive verb

e > ie	**o > ue**	**e > i**
cerrar *to close*	**acostar(se)** *to go to bed*	**decir** *to say or tell*
comenzar *to begin*	**almorzar** *to eat lunch*	**despedirse** *to say goodbye*
entender *to understand*	**contar** *to count*	**elegir** *to opt or elect*
mentir *to lie*	**costar** *to cost*	**medir** *to measure*
pensar *to think*	**dormir** *to sleep*	**repetir** *to repeat*
perder *to lose*	**encontrar** *to meet*	**seguir★** *to follow*
preferir *to prefer*	**recordar** *to remember*	**★ (yo sigo)**
querer *to want,*	**volver** *to return*	**servir** *to serve*

*to miss –
to lose weight*

*to want, to wish
to hope for*

■ The verb **jugar** *(to play)* is the only **u > ue** verb in Spanish.

j**ue**go, j**ue**gas, j**ue**ga, jugamos, j**ue**gan

■ The verb **decir (i)** *(to tell)* has an additional change in the **yo** form

Remember

digo, dices, dice, decimos, dicen

¡Recuerde! Stem-changing verbs, **e > ie, e > i,** and **o > ue,** change in all forms except **nosotros/as.**

Para practicar

A. ¡Yo también!   Break time. You are on break from your teaching duties in an elementary school, and you overhear two colleagues discussing how they handle things. Tell if you do the same things.

MODELO: Nosotros almorzamos en el escritorio mientras calificamos la tarea.
Yo almuerzo en la cafetería.

1.   Nosotros volvemos tarde a la clase después del almuerzo.
2.   Nosotros queremos ayudar a los estudiantes.
3.   Nosotros pensamos mucho en los estudiantes.
4.   Nosotros dormimos en la oficina.
5.   Nosotros servimos el almuerzo en la cafetería.
6.   Nosotros repetimos las instrucciones con paciencia.
7.   Nosotros mentimos a la directora.
8.   Nosotros preferimos trabajar en el patio de recreo

B. ¿Quién?   Tell if you, a teacher (**Yo**), your student (**Mis estudiantes**), or all (**Nosotros**) would do the following things in school.

MODELO: empezar a mirar un vídeo
Yo empiezo a mirar un vídeo.

[handwritten: I start to look at a video]

1.   _____ dormir mucho
[handwritten: No dormimos mucho en la escuela]

2.   _____ almorzar en la cafetería
[handwritten: Nosotros almorzamos en la cafetería]

3.   _____ volver a casa todos los días
[handwritten: Nosotros volvemos a casa todos los días]

4.   _____ recomendar mucho estudio
[handwritten: Yo recomiendo mucho estudio]

5.   _____ despedir a los estudiantes a las 3
[handwritten: Yo despido a los estudiantes a las tres]

6.   _____ preferir no tener tarea
[handwritten: to say goodby/fire]
[handwritten: Mis estudiantes prefieren no tener tarea]

C. Con un amigo.   You and a classmate have just been hired into a new job as recreation counselors at a school to ensure that after-school students are as happy and motivated as possible. The problem is that you and your friend have to make up the job description. Brainstorm a list of as many activities as possible for each of the actions below:

empezar   pedir   servir   jugar

MODELO: **empezar**
Empezamos un juego.   Empezamos un club de tarea.

Módulo 2

Más ayuda, menos problemas
Mae help, less problems

Jose is taller than

José es más alto que Juan y Juana

Bad
Malo
worse
Peor

Jorge Gómez

A   A+

Good
Bueno
¡Mejor!
Better/ ~~Best~~
la roca
the rock

Bok teble musik   D F

José

Juana es tan alta como Juan
is as tall as

frustrado con el problema
frustrated with the problem

A. ¿Mejor o peor? Tell which of these pairs is **mejor** and which is **peor**—in your opinion.

1. mejor
chocolate/vainilla

3. matemáticas/historia mejor

2. A+ / F mejor

4. béisbol/fútbol mejor

B. Asociaciones. Can you finish these popular similes with one of these words in Spanish?

a. relámpagos   b. casa   c. ratoncito   d. búho

1. Tan grande como una ___ b ___.

3. Tan sabio *(wise)* como un ___ d ___.

2. Tan silencioso como un ___ c ___.

4. Tan rápido como los ___ a ___.

La escuela

After receiving the results of his tests, Alejandro and his mother have learned that he is gifted but also has a combination of problems—a learning disability. One of the objectives in his IEP is to master storytelling in a logical sequence and to learn to express himself better orally. His Speech and Language teacher, Miss Hernández, has asked him to write about his changing feelings about school.

ALEJANDRO: Pues, ahora me gusta la escuela mucho más. Con la ayuda de mi familia y de mis maestros (tengo más maestros que los otros estudiantes,) ahora sé que puedo hacer el trabajo. El psicólogo dice que soy más inteligente que muchos de los estudiantes del segundo grado, pero el problema es que tengo que trabajar más que ellos. Para mí, las matemáticas son menos difíciles que la lectura. A veces lloro cuando no puedo hacer mi tarea, pero ahora hay menos lágrimas que risa cuando mi mamá me ayuda. Ella tiene más paciencia cuando hacemos la tarea, y si empiezo a llorar, me da unas galletas o yo salgo a jugar con mis amigos un rato. Ella siempre dice: "la frustración es peor que la equivocación". Dicen que la actividad física es tan importante como la tarea para mí, y ahora salgo al patio de recreo todos los días. Mi amigo, Juanito, es más atlético que yo, pero con mucha práctica, voy a ser tan fuerte como él. Es lo que dice la maestra—que con más práctica y más concentración voy a ser más fuerte en todo. (ja-ja). Cada noche cuando termino mi tarea para la clase de la Sra. Miller, tengo más tarea para la Srta. Hernández: miro mi programa favorito de televisión y después le cuento el programa a mi mamá. Si cuento todo el programa en orden, puedo jugar con mis nuevos juegos de vídeo por media hora. Mi salud es mucho mejor que antes también. Ahora no tengo dolores de estómago antes de ir a la escuela.

C. ¿Comprende usted? Tell whether the following statements are **Cierto (C)** or **Falso (F).** If a statement is false, provide the correct information.

1. Los resultados de las pruebas de Alejandro indican que no es muy inteligente.
2. Alejandro ahora tiene más autoestima.
3. Su mamá tiene más paciencia y él llora menos ahora.
4. Cuando está frustrado, su mamá grita mucho.

D. Los problemas del aprendizaje. Read the following list of potential warning signs of learning disabilities and see if any of the symptoms are familiar to you. Even if you do show some, it does not mean that there is a learning disability.

¿Cuáles son las señales de un problema de aprendizaje?

- Puede tener problemas para aprender el alfabeto, rimar las palabras o conectar las letras con sus sonidos;

- Puede cometer errores al leer en voz alta, y repetir o detenerse a menudo;

- Puede no comprender lo que lee;

- Puede tener dificultades al deletrear (spell) palabras;

- Puede aprender el lenguaje de forma atrasada y tener un vocabulario limitado;

- Puede tener dificultades para seguir instrucciones;

- Puede confundir los símbolos matemáticos y leer mal los números;

- Puede no poder repetir un cuento en orden (lo que ocurrió primero, segundo, tercero); o

- Puede no saber por dónde comenzar una tarea o cómo seguir desde allí.

E. Con frecuencia, a veces, nunca. Learning disabilities are difficult to diagnose and difficult to define. Everyone shows some symptoms from time to time, but it does not mean that they have a learning problem. Read through the list above and tell whether or not you have experienced each of the symptoms. If it is a frequent one for you, mark it **(frecuente).** If it is occasional, mark **(a veces)** and if you never experience it, mark it **(nunca).** Then compare your answers with two more students to see if you coincide.

Estructuras

Comparing and contrasting:
Los comparativos — *Comparatives* — put quality adjective noun here

- For comparisons of inequality (more than/less than), use **más... que** or **menos... que** with a noun, an adjective, or an adverb.

Hay **más** niños **que** niñas en la clase.	*There are more boys than girls in the class.*
Hay **menos** niñas **que** niños.	*There are fewer girls than boys.*
Esta clase es **más** grande **que** la otra.	*This class is larger than the other.*

- For comparisons of equality (the same as) use **tan... como** with adjectives and adverbs, and **tanto/a/os/as... como** with nouns.

Carola es **tan** alta **como** Juanito.	*Carola is as tall as Juanito.*
El proceso es **tan** útil **como** la respuesta.	*The process is as useful as the answer.*
Yo tengo **tantos** estudiantes **como** ellos.	*I have as many students as they do.*
Julio hace **tanto** trabajo **como** Ana.	*Julio does as much work as Ana.*

hacer = to do, make

the same as

- **Más, menos,** and **tanto como** can all be used with verbs to compare actions.

Yo trabajo **menos** ahora.	*I work less now.*
Nosotros estudiamos **más** ahora.	*We study more now.*
Ellos aprenden **tanto como** el año pasado.	*They learn as much as last year.*

- Use the following irregular comparisons to say *better, worse, older,* or *younger.*

better than
worse than
older than
younger than

Su nota es **mejor que** mi nota.	*Your grade is better than my grade.*
Mi nota es **peor que** su nota.	*My grade is worse than your grade.*
Pablo es **mayor que** Susana.	*Pablo is older than Susana.*
La directora es **menor que** el maestro.	*The principal is younger than the teacher.*

- To say *more than* or *less than* or *fewer than* with numbers, use **más de** or **menos de.**

Hay **más de** 15 clases aquí.	*There are more than fifteen classes here.*
Falta **menos de** una hora para el examen.	*There is less than an hour for the test.*

Para practicar

A. ¿Es fácil o difícil? Use **más que** or **menos que** to tell which of the following tasks is more difficult for you. If they are equally easy or difficult, use **tan... como** or **tanto... como.** Don't forget to make your adjectives match the nouns.

MODELO: el lenguaje o las matemáticas
Para mí, las matemáticas son más difíciles que el lenguaje.
Para mí, las matemáticas son menos difíciles que el lenguaje. or
Para mí, las matemáticas son tan difíciles como el lenguaje.

1. la clase de español o de matemáticas
2. el álgebra o la geometría
3. preparar un sándwich o una pizza
4. leer el periódico o leer Shakespeare
5. ir a la biblioteca o usar Internet para buscar información
6. hacer la tarea o mirar la televisión

B. ¿Para niños, para niñas o unisexo? Tell if you think the following things were **traditionally** used more by girls or boys, or whether they are used equally by both sexes.

MODELO: zapatos de tenis
Hay tantos niños como niñas que usan zapatos de tenis.

niños **1.** pantalones
niños. **2.** muñecas G.I. Joe
3. muñecas Barbie
niñas **4.** libros cómicos
niños

5. una pelota de fútbol
6. lápices
7. recursos educativos para resolver problemas *educational resources to solve problems*
8. cuerdas para saltar *jump ropes*

C. Comparaciones. Fill in the blanks with the name of a *famous* person to make the comparison. Then, compare your answers with another student's and together come up with five more "simile" comparisons.

MODELO: Tan alto como _____.
Tan alto como Yao Ming.

1. Tan inteligente como _____.

2. Tan rico como _____.

3. Tan bonita como_____.

4. Tan famoso como _____.

Módulo 2

Los mejores = The best

The Assembly

La asamblea

All the winners are also invited to a pizza party with the principal courtesy of Pizza Hut

Todos los ganadores también están invitados a una fiesta de pizza con la directora, cortesía de Pizza Hut

proud parents

padres orgullosos

sacar fotos — *take pictures*

Awards: november
Premios: noviembre

los trofeos y los certificados

The troplies and the certificates

entregar el premio) *to deliver / hand over the award / prize*

ganar el premio — *to win / earn the prize / award*

perder el dinero — *To lose the money*

A. ¿Cómo se dice?   Find the word in the drawing that best completes the following sentences.

1. Un documento que reconoce y confirma un logro (*accomplishment*) es un

_____.

2. Una estatua de metal que reconoce y confirma un logro es un

_____.

3. La persona que gana una competencia normalmente recibe un

_____.

4. Una emoción normal para los padres cuando sus hijos ganan un premio es

el _____.

B. Acciones.   Match the verbs on the left with an equivalent from the right.

1. _____ ganar   **a.** dar

2. _____ perder   **b.** ser "número uno"

3. _____ entregar   **c.** no saber dónde está una cosa o no recibir un premio

4. _____ sacar fotos   **d.** usar una cámara

Somos los mejores

What's wrong? It's Friday afternoon and a troubled Alejandro comes in the door. His mother knows that this is not the face of her happy little boy who seemed to be progressing so nicely with all of his new support and help. When she reads the note from the teacher, she is on the phone immediately.

MAMÁ: Sra. Miller, buenas tardes. Habla Ángela Braun, la madre de Alejandro. ¿Cómo está usted, señora?

SRA. MILLER: ¡Ay! Gracias por llamar tan rápidamente...

MAMÁ: Pues, Sra. Miller, en este momento tengo aquí al niño más triste del mundo. Claro que llamo inmediatamente. ¿No está progresando bien? El pobre está nerviosísimo.... ¿Hay algún problema...?

SRA. MILLER: ¡Ay, pobrecito! Él siempre anticipa las peores noticias. Al contrario, llamo con buenas noticias—pero es un secreto que usted tiene que guardar. El viernes que viene tenemos nuestra asamblea con los premios para reconocer a los mejores estudiantes del mes. Después de un voto de todos los maestros y empleados de Menlo Park, resulta que Alejandro va a ganar dos premios importantes: el del mejor estudiante de matemáticas y ¡ta-da!... **el premio mayor de la escuela: El de estudiante del mes.**

MAMÁ: Ayyy.

SRA. MILLER: Señora, ¿está llorando?

MAMÁ: De pura felicidad. Son las mejores noticias del mundo. No lo creo. ¡Mi hijo es el mejor estudiante de la escuela en la mejor escuela de la ciudad! Y con los mejores maestros del mundo.

C. ¿Comprende usted?   Answer the following questions based on the dialogue.

1. ¿Por qué está triste Alejandro cuando regresa de la escuela?

2. ¿Son buenas o malas las noticias de la Sra. Miller?

3. ¿Cuáles son los dos premios que gana Alejandro?

4. Describa las emociones que tiene su mamá.

D. Las mejores cosas… las peores. Here's the beginning of a worksheet a teacher has prepared to help his students identify feelings about different things. Fill in the blanks as if you were the student answering the questions.

My favorite things
Mis cosas favoritas

Me llamo_____ y mis cosas favoritas son:

1. Mi clase favorita es_____.

2. El estudiante más inteligente es_____.

3. El/La mejor maestro/a es_____.

4. La clase más difícil es_____.

5. El cantante más popular es_____.

6. La película más violenta es_____.

7. Mi comida favorita es_____.

8. El mejor restaurante es_____.

E. Más. This poor teacher is tired and can't think of any more categories of most and favorites for his students. With a partner, can you think of six more categories for the children? Write out the questions and then answer them.

MODELO: el programa de televisión/cómico

El programa de televisión más cómico es _____.

Estructuras

Comparing and contrasting:
Los superlativos *The superlatives*

- Use a superlative to express *the most* or *the least* when comparing more than two things.
- The superlative in Spanish uses the definite article **(el, la, los, las)** with the comparative form of the adjective.

Adjetivo:	Esta escuela es **moderna.**	*This school is modern.*
Comparativo:	Esa escuela es **más moderna.**	*That school is more modern.*
Superlativo:	La otra escuela es **la más moderna.**	*The other school is the most modern.*

- Adjectives that have irregular forms in the comparative use the same forms in the superlative, with the addition of the definite article → *el, la, los, las*

good better old- older
bueno > mejor   viejo > mayor
bad worse   young younger
malo > peor   joven > menor

Adjetivo:	Mario es un **buen** estudiante.	*Mario is a good student.*
Comparativo:	Enrique es un **mejor** estudiante.	*Enrique is a better student.*
Superlativo:	Pepe es **el mejor** estudiante de todos.	*Pepe is the best student of all.*

- Another way to give an adjective a superlative meaning of *extremely* or *very* is to add one of the forms **(-o, -os, -a, -as)** of the suffix **–ísimo/a.** If the adjective ends in a vowel, drop the final vowel and add the correct form of **–ísimo/a.**

Esta madre está **orgullosa.**	*This mother is proud.*
Esa madre está orgull**ísima.**	*That mother is extremely proud.*

- If the adjective ends in a consonant, add the suffix directly to the stem.

Darle una "F" a un estudiante es **difícil.**	*Giving an "F" to a student is difficult.*
Darle una "F" a un estudiante que se esfuerza es dific**ilísimo.**	*Giving an "F" to a student who is trying is extremely difficult.*

Para practicar

A. Asociaciones. Write down the names of the people, things, or places you associate with these descriptions and then compare your answers with a classmate.

1. la nota más baja para una boleta de calificaciones
2. el programa de televisión más popular entre sus amigos

3. la nota más alta para una boleta de calificaciones
4. el/la mejor maestro/a de español
5. la clase más difícil
6. el actor/la actriz más guapo/a

B. Extremísimo. Anything you can do, I can do better. You and a friend are having a discussion about personal and professional traits. For every statement that your friend makes, use an **–ísimo/a** adjective to show that you and yours are even more so.

MODELO: E1: Estoy cansada. ―*tired*
E2: *Yo estoy cansadísima.*

1. Soy inteligente.
2. Soy un estudiante malo.
3. Necesito mucha ayuda.
4. Tengo un problema difícil.
5. Mis notas son buenas.
6. Mi mamá está orgullosa.

C. En pareja. You and your partner are trying to organize the projects to be done by priority. As you look at each of these groups of three, put them into priority order according to the adjective given.

MODELO: serio: el problema con el equipo del gimnasio
el problema de la cafetera rota (*broken coffee pot*)
el problema con el niño perdido (*lost*)

El problema de la cafetera rota es serio.
El problema con el equipo del gimnasio es más serio.
El problema con el niño perdido es el más serio.

1. urgente: la llamada de teléfono de una madre furiosa
la llamada de su amigo
la llamada de unos televendedores (*telemarketers*)

2. fácil: buscar información para las clases en Internet
buscar información para las clases en la biblioteca
buscar información para las clases en el periódico

3. interesante: ir a otra ciudad para estudiar el sistema de educación
ir a otro país para estudiar el sistema de educación
navegar por Internet para estudiar otros sistemas de educación

4. económico: dar trofeos a todos los estudiantes que ganan premios
dar certificados a todos los estudiantes que ganan premios
dar una sonrisa (*smile*) a todos los estudiantes que ganan premios

Vocabulario Módulo 1

Sustantivos

el abrazo	*hug*	el impedimento	*impediment*
el ánimo	*encouragement*	el/la intérprete	*interpreter*
la boleta de calificaciones	*report card*	la materia	*subject*
el cambio	*change*	el mes	*month*
el/la cantante	*singer*	la nota	*grade, note*
el comentario	*comment*	el problema	*problem*
el comité	*committee*	el progreso	*progress*
el/la compañero/a	*companion*	la prueba	*examination*
el/la coordinador/a	*coordinator*	la raíz	*root, stem*
el/la ganador/a	*winner*	la seña	*sign*
		la silla de ruedas	*wheelchair*

Verbos

acostar (ue)	*to put to bed*	perder (ie)	*to lose*
almorzar (ue)	*to have lunch*	poder (ue)	*to be able, can*
comenzar (ie)	*to begin*	probar (ue)	*to attempt, try*
costar (ue)	*to cost*	quejarse de	*to complain about*
despedirse (i)	*to say goodbye*		
elegir (i)	*to opt, elect*	querer (ie)	*to want*
encontrar (ue)	*to find*	repetir (i)	*to repeat*
entender (ie)	*to understand*	seguir (i)	*to continue, follow*
medir (i)	*to measure*		
mentir (ie)	*to lie*	servir (i)	*to serve*
pedir (i)	*to ask for, order*	volver (ue)	*to return*

Adjetivos

ciego/a	*blind*	divertido/a	*fun, enjoyable*
desanimado/a	*discouraged*	fácil	*easy*
difícil	*difficult*	motivado/a	*motivated*
discapacitado/a	*disabled*	sordo/a	*deaf*

Otras expresiones

al contrario	*to the contrary*	según	*according to*
bastante	*enough*	un rato	*a while*
pues	*well*		

Módulo 2

Sustantivos

el aprendizaje	*learning*	el orgullo	*pride*
la asamblea	*assembly*	la patineta	*skateboard*
la ceguera	*blindness*	el/la primo/a	*cousin*
la creencia	*belief*	el promedio	*average*
la discapacidad	*disability*	la roca	*rock*
el diseño	*design*	la sonrisa	*smile*
la equivocación	*mistake*	la sordera	*deafness*
la felicidad	*happiness*	la suerte	*luck*
la foto(grafía)	*photo(graph)*	el/la tío/a	*uncle, aunt*
el fracaso	*failure*	el trastorno	*disorder*
la lágrima	*tear*	el valor	*value*
la mente	*mind*		

Verbos

animar	*to encourage*	guardar	*to keep*
anunciar	*to announce*	hacer (g)	*to do, make*
apagar	*to turn off*	mandar	*to send*
celebrar	*to celebrate*	quedarse	*to stay, remain*
comentar	*to comment*	sacar	*to take (out)*
compartir	*to share*	votar	*to vote*
entregar	*to hand over, deliver*		

Adjetivos

frustrado/a	*frustrated*	sano/a	*healthy*
orgulloso/a	*proud*		

Otras expresiones

aquí	*here*	ningún/guno/a	*none, not one*
como	*as, like*	peor	*worse*
conmigo	*with me*	tan	*so, as*
mejor	*better*	tanto/a	*as much*
menor	*younger*	tantos/as	*as many*
menos	*less*		

Síntesis

A escuchar

¿Por qué llama la maestra? Listen to the conversation and then tell if the following statements refer to **La maestra (M), el padre (P)** o **Gabriel (G).**

1. _____ Va a recibir un premio.

2. _____ Llama a la casa con buenas noticias.

3. _____ Sus notas y su comportamiento son mejores.

4. _____ Siente mucho orgullo.

A conversar

There are many ways that parents and other family members can help young children off to a good start in school—reading to them is the key. Read these suggestions and then with a partner explain each concept in your own words. Brainstorm a list of places where parents can find books at little or no charge.

> **¿Por qué debe leer con sus hijos?**
>
> 1. Cuando lee con sus hijos establece un ambiente de bienestar, intimidad y descanso que es algo raro en una familia muy ocupada.
>
> 2. Sus niños tienen más éxito en la escuela. Leyéndoles regularmente mejora su vocabulario y su concepto del mundo.
>
> 3. Por medio de la lectura de cuentos y noticias puede compartir sus valores y creencias con sus hijos. Los niños mayores tienen la oportunidad de compartir sus sentimientos con usted—fomentando la comunicación entre todos.
>
> 4. Sus niños aprenden por medio de su ejemplo que la lectura es divertida e informativa.

A leer

Mente sana en cuerpo sano. As important as mental activity is to young children and their education, we cannot forget the benefits of physical activity as a balance. Read the following tips for adding physical activity to a child's more sedentary day.

La pirámide de actividades para niños

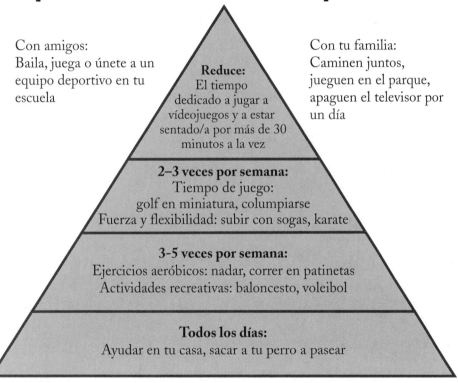

Con amigos:
Baila, juega o únete a un equipo deportivo en tu escuela

Con tu familia:
Caminen juntos, jueguen en el parque, apaguen el televisor por un día

Reduce:
El tiempo dedicado a jugar a vídeojuegos y a estar sentado/a por más de 30 minutos a la vez

2–3 veces por semana:
Tiempo de juego:
golf en miniatura, columpiarse
Fuerza y flexibilidad: subir con sogas, karate

3-5 veces por semana:
Ejercicios aeróbicos: nadar, correr en patinetas
Actividades recreativas: baloncesto, voleibol

Todos los días:
Ayudar en tu casa, sacar a tu perro a pasear

¿Y usted? After reading the **Pirámide de actividades,** invent one additional activity that the children can do in each of the following categories:

a. ejercicios aeróbicos b. juegos c. fuerza y flexibilidad d. actividades recreativas

Then choose one of the activities and explain to a classmate what you can do to help them be more active.

MODELO: ejercicios aeróbicos:
Podemos organizar carreras (races) *para los niños y dar premios.*

A escribir

A child has about two hours after school to do school work, be with family, and have some fun before bedtime. Organize and write a schedule of five different activities to contribute to a well-balanced life. Don't forget to include family members!

MODELO: *5:00-5:30 La tarea de la escuela. Si no hay tarea, puede leer un libro.*

Algo más

Ventana cultural

Did you know that many non-English speaking students have been mistakenly placed in Special Education classes? Often students perform poorly—not for lack of intellectual capability—but rather for lack of understanding in English. Efforts are being made nationwide to more accurately assess ELL (English Language Learner) students and to place them in the proper classrooms. Read this article for an example of parent education programs.

La escuela Corona y el Centro familiar ofrecen:

Clases gratis para los padres

PECES: Padres eficaces con entrenamientos sistemáticos

El programa PECES les ayuda a ser mejores padres

Ustedes aprenden:

• las formas de construir relaciones positivas con los niños

• las consecuencias lógicas y naturales como alternativas a los premios y castigos

• a enseñar al niño a ser responsable

• la comunicación—escuchar al niño

Curso básico para padres de niños de 2–12 años, 7 sesiones, comienza el 7 de septiembre.

Libro de trabajo gratuito; un grupo de apoyo sigue después de terminar el curso básico.

Se debe matricular antes de la clase.

Para obtener más información, llame al 800-653-2060

En mis propias palabras. Write four reasons why such a training class could have positive results for parents and students alike.

A buscar

There are many sources of support for Hispanics in the world of education—go to www.prenhall.com/rush and look under the topic Hispanic support/ Apoyo para hispanos. Print out a page from one specific site that you find of interest. What's the purpose of the organization? Who do they serve? Briefly report to the class on your findings.

A conocer: Yolanda Benítez.

Yolanda Benítez is Superintendent of the Rio School District in Oxnard, California, in charge of six elementary schools and one middle school, a position she's held since 1995. She graduated from California State University, Los Angeles, with a Bachelor's degree in Psychology, a degree in secondary education and a Master's degree in Statistics. In 1999, Benítez was honored by El Concilio del Condado de Ventura as one of nine individuals who have served as leaders for the Latino community. In her own words, "I see what I'm doing as affecting kid's lives, whether it's education or going into politics."

LECCIÓN 5

Security in school

La seguridad en la escuela

Módulo 1
- Las reglas de la escuela
- Making requests: *Los mandatos afirmativos informales*
- La disciplina
- Making requests: *Los mandatos formales; mandatos negativos informales*

Módulo 2
- En caso de emergencia
- Los mandatos: *Irregulares/con cambios ortográficos/con pronombres de objeto indirecto*
- No hay ningún peligro
- Expressing negative ideas: *Las expresiones afirmativas y negativas*

Consejera

Síntesis
- A escuchar
- A conversar
- A leer
- A escribir

Algo más
- Ventana cultural: Más hispanos abandonan la escuela temprano
- A buscar
- A conocer: Edward James Olmos

Módulo I

Las reglas de la escuela
School Rules

Admit the problems I caused to others
Remedy my mistakes and the problems I caused
Helping others for the benefit of all

I am a creator of peace. I promise:
Praise people for their good deeds
Stop insulting
Find sensible people like friends and counselors

Soy Creador de la Paz. Yo prometo:

1. Elogiar a las personas por sus buenas acciones
2. Dejar de insultar
3. Buscar a personas sensatas como amigos y consejeros
4. Admitir los problemas que causo a otros
5. Remediar mis errores y los problemas que causo
6. Ayudar a otros para el beneficio de todos

the signs of the gangs

El grafiti: las señas de las pandillas

homeboy
los vatos*

jacket
la chaqueta

danger
el peligro

pants
los pantalones

los tenis

los pantalones
Shorts cortos

shoes
los zapatos

los calcetines —
socks

la camisa — *Shirt*

la pelea
fight

threat with blade
amenaza con navaja

la falda y la blusa
skirt and blouse

una persona
sabia/sensata
wise person

el vestido — *dress*

María, gracias por ayudarme
en el patio.
Eres una buena amiga.

Note of praise
Nota de elogio

*Vatos is a slang term for *homeboy*.

peligroso/a = dangerous

el abrigo = winter coat

el traje = suit

la gorra = hat

la bufanda = scarf

los guantes = gloves

los mitones = mittens

How do you say?

A. ¿Cómo se dice?   Choose the correct Spanish word from the illustration for each description.

1. _____d_____ un conflicto violento y físico entre dos o más personas

2. _____d_____ "club" de jóvenes que defiende con violencia su "territorio"

3. _____b_____ un instrumento agudo (*sharp*) que se usa en las peleas

4. _____c_____ la ausencia de violencia; la tranquilidad

a. pandilla

b. navaja

c. paz

d. pelea

B. Acciones.   Replace the phrase in italics with one of the informal commands in the list below.

a. busca a	b. elogia a	c. remedia	d. renuncia a

1. *decir y escribir cosas positivas de* otras personas
2. *dejar de* insultar
3. *investigar e identificar* a amigos y consejeros sabios
4. *rectificar* problemas que notas o causas

I'm afraid →
(I have fear)

Tengo miedo

A new student at Elizondo Middle School is having a problem with some older students. How does he handle it? By trying to "build peace."

ANTONIO: Sr. Cooper, ¿tiene usted un momento?

SR. COOPER: Claro que sí, Antonio. Pasa y siéntate. Veo en tu cara que tienes un problema. Dime lo que pasa.

ANTONIO: Pues, Sr. Cooper, como usted sabe, soy un estudiante nuevo en esta escuela. Y es que... no sé explicarme. Tengo miedo.

SR. COOPER: ¿Miedo de las clases?

ANTONIO: No. De los estudiantes. De las pandillas. No es como mi escuela primaria.

SR. COOPER: Explica.

ANTONIO: A veces cuando salgo de la escuela me esperan unos miembros de una pandilla que me amenazan. Me dicen: "Declara tus colores y danos tu dinero." Mi chaqueta es de uno de los colores de una pandilla rival. Les digo que no soy miembro de los Conquistadores, y que mi uniforme es del color de la escuela, pero no me creen. Dicen: "Prueba que no eres miembro e iníciate en nuestro club." Creen en la violencia. Yo no quiero participar y tengo miedo. Usted es una persona sensata. Y uno de los mandatos de los Creadores de la Paz es: Busca a una persona sabia si hay peligro.

SR. COOPER: Gracias, Antonio, por confiar en mí. ¿Qué son los Creadores de la Paz? ¿Y los mandatos?

ANTONIO: En un centro de Creadores de la Paz, como mi escuela primaria, todos intentamos vivir los mandamientos todos los días para crear una comunidad positiva y resolver conflictos sin violencia. Hay seis mandamientos para ser Creador de la Paz.

SR. COOPER: Me parece un programa excelente. Antonio, ven conmigo. Vamos a hablar con otra persona sabia—el Director.

C. ¿Comprende usted? Answer the following questions based on the dialogue.

1. ¿Con quién quiere hablar Antonio de su problema?
2. ¿Qué quiere decir "Declara tus colores"? ¿Los colores de qué?
3. ¿Qué hacen los estudiantes en la primaria de Antonio para resolver conflictos?
4. ¿Por qué buscan Antonio y el Sr. Cooper al Director?

D. Los Creadores de la Paz. Read the following excerpt from the PeaceBuilders' manual and respond to the questions that follow.

El experimento de las dos escuelas

El compromise de los Creadores de la Paz:

Soy Creador de la Paz. Yo prometo:

1. Elogiar a las personas por sus buenas acciones
2. Dejar de insultar
3. Buscar a personas sensatas como amigos y consejeros
4. Admitir los problemas que causo a otros
5. Remediar mis errores y los problemas que causo
6. Ayudar a otros para el beneficio de todos

Imagínese dos escuelas. Las dos están situadas en el mismo distrito escolar y en el mismo barrio "de riesgo" (*at risk*). Los dos edificios son viejos y tienen la misma cantidad de dinero en sus fondos. Sin embargo, una de las escuelas tiene entre un 50 y un 75% menos actos de delincuencia juvenil que la otra, un 50% menos de abuso de drogas y alcohol y más estudiantes que completan su educación y sobresalen académicamente—incluso en las pruebas nacionales.

"Los Creadores de la Paz" establecen una norma para el comportamiento estudiantil a base de principios compartidos por los maestros, los padres y los estudiantes. Los adultos y los jóvenes trabajan juntos para "crear la paz". Los adultos son los modelos del comportamiento que los estudiantes deben copiar. Demuestran el lenguaje de la paz y abren el camino a la paz—y al éxito. Crear la paz consiste en esforzarse por crear el ambiente o atmósfera en que preferimos vivir—un ambiente positivo, sin violencia, y con todos los beneficios de una comunidad en armonía.

1. In your own words—in Spanish, of course—write a three to four sentence summary of the Peace Builders' vision.

2. Re-read the first paragraph about the two schools' experiment. In one or two sentences, write why you believe that that story is or is not possible.

E. Reflexiones de un estudiante del grado 8. Read the following thoughts written by a student and then answer the questions.

Cuando yo estaba en la primaria, recibía buenas notas. Los adultos siempre prestaban atención a las cosas buenas que hacíamos. Ahora que estoy en la escuela intermedia, nadie me elogia. Nadie me presta atención. Dejé de esforzarme. Mis calificaciones ya son malas. (J.C., May, 1999) Este año en el grado 8, nuestra escuela tiene PeaceBuilders. Al principio, yo creía que este grupo era realmente estúpido. Por todas partes de la escuela había estas **Notas de elogio.** Empezamos **Círculos de la paz.** Yo recibí **"Preferrals"** del director por las buenas cosas que hago. Mis calificaciones son mucho mejores ahora. Unas personas visitaron mi escuela para ver PeaceBuilders en acción. Me preguntaron mis impresiones sobre este grupo. Yo contesté: Al principio los estudiantes van a decir que es una tontería. Pero es porque tienen miedo de decir que les gusta. Después de un tiempo, es algo muy natural, como una costumbre. Estoy contento. Yo te diría: ¡simplemente hazlo! *(just do it!)*.

1. Para J.C., ¿cuál es la diferencia entre la escuela primaria y la intermedia?
2. ¿Por qué tiene calificaciones bajas en la escuela intermedia?
3. ¿Por qué cree que es tonto?
4. ¿Qué les recomienda J.C. a otros?

Estructuras   *Making requests: Los mandatos afirmativos informales*

Informal affirmative commands

- Nowhere in the Spanish language is the difference between formal address and informal address as evident and important as it is when giving commands. When an adult gives a child an order or a friend tells you to do something, the informal command will be used. With informal (**tú**) commands, you will use a different form when you are telling someone to *do something* (affirmative command) than you will use if you are telling someone *not* to do something (negative command.)

- When telling a friend or family member to do something as a command, use the third person in the present tense indicative (**él, ella** or **usted**) form of the verb:

Habla con un amigo sensato.	*Talk to a wise friend.*
Estudia las lecciones.	*Study the lessons.*
Come el sandwich.	*Eat the sandwich.*
Elogia a tus amigos.	*Praise your friends.*

- The affirmative **tú** commands for the following verbs are irregular.

say	**decir**	**di**	**salir**	**sal** *leave*
do	**hacer**	**haz**	**ser**	**sé** *be*
go	**ir**	**ve**	**tener**	**ten** *have*
put	**poner**	**pon**	**venir**	**ven** *come*

- As you will see in more depth later on, direct and indirect objects are always attached to the end of the affirmative command.

Dime la verdad.	*Tell me the truth.*
Háblame.	*Talk to me.*

Para practicar

A. Los sabios.   As a wise teacher, students are always seeking your advice. Here's a list of things this student needs to do. Put them into an informal command.

MODELO: hablar claramente   *Habla claramente.*

1. comer en la cafetería
2. jugar en el patio de recreo
3. escribir con pluma
4. elogiar a tus compañeros
5. esperar aquí

6.   estudiar mucho
7.   dejar de insultar
8.   cerrar la puerta
9.   buscar a personas sensatas
10.   prestar atención a la maestra

B. Más mandatos.   This student has gotten himself into some trouble. Put the following phrases into the **tú** command form to give him some guidance.

MODELO: ir a la oficina del director   *Ve a la oficina del director.*

1. hacer la tarea inmediatamente
2. decir la verdad
3. salir del baño inmediatamente

4.   tener paciencia
5.   venir acá en este momento
6.   poner la tarea en el escritorio

C. Maestros de la paz.   As school teachers, it is very important to model the behavior you want the students to use. With a classmate, write a list of ten commands you would give to another teacher to help him/her be a "PeaceBuilder."

MODELO: *Elogia a los estudiantes cuando estudian.*

Módulo I

La disciplina *Discipline*

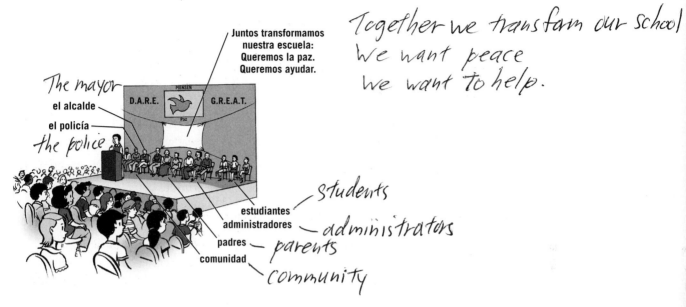

Juntos transformamos
nuestra escuela:
Queremos la paz.
Queremos ayudar.

Together we transform our school
We want peace
we want to help.

The mayor
el alcalde

el policía
the police

PIENSEN
D.A.R.E.   G.R.E.A.T.
Paz

estudiantes — *students*
administradores — *administrators*
padres — *parents*
comunidad — *community*

A. Contrarios. Each of the following groups of words is related, but one is the opposite of the rest. Circle the word that does not belong.

1. a. iniciativa estudiantil   **b.** coalición   **c.** activistas   **d.** pandillas

2. a. paz   **b.** violencia   **c.** tranquilidad   **d.** calma

3. a. ayuda   **b.** cooperación   **c.** alianza   **d.** hostilidad

4. a. elogio   **b.** amenaza   **c.** sospecha   **d.** miedo

B. Acciones. Using your imagination and memory, look at the following verbs and circle the option closest in meaning.

1. modelar: **a.** demostrar   **b.** coordinar   **c.** buscar

2. tolerar: **a.** eliminar   **b.** aceptar   **c.** buscar

3. buscar: **a.** explicar   **b.** transformar   **c.** identificar

4. pensar   **a.** amenazar   **b.** participar   **c.** crear una visión mental

Juntos

*With Mr. Cooper's help, Antonio has organized classmates in all of the grades to transform the school and eliminate violence and fear. The kids know they cannot do it alone. They have called a special assembly for students, parents, administrators, and community members to "kick-off" their **"JUNTOS"** program and outline their "do's and don'ts" for peace.*

Declaración de la Paz.

Amigo estudiante: Hazte un agente de la paz. Tú debes:

Participar. Participa en los clubes de la paz. **No participes** en las pandillas de violencia.

Buscar. Busca soluciones a los conflictos. **No busques** peleas.

Aprender. Aprende a expresarte con calma. **No aprendas** la violencia.

Comunicar. Comunica tus sospechas a un adulto. **No te comuniques** con personas peligrosas.

Venir. Ven a la escuela con entusiasmo. **No vengas** con armas, ni drogas, ni mal humor.
Pensar. Piensa Paz.

Padres: Háganse Agentes de la Paz.

Ustedes deben:

Participar. Participen en las actividades de la escuela. **No participen** en actividades ilegales.

Aprender. Aprendan los síntomas de los problemas con drogas o alcohol.
No aprendan a tolerarlos en su casa.

Modelar. Modelen un comportamiento responsable. **No modelen** un comportamiento violento.

Insistir. Insistan en el respeto de sus hijos. **No insistan** en nada que interfiera con los estudios.

Pensar. Piensen Paz.

Maestros, Administradores: Háganse Agentes de la Paz.

Deben:

Modelar.	**Modelen** el respeto mutuo y la cooperación.
Prometer.	**Prometan** a los estudiantes una escuela segura y sin violencia.
Pedir.	**Pidan** el apoyo y cooperación de los estudiantes y sus familias y de la comunidad y la policía.
Buscar.	**Busquen** líderes estudiantiles y **escuchen** sus opiniones.
Responder.	**Respondan** inmediatamente a cualquier incidente de violencia o falta de respeto.
Pensar.	**Piensen Paz.**

C. ¿Comprende usted?   Answer the following questions based on the dialogue.

1. ¿Qué debe modelar un estudiante?
2. ¿Qué debe modelar un padre?
3. ¿Qué deben modelar los maestros y administradores?
4. ¿Qué deben "pensar" todos?

Do not tell him

D. ¡Dile que no!   Read the following brochure on tips for staying alive and design a campaign to promote these tips at a local school or with a youth group. Make a list of four key strategies to impress the young people to "Just Say No!".

Buenos consejos

1. Nunca entres en un automóvil con un conductor que haya bebido. Llama a alguien para que venga a recogerte.
2. Aléjate de los jóvenes que beben. Ellos pueden parecer populares, pero no lo son; sólo se están maltratando a sí mismos y puede que a ti también.
3. Si te invitan a un lugar donde piensas que van a beber alcohol o tomar drogas, ¡no vayas!
4. Si estás pensando en beber, no lo hagas. Todo lo puedes hacer sin tener que beber.

MODELO: *No es necesario beber alcohol para tener una buena personalidad.*

Estructuras

Making requests: Los mandatos formales; mandatos negativos informales

■ You have already learned to use the affirmative **tú commands** when you are telling somebody *to do* something. When you are telling a friend *not to do* something, you use a different command form.

Enrique, **habla** de tus problemas.	*Enrique, talk about your problems.*
Enrique, **no hables** de tus problemas.	*Enrique, don't talk about your problems.*

The negative **tú** command, and *all* **usted** and **ustedes** commands, use the following basic format to show respect and courtesy as you tell people what to do—or not to do. To form these commands, drop the final **-o** from the **yo** form of the verb in the present tense (the **yo** form will give all necessary spelling changes) and add these endings:

For **-ar** verbs, add **-e**.

hablar	habl**o**	⇒	habl**e**	*speak*
llamar	llam**o**	⇒	llam**e**	*call*

For **-er** and **-ir** verbs, add **-a**.

aprender	aprend**o**	⇒	aprend**a**	*learn*
venir	veng**o**	⇒	veng**a**	*come*

For the **ustedes** form of these commands, add **-n**.

comer	com**a**	⇒	¡**Coman** un sandwich!	*eat*
venir	veng**o**	⇒	¡**Vengan** ustedes a la escuela!	*come*

For the negative **tú** command, add an **-s**.

comer	no com**as**	¡**No comas** mucho azúcar!	*eat*
venir	no veng**as**	¡**No vengas** mañana!	*come*

In order to preserve the original pronunciation of the verb, these commands for verbs ending in **-car**, **-gar**, and **-zar** have the following spelling changes:

bus**car** ⇒	bus**que**	**Busquen** a un adulto sensato.	*find*
entre**gar** ⇒	entre**gue**	**Entregue** la tarea mañana.	*deliver*
empe**zar** ⇒	emp**iece**	**No empieces** el proyecto sin un adulto.	*start*

Steps to forming a command:

1. go to the **yo** form
2. take off the **-o**
3. add the opposite ending.

Handwritten annotations:

Usted Form
* go to (yo)
drop the "o"
add the opposite vowel
ar → e
er > a
ir > a

Ustedes Form
go to yo
drop the "o"
add the opposite vowel
ar → e
er > a
ir > a
add "n"

Para practicar — *tips*

A. Consejos. You are a peer counselor working with a student who just cannot break old habits of violence. Using an appropriate **tú** form command, give him wise advice.

MODELO: Estudiante: ¡Estoy furioso!
Ud.: *¡No estés furioso!*

Find **1.** ¿Busco a los rivales para una pelea? *No ~~uses~~ busques*

visit **2.** ¿Visito la escuela de los rivales? *No visites*

put **3.** ¿Pongo grafiti con señas de la pandilla en el barrio? *No pongas*

come **4.** ¿Vengo a la escuela con una navaja? *No vengas*

write **5.** ¿Escribo obscenidades con pintura? *No escribas*

take **6.** ¿Tomo drogas para olvidar (*forget*)? *No tomes*

~~start~~ **7.** ¿Traigo alcohol a la escuela? *Bring (traer)* *No traigas*

8. ¿Amenazo (*threaten*) a los rivales? *No amendces*

— *The sensible teacher*

B. El maestro sensato. As a well-respected teacher you are often called upon to give students advice. Use formal commands (**ustedes**) to tell them whether or not they should do the following things.

MODELO: ¿Llamamos a la policía si un estudiante dice palabras malas?
No llamen ustedes a la policía si un estudiante dice palabras malas.

1. ¿Escribimos notas de elogio para los estudiantes responsables?
2. ¿Buscamos a un adulto si un estudiante trae armas a la escuela?
3. ¿Amenazamos con navaja a los estudiantes que no llevan el uniforme?
4. ¿Pedimos ayuda con problemas serios?
5. ¿Llegamos a las clases con armas?
6. ¿Reportamos peligros al director?

C. ¿El estudiante o los padres? As a school counselor, you often do "family therapy" sessions. Today you are working with Henry and his parents. Decide if the following suggestions are for the parents: (**ustedes**) or Henry (**tú**) and give the appropriate command form. Can you add three more for each?

MODELO: hacer la tarea todos los días
Henry, haz la tarea todos los días.

1. hablar con su hijo
2. buscar a nuevos amigos
3. no salir por la noche durante la semana
4. modelar el comportamiento que esperan

D. Con un amigo. You and a classmate are peer counselors trying to help two students who have been victims of the school bully. Make a list of five things these students should do and five things these students should not do—using **ustedes** form commands.

MODELO: *Busquen a un adulto.*
No busquen armas.

Módulo 2

En caso de emergencia

Lista de emergencias

Simulacro = práctica

 1. **incendio** —fire

 2. **terremoto** — earthquake

 3. **tornado/ciclón** cyclone

 4. **desastre químico** Chemical disaster

 5. **amenaza de bomba** bomb threat

 6. **amenaza de armas** weapons threat

7. **ataque terrorista** terrorist attack

(handwritten note, left margin) debajo de → under the

Evacuation route — **Ruta de evacuación**

Protected site — **Sitio amparado**

eyes **los ojos** — **la cabeza** head
la nariz nose — **la boca** mouth
las orejas ears — **los brazos** arms
las manos hands
las piernas legs
los pies feet

shoulders = hombros

A. ¿Cómo se dice?   What body parts would you associate with the following? Use as many as you can think of for each.

(handwritten note, left margin)
salir — leave
ir — go
dar — give

1. los anteojos (*eye glasses*)
2. la respiración
3. la música
4. el fútbol

B. ¿Evacuar o buscar un refugio?   Using your best judgment as you read the list of emergencies, decide whether it is better to **evacuar la clase (E)** o **buscar un refugio (R)** indoors.

(handwritten notes, left margin)
esconder = hide
guadar = keep, save
mover = move
llamar = call
cieren = close
abren = open
escapar = escape

1. _____ tornado
2. _____ incendio
3. _____ emergencia química
4. _____ amenaza de bomba

¿Simulacro para practicar o emergencia de verdad?

Just as Sr. Russo's seventh grade Spanish class is about to begin an exam, the school's emergency alert system alarm sounds. With so much news of terrible emergencies in the world, Sr. Russo and his student teacher, Srta. Marcos, have very nervous students on their hands.

SR. RUSSO: ¡Escuchen! ¡Escúchenme, por favor! Todos. ¡Estén tranquilos! Esta alarma indica una evacuación total por incendio u otro peligro. Con mucha calma, caminen al armario y rápidamente saquen las chaquetas. Cúbranse la cabeza, los brazos y la cara y rápidamente vayan a la salida del gimnasio. Espérenme allí en el patio. No hablen hasta llegar al patio donde recibiremos más instrucciones. Srta. Marcos, acompañe a la clase, por favor, y tome la lista de estudiantes para contarlos allí. Yo voy a ver si hay estudiantes en el baño. Niños. Caminen, no corran. Pero salgan rápidamente.

ARMANDO: ¡Oigan! No sean estúpidos. Es sólo un simulacro. No es para tanto.

MARGARITA: (llorando) Dicen en el pasillo que hay una bomba en la escuela. Tengo miedo. Quiero ir a mi casa.

ARMANDO: Margarita, eres una bebé. Es un simulacro.

RODRIGO: (en el patio) ¡Escuchen! Vienen los bomberos (*firemen*) y la policía. No es simulacro, Armando. Es una emergencia de verdad. Hay más policías con perros. Y allí están las ambulancias. Es una verdadera EMERGENCIA. Armando... no llores. Estamos seguros aquí en el patio.

C. ¿Comprende usted?   Decide if each of the statements is **Cierto (C)** or **Falso (F)** based on the dialogue. If the statement is incorrect, provide the correct information.

1. _____ Los estudiantes están en la clase de matemáticas.

2. _____ La alarma indica un tornado.

3. _____ La Srta. Marcos va a pasar la lista de estudiantes en el patio.

4. _____ Armando no cree que hay peligro, al principio.

D. ¡Terremoto! Read the instructions from the Red Cross on how to survive an earthquake. Have you ever experienced one? Decide which suggestions you followed or would follow in such a circumstance. Compare your choices with a classmate.

✚ CRUZ ROJA AMERICANA
✔ LISTA DE SUPERVIVENCIA PARA TERREMOTOS Y DESASTRES

Durante un terremoto:

1. Si usted está adentro, colóquese debajo de una mesa o escritorio. Tenga cuidado de las cosas que caen y de los objetos que vuelan por el aire. Permanezca lejos de las ventanas.
2. Si usted está afuera, muévase a un área amplia, lejos de edificios, árboles, postes de luz, paredes de ladrillo o de bloques y otros objetos que puedan caer.
3. Si usted está en un automóvil, pare y permanezca en él hasta que la sacudida pase. Evite parar debajo o cerca de árboles y cables de la luz o bajo pasos a desnivel *(overpasses)*.
4. Si usted está en un edificio alto, colóquese debajo de un escritorio. No use el ascensor para salir—use las escaleras.
5. Si usted está en un almacén, busque protección debajo de una mesa o de cualquier objeto pesado. Evite pararse debajo de cualquier cosa que pueda caer.

Después de un terremoto:

1. Use zapatos fuertes para evitar heridas al caminar sobre vidrios y deshechos.
2. Busque heridos y dé primeros auxilios.
3. Protéjase contra posibles incendios y sus peligros:
   - Si huele a gas o sospecha un escape, cierre la válvula principal, abra las ventanas y salga de la casa.
   - Si sospecha escapes de agua, cierre la llave principal.
   - Si sospecha de daños en el sistema de electricidad, cierre el circuito principal o retire los fusibles.
4. Prenda el radio y escuche las instrucciones.
5. No toque los cables caídos de la luz.
6. Haga limpieza de todo material potencialmente peligroso.
7. Inspeccione las tuberías antes de usar los baños.
8. Chequee la casa por daños en el techo, chimenea, etc.
9. No use el teléfono, excepto para una emergencia real.
10. Esté preparado para temblores recurrentes.
11. Abra los armarios cuidadosamente.
12. Coopere con las autoridades de seguridad pública.

Si usted tiene que evacuar:

1. Ponga en sitio visible un mensaje haciendo saber el lugar donde usted puede ser localizado.
2. Lleve con usted lo siguiente:
   - medicina y equipo de primeros auxilios
   - linterna, radio y baterías
   - papeles importantes y dinero
   - comida, sacos para dormir, cobijas y ropa extra

Estructuras   *Los mandatos: Irregulares/con cambios ortográficos/con pronombres de objeto indirecto*

- The following verbs have irregular **Ud./Uds.** and **negative tú** command forms:

ser	⇒	sea(n)	no seas tú
estar	⇒	esté(n)	no estés tú
ir	⇒	vaya(n)	no vayas tú
saber	⇒	sepa(n)	no sepas tú
dar	⇒	dé/den	no des tú

Commands and Indirect Object Pronouns

Use the pronouns **me** to mean *me, for me,* or *to me* and **nos** to mean *us, to us,* or *for us.* These pronouns are attached to the *end* of a command if it is affirmative—a "yes" command. When adding a pronoun to the end of affirmative commands of two or more syllables, be sure to place an accent mark above the stressed vowel in order to preserve the original pronunciation. If the command is negative, put the pronoun in front of the verb.

Explíque**me** el problema.	*Explain the problem to **me**.*
No **me** explique el problema.	*Don't explain the problem to **me**.*
¡Díga**nos** qué hacer!	*Tell **us** what to do!*
¡No **nos** diga mentiras!	*Don't tell **us** lies!*

Use the pronoun **le** to mean *to* or *for you, him,* or *her* and **les** to mean *to* or *for you (plural)* or *them.* Put it before negative commands and after affirmative ones. You may clarify any ambiguity by adding **a** + the person's name.

Escríba**le** un reporte.	*Write him a report.*
Escríba**le** un reporte al policía.	*Write a report to the policeman.*
¡No **les** des otra oportunidad!	*Don't give **them** another chance!*
¡No **les** des otra oportunidad **a los drogadictos!**	*Don't give the drug addicts another chance!*

Para practicar

A. Línea de emergencia.   You are helping out on the crisis center hotline where a caller is faced with an emergency. Use your best judgment and answer with a formal command.

MODELO: Persona: Tengo miedo.
No tenga miedo.

1. ¿Busco al policía?
2. ¿Voy por ayuda?
3. ¿Doy mi nombre y dirección?
4. ¿Traigo una pistola?
5. ¿Le explico el problema?
6. ¡Estoy nervioso!
7. ¿Tomo tranquilizantes?
8. ¿Espero aquí?

B. El incendio.   As you walk by the gymnasium with a group of visitors to the school, you smell smoke. In case it is serious, use the following list of commands to talk to each member of the group. Add any words necessary to complete the thought.

MODELO: buscar...
Busque la alarma de incendio.

1. llamar...
2. poner...
3. ir...
4. cubrir...
5. tomar...
6. cerrar...

C. La amenaza de bomba. You and your vice-principal have just been made aware of a bomb threat called into your school. Make a list of ten things that you will have to tell people to do using formal commands.

MODELO: Evacuar el edificio: *Evacúen el edificio.*

Módulo 2

No hay ningún peligro

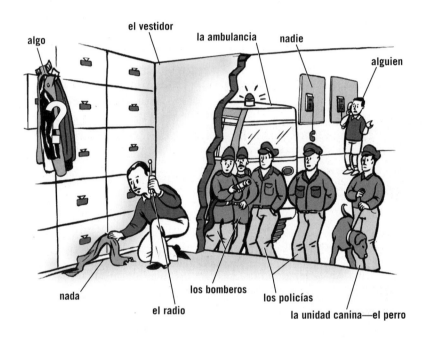

A. ¿Cómo se dice? Choose the correct Spanish word from column **A**, according to each definition in column **B**.

A	B
1. _____ Profesional que apaga los incendios.	**a.** ambulancia
2. _____ Profesional que lucha contra el crimen.	**b.** unidad canina
3. _____ Un equipo de hombre y perro contra el crimen.	**c.** bombero
4. _____ Transporte de emergencia médica.	**d.** policía

B. Contrarios. From the drawing and from memory, can you match up the opposites in meaning? Do you know what they mean?

1. _____ algunos   **a.** nada

2. _____ alguien   **b.** tampoco

3. _____ también   **c.** nadie

4. _____ algo   **d.** ningún

¿No hay ningún peligro?

*Mr. Russo has been searching the building for two missing students. As he moves through, he is in contact with "command central"—**el centro de control**—by radio.*

DIRECTOR:	Daniel, ¿me escuchas? ¿Dónde estás? ¿Por qué no estás con tu clase?
SR. RUSSO:	La Srta. Marcos está con ellos. Algunos estudiantes no están con el grupo. Voy a ver si hay alguien en el vestidor.
DIRECTOR:	¿Hay alguien?
SR. RUSSO:	No hay nadie aquí. John, estoy preocupado. Marco Antonio y Sebastián son buenos estudiantes. Nunca faltan a clase ni mucho menos a un examen. ¿Dónde están los bomberos?
DIRECTOR:	La unidad canina que busca la bomba está en la cafetería y algunos bomberos deben estar en el gimnasio en este momento.
SR. RUSSO:	Aquí no hay ningún bombero. A veces Marco Antonio y Sebastián juegan con las computadoras en la biblioteca. Ahora voy allí. No, tampoco están aquí. Un momento, John...
DIRECTOR:	Daniel, Daniel, ¿ves algo?
SR. RUSSO:	(sarcásticamente). Nada, John. Sólo a mis dos estudiantes que miran toda la actividad con mucha risa. Creen que son héroes frente a los otros estudiantes por llamar con la amenaza de bomba e interrumpir el examen de español. John, no hay ningún peligro. Repito. No hay ningún peligro—para nosotros. Pero para estos dos jóvenes, hay algunos problemas muy serios.

C. ¿Comprende usted? Answer the following questions based on the dialogue.

1. ¿Quién está con la clase de Daniel?

2. ¿Cómo se comunican Daniel y John?

3. ¿Por qué está en el vestidor Daniel?

4. ¿Dónde están Marco Antonio y Sebastián? ¿Por qué creen que son héroes?

D. La disciplina y el abuso infantil. There's a fine line between discipline and abuse. After reading this brochure, list two situations in which discipline by a parent is necessary; then categorize appropriate/inappropriate measures you might find a parent exercising. Compare your list with that of a classmate.

La disciplina y el abuso infantil

Hay una gran diferencia entre el abuso y la disciplina de los niños. La disciplina consiste en corregir la conducta de su hijo sin lastimarlo. El abuso consiste en lastimar al niño.

Cómo mantener la disciplina

Decida cómo recompensar la buena conducta—felicite a su hijo frecuentemente. Y decida qúe hacer cuando sus hijos se porten mal.

- No golpee a su hijo
- Mantenga la calma
- Establezca reglas
- Deles a sus hijos varias opciones
- Sea justo
- No les diga a sus hijos que son "malos"
- Demuéstreles a sus hijos amor y respeto

Jist Publishing

MODELO: *Situación: Un niño corre en un restaurante.*
Disciplina: Decirle: "No corras, siéntate." Abuso: Darle unas palmadas (spanking).

Estructuras

Expressing negative ideas: Las expresiones afirmativas y negativas

- In Spanish, sentences are made negative by placing either **no** or a negative expression *before* the verb. While double negatives are considered to be incorrect in English, they are often necessary in Spanish. The following affirmative expressions must be changed to their negative equivalents if one part of the sentence is negative:

alguien	*somebody*	**nadie**	*nobody*
algo	*something*	**nada**	*nothing*
también	*also*	**tampoco**	*neither*
siempre	*always*	**nunca**	*never*

—¿Hay **algo** en la mesa?   *Is there something on the table?*
—**No** veo **nada.**   *I don't see anything.*
—¿Hay **algo** en la otra mesa?   *Is there anything on the other table?*
—No, **no** veo **nada** allí **tampoco.**   *No, I don't see anything there either.*
—¿Hay **alguien** en el baño?   *Is there anyone in the bathroom?*
—**No, no** hay **nadie** allí.   *No, there is no one there.*
—Si no hay **nadie** allí, vamos al vestidor.   *If nobody is there, let's try the locker room.*

- **Alguno/a** and **ninguno/a** are usually used before a noun and must agree in number and gender with the noun they describe. **Ningún/ninguno/a** literally mean *not even one*. To indicate "there aren't any. . ." both the noun and **ningún/ninguno/a** become singular.

Hay algun**as** buen**as** ideas.   *There are some good ideas.*
No hay ning**una buena idea.**   *There are no good ideas. (There's not even one good idea.)*

- **Algún** and **ningún** are used before masculine singular nouns. **Ninguno/a** is not used in the plural unless no singular form of the noun exists: (i.e. **pantalones, tijeras** *(scissors)*)

Hay **algunos problemas** aquí.   *There are some problems here.*
No hay **ningún problema** aquí.   *There are no problems here. (not even one)*
Necesito **unas tijeras.**   *I need some scissors.*
No veo **ningunas tijeras.**   *I don't see any scissors.*

A. Siempre, a veces *(at times)*, **nunca...** Tell how often you do the following:

MODELO: leer todos los detalles de los desastres en el periódico
A veces leo los detalles de los desastres en el periódico.

1. ir a la clase de español en una ambulancia
2. llamar a la policía para reportar un problema
3. prestar atención a las sirenas de los vehículos de emergencia
4. llamar a la escuela con una amenaza de bomba
5. hacer la tarea durante la clase
6. traer armas a las clases
7. estar nervioso por un examen
8. tomar cerveza durante un examen

B. La madre impaciente. The school officials have their hands full with the mother who believes her son never is wrong. How will they respond to her complaints?

MODELO: —**Nunca** ayudan a los estudiantes.
—*Siempre ayudamos a los estudiantes.*

1. *Nunca* hay *nadie* para contestar mis preguntas.
2. Las recepcionistas *siempre* son antipáticas.
3. *Nunca* hay *nada* interesante en sus clases.
4. El comportamiento del profesor de español *siempre* causa problemas.
5. Mi hijo *tampoco* causa problemas a los otros estudiantes.
6. *Nadie* comprende nuestras necesidades.
7. *Alguien* causa los problemas y mi hijo *siempre* es víctima.
8. *Nunca* hay precauciones de seguridad.

C. ¿Tiene usted...? Tell whether or not you have any of the following right now.

MODELO: algunas preocupaciones por su seguridad *(safety)*
No tengo ninguna preocupación por mi seguridad.

1. algunos problemas en la escuela
2. algún amigo mexicano
3. algunos estudiantes con problemas con el inglés
4. algo importante que hacer mañana
5. algunas clases imposibles
6. algunos pantalones morados

D. Para mañana. You and your assistant are in the office at midnight trying to get ready for tomorrow's important emergency drill. Take turns asking and answering whether or not you need the following things to ensure everyone's safety.

MODELO: radios

> *Asistente: ¿Necesita algunos radios?*
> *Director/a: Sí, necesito algunos radios. or No, no necesito ningún radio.*

1. mapas de las rutas de evacuación
2. fotos de su familia
3. gatos
4. revistas para leer
5. instrucciones
6. números de teléfono del distrito

Vocabulario Módulo 1

Sustantivos

el abuso	*abuse*	**la falda**	*skirt*
la acción	*action*	**el grafiti**	*graffiti*
el/la agente	*agent*	**el héroe/**	
la alarma	*alarm*	**la heroína**	*hero*
el/la alcalde/sa	*mayor*	**el mandamiento**	*commandment*
la amenaza	*threat*	**el mandato**	*command*
el arma (f.)	*weapon*	**el/la modelo**	*model*
la ausencia	*absence*	**la navaja**	*knife, razor*
el beneficio	*benefit*	**la obscenidad**	*obscenity*
la blusa	*blouse*	**la oportunidad**	*opportunity*
los calcetines	*socks*	**la pandilla**	*gang*
la calma	*calm*	**los pantalones**	*pants*
el camino	*road*	**la paz**	*peace*
la cara	*face*	**la pelea**	*fight*
la chaqueta	*jacket*	**la pintura**	*painting*
el círculo	*circle*	**el rival**	*rival*
el conflicto	*conflict*	**la salida**	*exit*
el/la creador/a	*creator*	**la solución**	*solution*
el crimen	*crime*	**la sospecha**	*suspicion*
la declaración	*declaration*	**los tenis**	*tennis shoes*
el/la		**el territorio**	*territory*
drogadicto/a	*drug addict*	**el tranquilizante**	*tranquilizer*
el edificio	*building*	**el uniforme**	*uniform*
el elogio	*praise*	**el vestido**	*dress*
el entusiasmo	*enthusiasm*	**la violencia**	*violence*
el experimento	*experiment*	**el zapato**	*shoe*

Verbos

abrir	to open	**iniciar**	to initiate
acompañar	to accompany	**insistir en**	to insist on
admitir	to admit	**insultar**	to insult
causar	to cause	**intentar**	to attempt
comunicar	to communicate	**interferir (ie)**	to interfere
confiar	to confide	**interrumpir**	to interrupt
copiar	to copy	**modelar**	to model
crear	to create	**participar**	to participate
cubrir	to cover	**probar (ue)**	to prove
defender (ie)	to defend	**remediar**	to fix
dejar	to leave (behind)	**renunciar**	to renounce
elogiar	to praise	**resolver (ue)**	to resolve
esperar	to wait for, hope	**tolerar**	to tolerate
explicar	to explain	**transformar**	to transform
expresar	to express		

Adjetivos

canino/a	canine	**impaciente**	impatient
corto/a	short (length)	**sabio/a**	wise
estúpido/a	stupid	**sensato/a**	sensible
ilegal	illegal	**violento/a**	violent

Otras expresiones

al principio	at the beginning	**me**	me, to me
allí	there	**nos**	us, to us
le	to him/her/you (for.)	**nunca**	never
		tampoco	neither
les	to them/you (pl.)	**te**	you, to you (fam.)

Módulo 2

Sustantivos

el almacén	department store	**la disciplina**	discipline
la ambulancia	ambulance	**el ejemplo**	example
el ascensor	elevator	**la escalera**	stairway
el automóvil	automobile	**la evacuación**	evacuation
la bomba	bomb	**la fila**	line, queue
el/la bombero/a	firefighter	**la herida**	wound
el ciclón	cyclone	**el/la**	
la cobija	blanket	**hispanohablante**	Spanish speaker
la conducta	conduct, behavior	**el incendio**	fire
		el juicio	judgement
la cruz	cross	**el lado**	side
el desacuerdo	disagreement	**la limpieza**	cleaning

la llave	*key*	**el simulacro**	*simulation*
el nivel	*level*	**el techo**	*roof, ceiling*
la pared	*wall*	**el terremoto**	*earthquake*
la práctica	*practice*	**el tiempo**	*time*
el/la radio	*radio*	**el tornado**	*tornado*
el refugio	*refuge*	**la unidad**	*unit*
la ruta	*route*	**el vestidor**	*dressing room*
la seguridad	*security*		

Verbos

afectar	*to affect*	**inspeccionar**	*to inspect*
alejarse de	*to move away from*	**lastimar**	*to injure*
		maltratar	*to mistreat*
cocinar	*to cook*	**oler (ue)**	*to smell*
cooperar	*to cooperate*	**parar**	*to stop*
corregir (i)	*to correct*	**pasear**	*to stroll*
decidir	*to decide*	**prender**	*to turn on*
establecer (zc)	*to establish*	**recoger**	*to pick up*
golpear	*to hit*	**tocar**	*to touch*

Adjetivos

entorpecido/a	*slowed down, dulled*	**pesado/a**	*heavy*
		público/a	*public*
escondido/a	*hidden*	**químico/a**	*chemical*
infantil	*childish*	**terrorista**	*terrorist*
justo/a	*fair*		

Otras expresiones

abajo	*under*	**arriba**	*above*
alguien	*somebody, anybody*	**enfrente de**	*in front of*

Síntesis

A escuchar

La recepcionista recibe una llamada interesante. Listen to the following phone call and answer the questions.

1. ¿Quién contesta el teléfono?
2. ¿Por qué tienen que evacuar la escuela?
3. ¿Cómo se llama la persona que llama?
4. ¿Cómo sabe la recepcionista que es Marco Antonio?

A conversar

Much controversy surrounds the use of marijuana—is it harmful?, medicinal? Read these effects of marijuana use from the National Institute on Drug Abuse and discuss your views with classmates.

- Problemas de memoria y de aprendizaje
- Percepción distorsionada (visual, auditiva y del tacto), y del sentido del paso del tiempo
- Problemas para pensar claramente
- Menor coordinación física
- Ansiedad, ataques de pánico y taquicardia

A leer

Read the following informational brochure on alcohol and children and then complete the activity by writing **Sí** or **No** for each statement. Correct any incorrect information.

Cómo ayudar a su hijo a decir "NO" al alcohol

Éstas son ocho maneras en las que usted puede ayudar a su hijo a decir "NO" al alcohol.

1. Sea un ejemplo
2. Hable con su hijo
3. Enséñele valores
4. Establezca reglas
5. Elogie a su hijo
6. Dé ánimos
7. Comparta las responsabilidades
8. Acepte los errores y desacuerdos

---

1. _____ Es importante ser un ejemplo.

2. _____ El niño forma sus propios _(own)_ valores.

3. _____ Hablar y elogiar a su hijo es muy importante.

4. _____ No es necesario aceptar los errores y desacuerdos.

A escribir

Juego de palabras: Algunas de las palabras en la lista **A** son nombres de las partes del cuerpo afectadas por el alcohol. Otras palabras describen cómo el alcohol puede afectarnos. La lista **B** tiene algunas de las cosas que podemos hacer en vez de beber. Todas las palabras están escondidas entre las letras—de arriba a abajo, de abajo a arriba, de lado a lado y diagonalmente. Dibuja un círculo alrededor de las letras que forman las palabras.

Lista A: discernimiento, cerebro, corazón, mente, entorpecido, hígado, dolor de cabeza, sangre, triste, tosco, vahído, ojos, juicio

Lista B: muñequitos, leer, deportes, diario, computadoras, vídeo, dibujar, cocinar, bailar, salir a paseo

```
M U Ñ E Q U I T O S C D O A
D I B U J A R M O P U I V Z
S C E D O M A E A N T A I E
E E O R E E L N T E R R D B
T M I C S A I L U N D I E A
R S A L I R A P A S E O O C
O N E O L N B O P I E M D E
P O R N S E A S O J O S E D
E D G E T S I R T C N O P R
D A N O Z A R O C C S O O O
M G A I E N V A H I D O R L
D I S C E R N I M I E N T O
S H O D I C E P R O T N E D
E C O M P U T A D O R A S S
J U I C I O C E R E B R O O
```

Algo más

Ventana cultural

Hispanics are now America's largest minority, as their number grew 50% in the last decade. When it comes to college, however, just 10% of Hispanics aged 25–29 hold bachelor's degrees, compared to 32% of whites. And their high school dropout rate is expected to double in the next decade, to 32%.

Más hispanos dejan los estudios a nivel secundario

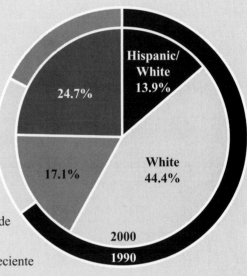

El número de hispanos que dejan los estudios a nivel secundario antes de completarlos, o de aquellos que no comenzaron la educación secundaria, aumentó en más del 50% en la década de los 90, especialmente en el sur y en el oeste del país, donde muchas escuelas trataron de acomodar a la población creciente de hispanohablantes.

El 67% de jóvenes hispanos viven en familias donde ninguno de los padres tiene un diploma secundario. De los 1.56 millones de jóvenes que abandonan la educación secundaria entre las edades de 16 a 19 en Estados Unidos, hay más hispanos que hace 10 años. Casi un 34%, o más de 528,000, son hispanos, más del 22%, o 346,000, del total en 1990. Con las iniciativas positivas de muchas organizaciones que ofrecen apoyo al estudiante latino, esperamos ver un mejoramiento en estos números en el futuro.

Para obtener más información: www.census.gov

En mis propias palabras. Why do you think Hispanics lag in school? Jot down at least four points to consider and compare your thoughts with those of a classmate.

A buscar

D.A.R.E. has its manual online in Spanish. Go to www.aepap.org/pedev/daremanual.htm and see what information you can find. You might look for other sites with information on drugs and alcohol in Spanish also.

A conocer: Edward James Olmos

Edward James Olmos, as an actor, activist, and advocate, embodies the strong characters he plays on screen, such as his Oscar-nominated role of Jaime Escalante in 1987's *Stand and Deliver*, the true story of helping 18 students at Garfield High School in Los Angeles pass the Advanced Placement calculus test. "I'm just coming into my own," he says. His PBS series, *American Family*, profiles Latinos. He is one of the co-founders of the Los Angeles Latino Film Festival, now in its sixth year, and of the Latino Book and Family Festival, founded in 1997. He commits to an average of 150 speaking engagements a year to help show disadvantaged youths that they can affect their future and make the decision to stay away from gangs and drugs.

$\mathcal{L}$ECCIÓN 6

Repaso I

Lección 1: Vamos a la escuela
- La hora
- **Ser** + adjetivos
- Las preguntas
- Los artículos

Lección 2: ¡La vuelta al cole!
- Más sobre los adjetivos
- Los verbos que terminan en **–ar**
- Los verbos que terminan en **–er, –ir**
- Expresiones con **tener** y **estar**

Consejera

Lección 3: La oficina de salud
- El presente progresivo
- **Ser** y **estar**
- El verbo **ir** y el futuro inmediato
- Verbos irregulares en el presente

Lección 4: El personal de la escuela
- Los adjetivos posesivos
- Los verbos con cambios de raíz
- Los comparativos
- Los superlativos

Lección 5: La seguridad en la escuela
- Los mandatos afirmativos informales
- Los mandatos formales; mandatos negativos informales
- Los mandatos irregulares/con cambios ortográficos/con pronombres de objeto indirecto
- Las expresiones afirmativas y negativas

Lección I

Vamos a la escuela

Módulo I

A. El/La secretario/a. Part of your job as school secretary is taking information from the new students and their families. Write the question you would ask to get the information provided.

MODELO: 6 años
¿Cuántos años tienes tú?

I. 153 calle Concordia   **4.** Hispano
2. (603) 435-7768   **5.** Irene Velázquez
3. el 6 de enero de 1997 (mil novecientos noventa y siete)

B. ¡Hola! Another of your jobs as a secretary is to give teachers a 15-minute advance reminder before their next parent meeting. As you contract them by intercom, greet each of the faculty with the appropriate greeting for the time of day, tell what time it is now, and at what time the meeting will be.

MODELO: 10:05 A.M.
Buenos días. Son las diez y cinco de la mañana. La reunión es a las diez y veinte.

I. 1:05 P.M.   **4.** 12 noon
2. 6:15 P.M.   **5.** 8:30 A.M.
3. 7:00 A.M. on the dot   **6.** 9:55 P.M.

C. En la sala de espera. While anxiously awaiting your turn with your child's principal, you make the following observations. Use the verb **ser** to link the subjects and verbs, and don't forget to match nouns and adjectives!

MODELO: La sala de espera/moderno
La sala de espera es moderna.

I. Las revistas/viejo   **5.** Las pinturas/interesante
2. Las recepcionistas/simpático   **6.** Las manzanas (*apples*)/rojo
3. Los asistentes/eficiente   **7.** El sistema telefónico/complicado
4. El maestro joven/guapo   **8.** La espera/largo

D. Problemas, problemas. You are the receptionist in the school office two days before classes are set to begin. The line of families who want to register in your school is out the door. Speed up the process by completing the information for two at a time and interview two classmates to fill in the forms. Remember. They don't have to tell the truth—just use good grammar!

Apellido(s)_____ Nombre_____	Apellido(s)_____ Nombre_____
Dirección_____	Dirección_____
Ciudad_____ Estado_____Código postal_____	Ciudad_____ Estado_____Código postal_____
Teléfono_____ Etnicidad_____	Teléfono_____ Etnicidad_____
Fecha de nacimiento_____ Edad_____	Fecha de nacimiento_____ Edad_____

Módulo 2

A. Un jefe sin memoria. You have a wonderful new boss, but he sometimes has a tendency to forget the words he is trying to say. Read the descriptions and supply the missing term.

MODELO: la mesa donde trabajo; tiene mi teléfono y mi computadora…
¡Ah!, el escritorio.

1. las mesas y sillas donde los estudiantes trabajan
2. los juguetes como Barbie y Ken y G.I. Joe
3. la clase en la que los niños aprenden números y cálculos
4. la reacción de las personas cuando algo es cómico
5. jirafas, pingüinos, tigres y elefantes
6. el lugar donde tenemos asambleas

B. Muchas preguntas. You are sitting in the waiting room of a school anticipating your meeting with a teacher. As you sit there, a new parent is on the phone trying to get as much information as possible about the school. You can only hear the answers the receptionist is giving. Now write down the question that the parent must have asked.

Hola...

MODELO: Estamos en la calle Main.
¿Dónde están ustedes?

1. Hay catorce maestros.
2. Las clases empiezan el lunes.
3. Usted necesita tener el acta de nacimiento del niño y el certificado de salud.
4. La directora se llama Dra. González.
5. Hay veinte estudiantes en las clases.

C. Direcciones. While you are on hall duty, a series of visitors stop by to ask you where they might find the following things or people. Use your best Spanish to tell them—some things may be found in more than one place.

MODELO: un sandwich
En la cafetería

1. las pelotas y juegos
2. asistencia médica
3. el director de la escuela
4. muchos libros para seleccionar
5. la asamblea para los premios
6. el conserje

D. Las relaciones humanas.   Maintaining good relationships with co-workers is often a key to your long-term success. Tell what question you would have asked to get the following answers from colleagues.

MODELO: Hoy estoy bien, gracias.
            ¿Cómo está usted hoy?

I.   Me llamo Mario Andaloro.
2.   Trabajo en la oficina.
3.   Tengo tres hijos.
4.   Hablo dos idiomas: inglés y español.
5.   Los maestros son simpáticos.
6.   Trabajo aquí porque la directora es excelente.

Lección 2

¡La vuelta al cole!

Módulo I

A. En la escuela.   Can you identify these school-day terms by their description?

I.   Un símbolo rojo, blanco y azul del patriotismo es _____.

2.   La práctica de las lecciones que los estudiantes hacen en casa es su

_____.

3.   Los estudiantes que quieren aprender a cantar en un grupo participan en el

_____.

4.   La organización de los padres que quieren apoyar la escuela es la

_____.

B. ¿Qué hace usted?   A confused teaching assistant is trying to deliver several orders of supplies to the correct places. Please match the supply with the room.

I.   Salón de arte   **a.**   galletas
2.   Centro de música   **b.**   crayones
3.   Gimnasio   **c.**   computadoras
4.   Cafetería   **d.**   violines y flautas
5.   Centro de matemáticas **e.**   pelotas
6.   Centro de tecnología   **f.**   libros de fracciones

C. Optimismo.   If only the world worked exactly the way we would like it to! Pretend that it is an ideal world and find an adjective to describe these nouns. Compare your list with a classmate's to see if you think alike.

MODELO: mi profesor/a
E1: *Mi profesor es excelente.*
E2: *Mi profesor es guapo.*

1. los estudiantes
2. la tarea
3. mis calificaciones
4. la maestra
5. mi amigo/a
6. yo

D. La división del trabajo.   You have been sent by the school district to be sure that everyone at the school is doing his or her job. Look at the following list of tasks and tell who does each one using the job categories below.

Las secretarias, el conserje, los maestros, la directora, los niños, las señoras de la cafetería, or all of us—**nosotros**

MODELO: contestar el teléfono
Las secretarias contestan el teléfono.

1. limpiar la escuela
2. preparar la comida
3. enseñar a los estudiantes
4. ayudar a los niños y sus familias
5. estudiar las lecciones
6. vigilar el patio de recreo
7. contestar muchas preguntas
8. preparar las lecciones

Módulo 2

A. ¿Dónde?   Can you match the following after-school activities with the place they will be held?

1. audiciones para el drama del 3er grado
2. el club de cocina
3. el club deportivo
4. el club de tecnología

a. en la cafetería
b. en el patio de recreo
c. en el laboratorio de computadoras
d. en el "teatro" del salón 101

B. ¡Rápido!   Oh, no! Your new after-school program opens in two days and you still don't have all of the activities planned nor the school supplies you will need. Brainstorm at least two activities and a "shopping list" of at least two materials or supplies you will need for each of the following clubs. Money is no object. But speed is! **Uno, dos, tres... ¡YA!**

Club deportivo	Club de computadoras	Club de arte	Club de juegos
jugar al fútbol pelotas			

C. ¿Qué hacen?   Turn the following subjects and verbs into complete sentences by supplying a logical ending.

MODELO: Los estudiantes/escribir
Los estudiantes escriben la tarea.

1. Los niños/comer en
2. La recepcionista/recibir
3. En la sala de espera, yo/leer
4. Cuando tenemos mucha sed, nosotros/beber
5. En el formulario de información personal, los padres/escribir
6. La directora/mirar

D. Expresiones.   Simplify the following situations for your child by using a logical **tener** expression.

MODELO: Las maestras necesitan calefacción.
Tienen frío.

1. Después de jugar mucho durante la hora de recreo, los niños quieren comer.
2. La maestra busca el termostato: necesita bajar la temperatura.
3. Los padres del niño muy enfermo *(sick)* llevan tres días sin dormir.
4. El estudiante nació *(was born)* en 1998.

Lección 3

La oficina de salud

Módulo 1

A. Identificación.   Can you complete each line with a logical vocabulary word related to playground safety?

1. Los adultos que vigilan a los estudiantes en el patio de recreo son

   _____.

2. En caso de accidente, es importante dar los _____ inmediatamente a la víctima.

3. El _____ y el _____ son dos equipos populares en el patio de recreo.

4. En el patio de recreo, los niños hablan en voz muy A–L–T–A. Ellos

   _____.

B. La familia.   Can you define the following family members—in Spanish? Follow the form for your answers.

MODELO: abuela
   La abuela es la mamá de mi mamá.

1. el tío
2. la hermana
3. los nietos
4. los padres

C. Modelo de conducta.   It's after-school hours and you are staying late to take care of paperwork and other odds and ends in your classroom. One of your most devoted students has volunteered to help you. Your student is particularly curious and wants to know exactly what you are doing at every moment. Answer all of the following questions with a logical response and the present progressive tense.

MODELO: ¿Qué lee usted?
   Estoy leyendo las tareas de los estudiantes.

1. ¿Qué escribe?
2. ¿Qué mira?
3. ¿Qué prepara?
4. ¿Por qué duerme?

SPANISH FOR SCHOOL PERSONNEL

D. Centro de información. As the secretary to a principal who is also an education professor at a prestigious university, you are often called on to give information about your boss. Use the correct form of **ser** or **estar** to complete the following sentences.

MODELO: El Dr. Caso... en México con su familia.
El Dr. Caso está en México con su familia.

1. El Dr. Caso originalmente... de Argentina.
2. El Dr. Caso y sus estudiantes... en una reunión en la universidad.
3. El Dr. Caso... experto en la educación bilingüe.
4. El Dr. Caso... muy cansado después de investigar el vandalismo toda la noche.
5. Este plan para la escuela... del Dr. Caso.
6. La clase en la universidad... a las ocho de la noche.
7. Los empleados del Dr. Caso... muy contentos de verlo.
8. El Dr. Caso y los maestros... hablando en la sala de conferencias.

Módulo 2

A. En el centro de salud. You are working at the school's health center and it seems that suddenly everyone is showing symptoms. Identify the following problems that the students describe to you.

MODELO: Tengo la temperatura elevada.
Tú tienes fiebre.

1. Tengo dolor de cabeza y no puedo respirar por la nariz.
2. El almuerzo regresa por la boca.
3. Tengo la cara muy rosada con comezón.
4. Desde *(since)* el partido de fútbol durante el recreo, tengo el tobillo hinchado y dolorido.

B. ¿Para qué sirven? Can you explain—in Spanish, of course—what you would need the following for?

MODELO: loción de calamina
Necesito loción de calamina para una erupción.

1. mensaje
2. teléfono
3. un médico
4. aspirina

C. ¿Qué va a hacer? Tell what you are going to do to remedy the following situations.

MODELO: Hay un niño muy enfermo en el centro de salud.
Voy a llamar a sus padres.

1. Hay un examen en su clase de español.
2. La habitación está sucia.
3. Usted necesita hacer ejercicio.
4. Usted está muy cansado.
5. Ustedes tienen hambre.
6. Hay una emergencia médica en la escuela.

D. ¿Quién o quiénes? You are the principal of a large school during the week before opening in the fall. Tell in a complete sentence if you (**yo=el/la director/a),** the school staff **(los empleados),** or all of us **(nosotros)** do the following things.

MODELO: (hacer) la limpieza
Los empleados hacen la limpieza.

1. _____ (conducir) los autobuses escolares

2. _____ (hacer) llamadas de larga distancia

3. _____ (traer) pizzas para los empleados

4. _____ (salir) de la escuela para ir a una reunión

5. _____ (poner) más papel y tiza en cada salón

6. _____ (saber) el número de emergencias

Lección 4

El personal de la escuela

Módulo I

A. El secreto de las calificaciones. Any teacher will tell you that giving grades is often the most difficult task of the year. Look at the comments that the following student has received during the quarter and give a grade of A, C, or F in the appropriate subject. Then compare your grading system with another student's.

El estudiante...

Calificaciones

1. Copia las tareas y exámenes de otros estudiantes.

2. Sabe escribir bien todas las palabras.

3. Lee mucho, pero comprende poco.

4. Sabe multiplicar y dividir

5. No es muy atlético, pero participa bien en los equipos.

a. ortografía _____

b. lectura _____

c. matemáticas _____

d. educación física _____

e. comportamiento _____

B. Identificación. Can you define in your own words (in Spanish, of course!) these people, disabilities, or accommodations related to Special Education?

MODELO: ceguera

Es una discapacidad en que la persona no puede ver.

1. sordera
2. lenguaje por señas
3. psicólogo escolar
4. batería
5. problemas de aprendizaje
6. silla de ruedas

C. Posesión.   Use the appropriate form of the possessive adjectives **mi(s),** **tu(s), su(s),** or **nuestro/a/os/as** to describe the relationships that follow.

MODELO: Tengo un tío que es maestro.
_Mi_ tío es bilingüe.

1. Ustedes tienen una escuela moderna.   _____ escuela es moderna.

2. Nosotros tenemos maestros
    excelentes.   _____ maestros son excelentes.

3. Elena tiene varios problemas.   _____ problemas son serios.

4. Tú tienes buenas calificaciones.   _____ calificaciones son buenas.

5. Ellos tienen una bandera mexicana.   _____ bandera es mexicana.

6. Ellos tienen dos revistas españolas.   _____ revistas son españolas.

7. Usted tiene un periódico venezolano.   _____ periódico es venezolano.

8. Usted tiene dos amigas colombianas.   _____ amigas son colombianas.

D. Personas diferentes.   You and your friend Eduardo are just the opposite of the two other first grade teachers, Juan and Lucía. Explain how by finishing the following sentences.

MODELO: dormir mucho en la sala de descanso
Eduardo y yo no dormimos mucho en la sala de descanso. Juan y Lucía
duermen mucho.

1. preferir a los estudiantes perezosos
2. pensar mucho antes de llenar las boletas de calificaciones
3. siempre perder las tareas de los estudiantes
4. almorzar en la cafetería
5. empezar el día temprano
6. pedir donativos (_donations_) a los padres de los estudiantes
7. querer ser maestros excelentes
8. decir siempre la verdad

Módulo 2

A. Servicios para el estudiante especial. Schools are required to offer many services to students and their families from the classroom to the playground, to the lunch room to specialized educational services. Read the following scenarios and indicate whether the school is offering better than average service **M** (**Mejor**) or worse than average service **P** (**Peor**).

MODELO: Estudiante: Tengo una pregunta.
_____P_____ _Maestro: Estoy ocupado._

1. Madre: Sra. Shrader, ¿a qué hora sale de la escuela? Quiero hablar con usted pero no puedo llegar hasta las 4.

   _____ Maestra: A las tres. Pero si quiere, puedo esperar.

2. Padre: Mi hijo tiene muchos problemas con las matemáticas. Quiero pedir una evaluación para ver si tiene problemas de aprendizaje.

   _____ Psicóloga: ¡Ja, ja, ja!

3. Estudiante: No comprendo la tarea para mañana.

   _____ Maestro: Un momento, mi hijo, y te explico la tarea.

4. Padres: Estamos interesados en apoyar a la escuela participando en la Organización de padres, pero no hablamos mucho inglés.

   _____ Directora: No se preocupen. Es importante que participen. En esta escuela tenemos intérpretes bilingües en todas las reuniones de la Organización de padres.

B. El superintendente que no recuerda nada. Your aging boss is having one of his forgetful spells again. Help him by supplying the word he is trying to describe.

MODELO: Superintendente: el evento donde los estudiantes excelentes reciben premios.
Usted: _La asamblea de honores_

1. Un documento que reconoce los logros de un estudiante
2. Cuando los padres orgullosos usan una cámara
3. El niño que recibe más votos de los maestros ese mes para recibir el premio
4. El premio de metal—una estatua

C. Las clases en mi escuela.   In my school, there are two very competitive teachers. One is Sr. Vargas with the third grade, and the other is Srta. Santana with the fourth grade. They are constantly comparing their classes. Using the following list, make at least three comparative statements of equality **(tan/tanto... como)** and three statements of inequality **(más... que, menos... que).**

MODELO: El Sr. Vargas habla tres idiomas. La Srta. Santana habla dos idiomas.
El Sr. Vargas habla más idiomas que la Srta. Santana.

Sr. Vargas	**Srta. Santana**
34 estudiantes	34 estudiantes
muy interesante	no muy interesante
perezoso	trabajadora
Hay 2 estudiantes del mes en su clase.	Hay 1 estudiante del mes en su clase.
5 estudiantes reciben trofeos hoy.	5 estudiantes reciben trofeos hoy.
Tiene dos conejos (*rabbits)* en el salón.	Tiene dos conejos en el salón.
Es un buen maestro.	Es muy buena maestra.

D. La mejor clase de la escuela.   Using the chart above, draw two conclusions about the best and worst classes in the school. Then write a sentence with **–ísimo/a/os/as** to explain.

MODELO: *La Srta. Santana es la mejor maestra de la escuela.*
Es buenísima.

Lección 5

La seguridad en la escuela

Módulo I

A. El director olvidadizo. Your forgetful boss is having trouble remembering the word he needs to use. Please help him out by supplying the word he is trying to describe.

MODELO: La parte de la escuela donde los estudiantes juegan al fútbol o a la rayuela
¿El patio de recreo?

1. La ropa que se pone encima de la camisa cuando tiene frío
2. La ropa que usan las muchachas: blusa y falda en una sola pieza
3. Un conflicto físico entre personas
4. La falta de conflictos; la tranquilidad
5. Decir cosas ofensivas de una persona
6. Un grupo de jóvenes que se identifica con un "territorio"

B. ¿Los clubes escolares o las pandillas? Which of the following items do you associate more with **clubes (C)** and which do you associate with **pandillas (P)?**

1. _____ la violencia
2. _____ los elogios
3. _____ la amenaza
4. _____ la paz
5. _____ el grafiti y las señas
6. _____ una navaja

C. Los consejos. As a school monitor, you frequently tell students what they should be doing. Use a **tú** command form to tell each student what he or she ought to be doing.

MODELO: tomar el refresco en la cafetería, no en la biblioteca
Toma el refresco en la cafetería, no en la biblioteca.

1. leer bien la lección
2. tener cuidado en el gimnasio
3. practicar el instrumento musical
4. buscar información en Internet
5. venir acá inmediatamente
6. salir por la puerta, no por la ventana

D. Traviesos.   Each of the students you encounter right now is doing something they should not be doing. Your first job is to tell each one not to do it using negative **tú** commands. Then warn the other students not to do it either, using **ustedes** commands.

MODELO: masticar chicle (*chew gum*) en la clase
No mastiques chicle. Y ustedes, no mastiquen chicle tampoco.

1. no decir mentiras

2. no traer armas a la escuela

3. no salir de la escuela para almorzar

4. no poner chicle en la computadora

5. no hacer señas de pandillas en la escuela

6. no escribir en las paredes (*walls*)

Módulo 2

A. ¿Hay peligro?   Since the director is away from school and you are in charge, it is up to you to decide if the school is in danger (**Hay peligro**) or not (**No hay peligro**) when the following things happen.

MODELO: Hay un intruso con una pistola.
Hay peligro.

1. Un estudiante accidentalmente rompe una ventana.

2. Hay un simulacro de incendio.

3. Hay un tornado en otra ciudad.

4. Hay un incendio en la cafetería.

5. Hay un terremoto bastante fuerte.

6. Dos estudiantes se pelean.

B. Respuesta a los desastres.   For each of the listed disasters, tell your assistant to call the appropriate response agency and then tell the teachers where to take their students.

MODELO: Hay un incendio en la cafetería.
Llama a los bomberos. Lleven a los estudiantes al patio de recreo.

1. Hay drogas en la escuela.

2. Hay una persona con una pistola.

3. Hay una amenaza de bomba.

4. Hay un accidente en el laboratorio de química.

5. Hay una pelea entre pandillas rivales. Traen navajas.

6. Hay una explosión en el laboratorio.

C. ¡Emergencia!   Tell the following people what they need to do in the emergency. Be polite! Use formal **usted** commands.

MODELO: buscar al director
Busque al director.

1. ir al gimnasio con los estudiantes
2. saber bien la ruta de evacuación
3. no tener miedo
4. dar su nombre y dirección
5. explicarle el problema al policía
6. empezar los primeros auxilios

D. Los dos maestros enemigos.   Ernesto and Paloma are two teachers who are always disagreeing. For every statement that Ernesto makes, give the opposite one that Paloma would make.

MODELO: Siempre llegas tarde a tu clase.
Nunca llego tarde a mi clase.

1. Siempre repites la misma lección.
2. Nunca tienes las boletas de calificaciones preparadas.
3. Siempre tienes algunas cervezas en el escritorio.
4. Nunca dices nada interesante.
5. Tus estudiantes tienen algunos problemas con la gramática, también.
6. Alguien te amenaza.

𝓛ECCIÓN 7

La educación alternativa

Módulo 1
- Se ofrecen alternativas
- Expressing generalizations and expectations, and the passive voice: *Se impersonal*
- La educación a distancia
- The recent past: *Acabar de* + *infinitivo*

Consejera

Módulo 2
- El salón virtual
- Expressing likes and dislikes: *Gustar*
- El proyecto virtual
- Numbers: *De cien a millones; los números ordinales*

Síntesis
- A escuchar
- A conversar
- A leer
- A escribir

Algo más
- Ventana cultural: ¿Quién sabe más de Latinoamérica?
- A buscar
- A conocer: www.SuperOnda.com

Módulo 1

Se ofrecen alternativas

A. ¿Cómo se dice?   Use la memoria, la imaginación y el dibujo para indicar una definición lógica para este vocabulario.

1. _____ alternativas
2. _____ particular
3. _____ multicultural
4. _____ la matrícula

a. el dinero que se paga para asistir a una escuela

b. de mucha diversidad étnica, religiosa o nacional

c. opciones o posibilidades adicionales

d. no para el público; privado

B. ¿Dónde?   Indique en qué escuela se pueden encontrar las siguientes especialidades.

a. bellas artes **b.** Tecnología **c.** Ciencias y Matemáticas **d.** valores multiculturales

1. _____ la danza, la ópera y la pintura
2. _____ la programación y las Ciencias de computación (o informática)
3. _____ Química, Física y Álgebra avanzada
4. _____ estudios de festivales, valores y costumbres étnicas

Los amigos

Las madres de Beto Morales y Pepe Brito piensan que estos dos niños son mucho más que amigos inseparables—son iguales en casi todo. Les gustan las mismas actividades, las mismas materias en la escuela y los mismos deportes. También tienen los mismos problemas con la escuela. Esta mañana las dos mamás hablan de los niños y de su escuela intermedia mientras toman un café.

SRA. MORALES: Se dice que el Sr. Porter está muy enfermo y ya no regresa a la escuela.

SRA. BRITO: ¿El maestro joven de ciencias? ¡Qué lástima! Es por su entusiasmo y determinación que la escuela tiene este programa de tecnología especial con el laboratorio—y la razón por la que Beto y Pepe tienen tanto interés en Ciencias y Matemáticas. Estos maestros tan creativos no se reemplazan fácilmente.

SRA. MORALES: Lo sé. Según la directora, es evidente que se eliminan los programas del Sr. Porter—y los de Arte y Música también por razones económicas. Por eso quiero hablarte del año que viene. ¿Sabes algo de las escuelas chárter?

SRA. BRITO: Nada. ¿Qué son?

SRA. MORALES: Son escuelas que nos dan alternativas a la educación tradicional. Se ofrecen clases más pequeñas y una variedad de programas especializados.

SRA. BRITO: ¿Qué clase de programas especializados?

SRA. MORALES: En esta parte de la ciudad hay unas que se especializan en las bellas artes; una que se especializa en los deportes y el atletismo, una que se especializa en la Tecnología, dos que se especializan en las Ciencias y Matemáticas y otra que se especializa en valores multiculturales. Se dan también opciones bilingües donde se enseñan español e inglés u otro idioma e inglés.

SRA. BRITO: ¿Y las otras clases básicas?

SRA. MORALES: También se requieren todas las clases básicas para cumplir con los requisitos del Estado. Se parecen mucho a las escuelas privadas, pero por ser parte de la educación pública, no se paga nada—son gratis. ¿Qué opinas?

SRA. BRITO: Si se habla español, se ofrecen clases más pequeñas con más atención individual y si no se paga matrícula, vamos. Investigando se aprende mucho.

C. ¿Comprende usted?   Conteste las preguntas según la información del diálogo.

1. ¿Quién es el Sr. Porter?
2. ¿Qué programas va a perder la escuela? ¿Por qué?
3. ¿Qué son las escuelas chárter?
4. ¿Qué especialidades ofrecen las escuelas chárter en esta parte de la ciudad?

D. Escuelas para su elección.   Lea el anuncio que sigue y prepare un resumen de cinco líneas explicando este programa.

Distrito escolar unificado de Arroyo Grande

Escuelas para su elección
Período de las solicitudes para el año escolar 2003–2004
Del 31 de enero al 11 de febrero de 2003

La ley:

- Les permite a los padres de niños en edad escolar que residen en el distrito seleccionar la escuela que ofrece el mejor beneficio para sus hijos.

- Mantiene el balance racial y étnico apropiado.

- Requiere un proceso de selección al azar e imparcial en la elección.

Preguntas sobre los procedimientos:

- ¿Están disponibles todas las escuelas para los solicitantes *(applicants)*? Sí, todas las escuelas primarias (K–5), secundarias (6–8) y preparatorias integrales (9–12) están abiertas, pero el cupo *(quota)* es muy limitado. La solicitud para los programas de escuelas especializadas tiene otros criterios de admisión.

- ¿Cómo se selecciona a los alumnos? Después del período de matrícula hay un sorteo. Se anuncian los resultados en marzo.

- ¿Existe una lista de espera? Sí, después del sorteo, si hay más vacantes, hay otro sorteo de esa lista.

- ¿Hay transporte a la escuela de su elección? No hay transporte fuera del área de asistencia de la escuela.

E. ¿Cuál es la mejor escuela para mi hijo/a?   Hable con un/a compañero/a de tres razones para elegir el mejor lugar para la educación de su hijo/a. Si no tiene hijos, mencione factores importantes al escoger una escuela.

MODELO: *Para mí, la escuela debe estar cerca de mi casa.*

Estructuras   *Expressing generalizations, and expectations, and the passive voice: Se impersonal*

- Use **se** to state generalizations about what is or is not done. Phrases with **se** are expressed in the following ways in English.

Se habla español en aquella escuela.	*They speak Spanish at that school.*
	One speaks Spanish at that school.
	Spanish is spoken at that school.
¿Se aprende inglés así?	*Does one learn English this way?*
	Do people learn English this way?
	Is English learned this way?
¿Cómo **se dice** "Charter School" en español?	*How is 'Charter School' said in Spanish?*
	How do you say 'Charter School' in Spanish?
	How do people say 'Charter School' in Spanish?

■ With **se**, use the third person form (**él**, **ella**, **usted**, **ellos**, **ellas**, **ustedes**) of the verb. It may be singular or plural, depending on the subject. To make the verb plural, simply add an **-n.**

Se aprende inglés en la escuela.	*English is learned at school.*
Se aprenden inglés y español en la escuela.	*English and Spanish are learned at school.*
Se vende el libro en la librería.	*The book is sold at the bookstore.*
Se venden los libros en la librería.	*The books are sold at the bookstore.*

■ Use a singular verb with people introduced by the personal **a** and with infinitive verbs used as subjects, even if referring to more than one person or action.

Se ve a muchas familias en la escuela.	*You see many families at school.*
Se puede investigar mucho por Internet.	*One can research a lot on the Internet.*

Para practicar

A. ¿Adónde se va? Identifique un sitio donde se venden las siguientes cosas escolares.

MODELO: diccionarios
Se venden diccionarios en la librería.

1. zapatos tenis
2. mochilas
3. lápices, plumas y papel
4. sándwiches para el almuerzo
5. equipo para los deportes
6. ropa para deportes

B. El extraterrestre. Usted tiene un visitante de otro planeta que no comprende nuestras costumbres. Explíquele lo que hacemos en este planeta con las siguientes cosas.

MODELO: el lápiz
Se escribe con el lápiz.

1. el agua
2. los libros
3. el almuerzo
4. los diccionarios
5. el dinero
6. los programas educativos de televisión

C. ¿Qué se hace con...? Escriba una oración usando **se** para explicar para qué se necesitan las siguientes personas.

MODELO: los maestros

Se necesitan los maestros para enseñar a los estudiantes.

1. los estudiantes	**4.** un/a director/a
2. las secretarias	**5.** los conserjes
3. el consejero	**6.** la enfermera de la escuela

Módulo 1

La educación a distancia

El salón virtual

el URL: www.si.edu
(el sitio web del Smithsonian Institute)

la pantalla

Clases en línea: Ciencias

navegar por la Red (Internet)

¡Usted tiene correo!

el correo electrónico

La educación a distancia

A. ¿Cómo se dice?   Llene el espacio con la palabra o frase del dibujo que mejor define estas descripciones de la "educación-e".

1. Una aula (*classroom*) formada por estudiantes en diferentes lugares

conectados por computadoras es un _____.

2. Ahora muchas personas usan _____ para sus comunicaciones en vez del servicio postal.

3. La dirección oficial de un sitio web es su _____.

B. En mis propias palabras.   Escriba una definición de las siguientes frases conectadas con la educación virtual.

1. navegar por la Red
2. la educación a distancia
3. estar "en línea"

¡Las clases en línea!

Las mamás de Beto y Pepe otra vez están tomando su café esta mañana y conversando sobre su tema favorito—sus hijos y su educación. Tratan de resolver muchos problemas de la escuela, del maestro Porter, y de sus hijos con una sola idea— "virtualmente" brillante.

SRA. MORALES: Acabo de recibir un correo electrónico del maestro Porter contestando mi nota de la semana pasada. Está mejor, pero su recuperación en casa va a ser prolongada. No puede regresar a la escuela este año.

SRA. BRITO: ¡Pobrecito! Y, ¡pobres niños! Van a estar muy tristes al saber que no pueden participar en la Feria de Matemáticas, Ciencias y Tecnología este año. Pepe y Beto tienen una idea fenomenal para su proyecto. Pero necesitan la ayuda del maestro.

SRA. MORALES: ¿Podemos ayudarlos nosotras dos? Podemos investigar el tema en línea por Internet...

SRA. BRITO: ¡Por Internet y por correo electrónico! ¡Eres brillante! ¡Así es! ¡Qué inspiración!

SRA. MORALES: ¿Cómo? No te comprendo. No es una idea nueva—investigar un tema por la Red. ¿Por qué te pones tan animada?

SRA. BRITO: Porque acabas de resolver todos los problemas: de la escuela, del maestro Porter y de los niños y la Feria.

SRA. MORALES: ¿Al mencionar la Red?

SRA. BRITO: Clases en línea. ¿Conoces el servicio de "Salones virtuales" que la escuela acaba de anunciar para los estudiantes que no pueden asistir a las clases? Hay clases y tutores interactivos en línea. Los niños usan la computadora en casa para estudiar las lecciones, hacer preguntas, hablar con otros estudiantes en las salas de conversación y hacer sus exámenes. Nosotros podemos hacerlo al revés: tener una clase virtual con un maestro enfermo que no puede asistir físicamente a la clase.

SRA. MORALES: ¿Cómo funciona?

SRA. BRITO: El maestro Porter puede crear los módulos y simulaciones en línea desde su computadora en casa. Después de completar cada módulo, los niños pueden navegar por la Red para buscar más información. Así, en línea, Pepe y Beto y sus compañeros pueden mantener el contacto con su maestro favorito y él puede ayudarlos con sus proyectos.

C. ¿Comprende usted?   Conteste las preguntas según la información del diálogo.

1.   ¿Por qué no puede asistir a la escuela el Sr. Porter?
2.   ¿Por qué están tristes Pepe y Beto?
3.   ¿Cómo pueden asistir a clases los estudiantes enfermos?
4.   ¿Cómo se pueden resolver los problemas del maestro y los estudiantes?

D. ¡Bienvenido a *Busca y captura* en español!   Usted quiere explorar Internet en español y *Busca y captura* le ofrece un mes de servicio incluyendo hasta 150 horas gratis. Después de leer sobre su programa, que cuesta solamente $9.95 por mes, escriba dos razones por las cuales desea aceptar su servicio y dos en contra de aceptarlo. Compare su decisión con la de su compañero/a.

MODELO: *A favor:*   *El programa traduce texto y páginas web y navega por Internet en español.*

En contra: *Ya tengo servicio de Internet con AOL.*

Busca y captura en español
Preguntas más frecuentes

¿Qué es Busca y captura?

Busca y captura es un servicio de acceso a Internet que está disponible a través de miles de números de acceso en Estados Unidos. Mediante *Busca y captura*, usted puede acceder a millones de sitios web en español e inglés. Independientemente de sus preferencias particulares (noticias, información sobre el estado del tiempo, entretenimientos, finanzas, deportes, compras o sitios para niños), *Busca y captura* le ayuda a encontrar los sitios más interesantes de Internet.

¿Qué es Busca y captura *en español*?

Busca y captura en español es un servicio de acceso a Internet en español. Puede navegar por Internet y charlar con gente de todas partes del planeta. Si busca un servicio que le facilite la búsqueda de información en español, este servicio es para usted.

¿Cómo puedo acceder a Busca y captura *en español*?

Cuando instale el disco adjunto, puede configurar su cuenta y comenzar a utilizar la muestra o versión gratuita *Busca y captura*. Todo lo que tiene que hacer es insertar el CD-ROM en su computadora y seguir las instrucciones que aparecen en la pantalla.

¿Cuáles son los gastos telefónicos?

Cuando utiliza *Busca y captura*, su computadora se conecta a Internet a través de la línea telefónica. Nosotros ponemos a su disposición miles de números telefónicos en EE. UU. En caso de no estar seguro de si el número de acceso es o no es un número local, verifique con su compañía telefónica local.

¿Qué necesito para utilizar Busca y captura *en español*?

Necesita una PC (486 o más veloz) con un módem de 9.600 baudios (se recomienda un módem de al menos 14.400 baudios) y que ejecute Microsoft Windows 95, 98 o NT 4.0. También necesita una unidad de CD-ROM, un mouse, y un monitor SVGA, además de 8MB de RAM como mínimo y 20MB de espacio libre en el disco duro.

E. Un gran debate. Las escuelas ya tienen computadoras con acceso a Internet. ¿Los estudiantes deben tener acceso restringido o no filtrado? Expresen sus opiniones.

MODELO: *Los estudiantes NO deben visitar sitios con material obsceno.*

Estructuras   *The recent past: Acabar de + infinitivo*

- To say what you have just done, use the phrase **acabar de +** *infinitive.* Conjugate **acabar** as a regular **-ar** verb.

Acabo de hablar con el Director.	*I have just spoken with the Principal.*
El estudiante **acaba de terminar** su tarea.	*The student has just finished his assignment.*
Acabamos de resolver el problema.	*We have just solved the problem.*
Ellos **acaban de crear** un sitio web.	*They have just created a website.*

- When talking about recently completed acts, you may find it useful to establish how long ago the event took place. Use **hace +** *a period of time* to tell how long ago the action happened.

Acabo de recibir buenas noticias.	*I have just gotten some good news.*
¿Cuándo?	*When?*
Hace diez minutos.	*Ten minutes ago.*

- Additional time phrases to tell how long ago something happened are:

hace dos días	*two days ago*
hace una semana	*a week ago*

- The following time phrases express specific moments in time. **Hacer** is not used with these phrases.

ayer	*yesterday*
anoche	*last night*
anteayer	*the day before yesterday*
la semana pasada	*last week*

Para practicar

A. Las tareas.   El director de su escuela está muy nervioso hoy. Quiere saber cuándo usted y sus compañeros de trabajo en la escuela van a hacer las siguientes tareas. Ustedes son muy eficientes. Use **acabar de** para decirle que todo está bajo control.

MODELO: ¿María va a llamar a los sustitutos?
María acaba de llamar a los sustitutos.

1.   ¿El conserje va a limpiar las aulas?

2.   ¿Usted va a contestar su correo electrónico?

3.   ¿Los estudiantes de kínder van a almorzar?

4.   ¿Las secretarias van a poner la información en el sitio web?

5.   ¿Los maestros van a hacer sus planes para la semana que viene?

6.   ¿Los niños van a tener un simulacro de incendio?

B. ¿Cuándo?   Acaban de suceder (*happen*) los siguientes eventos. Primero, explique lo que pasó usando **acabar de** y después indique **cuándo**.

MODELO: yo/terminar mi clase en línea/tres horas
Yo acabo de terminar mi clase en línea hace tres horas.

1.   los estudiantes/regresar del recreo/media hora

2.   nosotros/navegar por la Red/20 minutos

3.   los maestros/preparar clases en línea/dos horas

4.   las madres/tener una idea brillante/cinco minutos

5.   los miembros del PTA/reunirse/anoche

6.   el estudiante/enfermo/ir a su casa/dos minutos

C. ¿Y usted?   Escriba cinco actividades que usted acaba de hacer antes de venir a clase hoy.

MODELO: *Acabo de terminar los ejercicios A y B.*

Módulo 2

El salón virtual

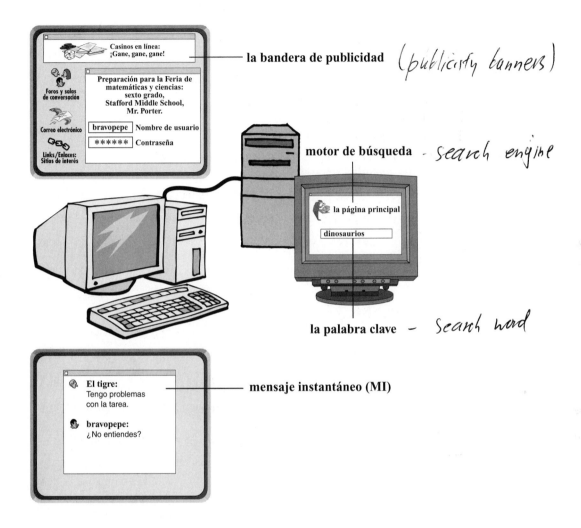

Casinos en línea:
¡Gane, gane, gane!

la bandera de publicidad *(publicity banners)*

Foros y salas
de conversación

Preparación para la Feria de
matemáticas y ciencias:
sexto grado,
Stafford Middle School,
Mr. Porter.

Correo electrónico

bravopepe Nombre de usuario

****** Contraseña

Links/Enlaces:
Sitios de interés

motor de búsqueda - *search engine*

la página principal

dinosaurios

la palabra clave - *search word*

El tigre:
Tengo problemas
con la tarea.

bravopepe:
¿No entiendes?

mensaje instantáneo (MI)

A. ¿Cómo se dice?   Use la memoria, la imaginación y el dibujo para emparejar estas frases que describen Internet con una definición lógica.

1. _____ una carta que llega por el ciberespacio
2. _____ una palabra secreta que verifica su identidad
3. _____ un programa que ayuda con la investigación en la Red
4. _____ una conversación electrónica entre dos usuarios en "tiempo actual"

a. mensaje instantáneo

b. motor de búsqueda

c. correo electrónico

d. contraseña

B. En sus propias palabras. ¿Puede definir estos conceptos en sus propias palabras?

1. nombre del usuario
2. mensaje instantáneo
3. salón de conversación
4. página principal

Nos gusta estudiar así

El maestro Porter está encantado con la idea de dedicar su tiempo de recuperación ayudando a los estudiantes por medio de la educación a distancia. Ellos no sólo tienen que diseñar y realizar sus proyectos por medio del ciberespacio, también tienen que mantener una lista de lo bueno y de lo malo del salón virtual. Aquí hay una compilación de las impresiones.

A favor del estudio virtual:

ROSA: Me gusta mucho participar en las conversaciones con los astronautas de NASA durante una misión. Mi proyecto tiene que ver con la exploración del espacio.

PABLO: A mí me gustan los "tours" virtuales de los museos y los sitios arqueológicos. Hay un sitio interactivo donde se puede conversar con los paleontólogos de los dinosaurios.

PEPE Y BETO: Nos gustan los foros con los expertos donde podemos hacer preguntas sobre la tecnología— ¡y recibir respuestas inmediatas!

SARA Y SUSANA: A nosotras nos gusta practicar español e inglés con personas de diferentes naciones. Es verdad que es una clase para hacer proyectos de ciencias y tecnología (☹), pero nos gustan más los idiomas (☺).

ALEJANDRO: Me gusta tener mi propio nombre de usuario, mi propia contraseña y mi propio correo electrónico. Y los mensajes instantáneos me permiten colaborar con mis compañeros del proyecto durante la noche o durante los fines de semana cuando es imposible reunirnos. Me gusta mucho la independencia.

SERGIO: Me gustan los sitios de música y juegos. Quiero un reproductor de MP3. Me interesa ser diseñador de juegos de vídeo en el futuro.

KAREN Y DOLLY: Los motores de búsqueda son fabulosos. Sólo ponemos una palabra clave en la búsqueda y nos da toda la información que necesitamos. A veces pasamos horas siguiendo todos los enlaces y tenemos que recordar que hay una tarea para completar.

En contra del estudio virtual:

TODOS: No nos gustan: los anuncios "pop-up", ni la pornografía, ni los viruses de la computadora, ni cuando la conexión se corta. Y no nos gusta estar tan lejos del maestro Porter.

C. ¿Comprende usted? Diga usted si las oraciones son **Ciertas (C)** o **Falsas (F).** Si son falsas, corríjalas.

1. _____ Un beneficio de la clase en línea es la independencia y la flexibilidad.

2. _____ Todos los estudiantes tienen mucho interés en completar los proyectos para la Feria.

3. _____ Hay más negativos que positivos en cuanto a las clases en línea.

4. _____ A todos les gustan mucho los anuncios comerciales.

D. Escuelas virtuales. Después de leer el artículo de una escuela virtual, hable con dos o tres compañeros de las ventajas y/o desventajas de estudiar por Internet.

MODELO: *¡Me gusta mucho estudiar así porque no tengo que salir de casa! Hay poca interacción con otros estudiantes, pero no me importa porque aun así aprendo.*

Una ciberescuela

¿Asistir a clase sin tener que salir de casa? Puede ser una solución para muchos estudiantes que tienen problemas para asistir a la escuela. Una escuela en Nebraska utiliza Internet para atraer a familias que rechazan el sistema público de educación. Ya tienen la posibilidad de educar a sus hijos desde su propio hogar.

La escuela virtual es una experiencia piloto dentro de un sistema oficial. Empezó en 1997 con 60 estudiantes y en 2000 ya contaba con 400. Aunque está regulada según la constitución, no está limitada por las mismas restricciones que afectan a otras escuelas. "No se trata de motivos religiosos ni políticos; los estudiantes que escogen la escuela virtual consideran que tienen más posibilidades de aprender que haciéndolo en una escuela pública tradicional que nunca cambia." Los cursos en Internet están basados en un sistema efectivo, manteniendo una cierta libertad de elección. Hay pruebas de aprendizaje "en línea".

Muchos educadores consideran este tipo de enseñanza como el modelo del futuro; otros creen que la escuela virtual es sólo una respuesta a las necesidades de un tipo determinado de estudiantes.

Estructuras   *Expressing likes and dislikes: Gustar*

- While the most convenient English translations of **me gusta** and **le gusta** are *I like* and *you/he/she likes,* they literally mean *(it) is pleasing to me* and *it is pleasing to you/him/her.*
- Use the following forms to tell if people are pleased or displeased by something.

Me gusta navegar por la Red.	*I like to surf the web.*
Te gusta seguir los enlaces.	*You like to follow the links.*
Le gusta consultar a los expertos.	*You (formal)/he/she likes to consult experts.*
Nos gusta ayudar a otros estudiantes.	*We like to help other students.*
Les gusta estudiar así.	*You (plural)/they like to study this way.*

- If the noun following the verb is plural, or if the verb is followed by a series of items, use **gustan**. If the verb is followed by one infinitive or a series of infinitives, use **gusta**.

Me gustan los sitios interactivos.	*I like interactive websites.*
Me gusta estudiar, conversar y explorar.	*I like to study, chat and explore.*

- To tell or ask the name of the person who is pleased or displeased by something, use **a** before the name. The use of **a** + *personal pronoun* before **me gusta, le gusta,** etc. is optional and can be used to emphasize the person who is pleased or displeased or to clarify any ambiguity.

A José no le gusta esperar.	*José does not like to wait.*
(A mí) me gustan los idiomas.	*I like languages.*
(A ti) te gusta la independencia.	*You like the independence.*
(A él/a ella/a usted) le gusta la ciencia.	*He/she/you like science.*
(A nosotros/as) nos gusta el maestro.	*We like the teacher.*
(A ellos/a ellas/a ustedes) les gusta trabajar.	*They/you like to work.*

[handwritten notes:]

(Backward Verbs)

gustar = to be pleasing
= is pleasing to
= Indirect Object Pronouns

to me
To you
→ to you/him/her
to us
to them / you (plural)

When using action (infinitive) use the singular

encantar = to really like

Para practicar

A. A usted, ¿qué le gusta más?   Diga cuál de estas opciones le gusta más.

MODELO: ir a la biblioteca o navegar por la Red.
Me gusta más navegar por la Red.

1. las clases tradicionales o las clases en línea
2. los chocolates o la cerveza
3. los idiomas o las ciencias
4. pedir ayuda o leer las instrucciones
5. esperar hasta el último momento o completar las tareas temprano
6. estudiar o mirar la televisión

B. ¿Le gusta o no le gusta?   Diga si a las siguientes personas les gustan o no estas cosas.

MODELO: Bill Gates/las computadoras
A Bill Gates le gustan las computadoras.

1. los maestros/las clases con estudiantes perezosos
2. un estudiante perezoso/muchas clases difíciles
3. un navegador de Internet/una conexión muy lenta *(slow)*
4. unos navegadores de Internet/muchas conexiones cortadas
5. los niños de tercer grado/el recreo
6. los maestros/los sábados

C. Las entrevistas.   Prepare una lista de cuatro preguntas y pregúnteles a tres de sus amigos o familiares qué les gusta hacer por Internet.

MODELO: Usted: ¿*Te gusta navegar por la Red durante el tiempo libre?*
Amigo: Sí, me gusta navegar por la Red.
Usted: A mi amigo le gusta navegar por la Red.

Módulo 2

El proyecto virtual

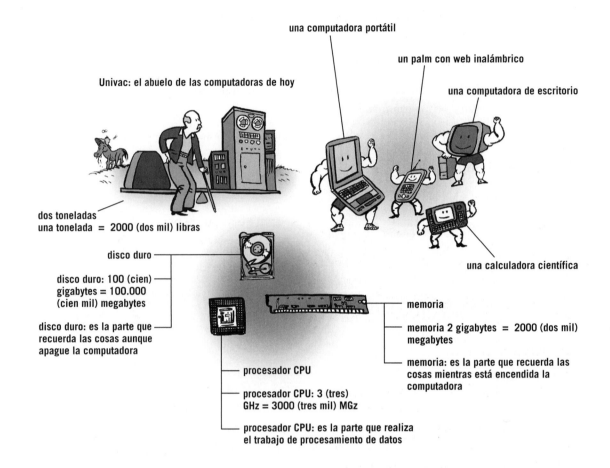

una computadora portátil

un palm con web inalámbrico

una computadora de escritorio

Univac: el abuelo de las computadoras de hoy

dos toneladas
una tonelada = 2000 (dos mil) libras

una calculadora científica

disco duro

disco duro: 100 (cien)
gigabytes = 100.000
(cien mil) megabytes

disco duro: es la parte que
recuerda las cosas aunque
apague la computadora

memoria

memoria 2 gigabytes = 2000 (dos mil)
megabytes

memoria: es la parte que recuerda las
cosas mientras está encendida la
computadora

procesador CPU

procesador CPU: 3 (tres)
GHz = 3000 (tres mil) MGz

procesador CPU: es la parte que realiza
el trabajo de procesamiento de datos

A. ¿Cómo se dice?   Use la memoria, la imaginación y el dibujo para emparejar estas partes de la computadora con su descripción.

a. el CPU   b. el disco duro   c. la memoria   d. servidor

1. _____ es la parte de la computadora que contiene la información—aun cuando la computadora está apagada (*turned off*)

2. _____ es el nuevo nombre para una macrocomputadora

3. _____ es la parte que recuerda la información mientras usted está trabajando en la computadora.

4. _____ es la parte que procesa y organiza los datos en la computadora

B. Los aparatos.   Identifique el aparato por su descripción.

1. _____ hace cálculos complejos "gráficamente"

2. _____ es una computadora tan pequeña que la puedo poner en el bolsillo de mi camisa o tenerla en la mano

3. _____ es una de las macrocomputadoras "primitivas"

4. _____ es una computadora completa que puedo llevar en mi mochila o portafolio

La primera feria

Mañana Pepe y Beto van a hacer su presentación de multimedia en la Feria de matemáticas, ciencias y tecnología. Su animación original: **Univac, el abuelo de la nueva tecnología,** *no va a ganar un premio, pero sí va a recibir una mención honorable. Pepe y Beto están muy nerviosos y entusiasmados y están mirando la presentación por décima vez. Escuchemos una porción de su dibujo animado donde el abuelo Univac está hablando con las calculadoras y computadoras de hoy.*

EL ABUELO UNIVAC: (*nostálgico*) Es el año 1961 (mil novecientos sesenta y uno). Yo soy Univac y soy el fenómeno de la tecnología. Soy la primera macrocomputadora (servidor) moderna. Peso más de dos toneladas (¡cuatro mil libras!) y soy más grande que un salón de clase. Tengo un disco duro con capacidad de cien megabytes, una velocidad de 1.3 (uno con tres) MHZ y .5 (punto 5) megabytes de memoria. Lo sé, lo sé. Ustedes van a decir que hoy el control remoto de un televisor tiene más potencia. Pero recuerden que soy de los años sesenta, y para aquella época, con un costo de más o menos $1.6 millones de dólares (un millón, seiscientos mil dólares), soy una maravilla.

PALM CHIQUITO: Pero Abuelo Univac, con .5 megabytes de memoria, ¿cómo es posible navegar por Internet?

UNIVAC: ¡Ay, chicos! En esta época, todavía no hay Internet. Mi única función es resolver problemas matemáticos.

CALCULADORA CIENTÍFICA: ¿Como yo?

UNIVAC: Tú lo haces mejor y mil veces (1000 X) más rápidamente que yo. Además tienes juegos. Palm, ¿de qué velocidad eres?

PALM: Tengo una velocidad de 400 MHz con 128 megabytes de memoria. Y tengo teléfono con acceso a Internet también. Soy maravilloso.

UNIVAC: Gracias al microchip. Pero recuerden, niños. En dos o tres años, la nueva generación de la tecnología va a verlos y va a pensar: *"Palm, qué primitivo eres"*.

C. ¿Comprende usted? Diga usted si las oraciones son **Ciertas (C)** o **Falsas (F).** Si son falsas, corríjalas.

1. _____ Univac es una computadora primitiva.

2. _____ Univac tiene más potencia que un control remoto de un televisor de hoy.

3. _____ Un procesador de 1.3 MHz es rapidísimo.

4. _____ Durante la época de Univac, no era posible navegar por la Red.

D. Equipo multifunción en color. Su impresora ya no funciona—¿por qué no compra una máquina que lo hace todo? Después de leer la publicidad de Amigo, termine la actividad.

Equipo multifunción en color

 Fax de papel normal: transmite rápidamente y tiene memoria de 8 MB para no perder sus mensajes en caso de recibir faxes y no quedar papel en la bandeja

 PC Fax en color: envía un documento en color sin acceso a Internet a otro usuario utilizando el visor de fax en color

 Interfaz de captura de vídeo: puede imprimir las imágenes de vídeo directamente desde la fuente de origen al conectar su cámara de vídeo o cámara digital al puerto de captura

 **Copiadora en color:** le ofrece copias de excelente calidad, con alimentador automático de hasta 50 originales, la posibilidad de reducir y ampliar desde el 25% hasta el 400% y de realizar múltiples copias (hasta 99) e incluso de clasificar

Impresora en color: imprime con una resolución de hasta 1.440 x 720 ppp, con bandeja de alimentación de hasta 250 hojas

Escáner plano en color: obtiene color real con 16.7 millones de colores para conseguir unas impactantes imágenes

Con seis funciones integradas en una unidad, el Amigo 2000 es un producto fácil de utilizar, con la potencia y versatilidad necesarias para satisfacer todas sus necesidades. Es un producto de fácil manejo y de alta calidad que le ahorra tiempo y espacio, y todo esto a un precio inferior al de los productos independientes.

1. Es posible reducir y ampliar las copias desde _____ hasta

_____ .

2. La calidad de las imágenes obtenidas por el escáner es _____ .

3. Se puede enviar un documento en color sin usar Internet por

_____ .

4. Es posible imprimir las imágenes de vídeo directamente desde

_____ .

5. El Amigo 2000 le ahorra _____ y _____ .

E. El precio se baja. Los precios de computadoras son ahora más baratos que nunca antes. Hable con compañeros de los precios de hoy para comprar un buen sistema.

MODELO: *Se puede comprar una computadora con impresora, módem, altavoces y copiadora de CD ROM por menos de $1.000.*

Estructuras   *Numbers: De cien a millones; los números ordinales*

- Use the following numbers to count from 100–1000.

100	**cien**	500	**quinientos**
101	**ciento uno**	600	**seiscientos**
102	**ciento dos**	700	**setecientos**
200	**doscientos**	800	**ochocientos**
300	**trescientos**	900	**novecientos**
400	**cuatrocientos**	100	**mil**

- Use **cien** to say *one hundred* exactly and if a larger number such as **mil** or **millones** follows **(cien mil),** but use **ciento** in 101–199 **(ciento uno, ciento dos. . . , ciento noventa y nueve).** Never use the word **un** before **cien** or **ciento** or **mil.** Although **cien** is used before both masculine and feminine nouns, multiples of one hundred (200, 300, etc.) agree in gender with the nouns they modify.

  trescient**os** dólares

  trescient**as** personas

- **¡OJO!** Remember that **uno** drops the **-o** before masculine nouns, and always uses an **-a** before feminine nouns:

131 libros	ciento treinta y **un** libros
131 computadoras	ciento treinta y **una** computadoras

- Most Spanish-speaking countries use a period **(.)** to designate numbers in the thousands and a comma **(,)** to designate decimal points.

Spanish: **1.543** (English **1,543**)	mil quinientos cuarenta y tres
Spanish: **1,5** (English **1.5**)	uno con cinco *or* uno coma cinco

- The word for thousand is **mil. Mil** is not pluralized when counting.

1.543	**mil** quinientos cuarenta y tres
2.002	**dos mil dos**
7.033	**siete mil** treinta y tres

- When expressing the year, use **mil.**

2002	**dos mil** dos
1999	**mil novecientos noventa y nueve**

- When counting in the millions, use **un millón, dos millones, tres millones,** etc. Use **de** before a noun that directly follows **millón** or **millones.** If another number is between the word **millón** or **millones** and the noun, omit **de.**

un millón de dólares   **un millón trescientos mil** dólares

Los números ordinales

- To express numerical order in Spanish, use ordinal numbers.

★ **primer/o/a/os/as**	*first*	**sexto/a/os/as**	*sixth*
segundo/a/os/as	*second*	**séptimo/a/os/as**	*seventh*
★ **tercer/o/a/os/as**	*third*	**octavo/a/os/as**	*eighth*
cuarto/a/os/as	*fourth*	**noveno/a/os/as**	*ninth*
quinto/a/os/as	*fifth*	**décimo/a/os/as**	*tenth*

- The ordinal numbers have masculine and feminine, singular and plural forms, depending on the noun that follows them.
- Drop the **-o** of **primero** and **tercero** before masculine singular nouns.

el prime**r** premio	*the first prize*
la primer**a** computadora	*the first computer*
el terce**r** premio	*the third prize*
la tercer**a** computadora	*the third computer*

Para practicar

A. El inventario.   Usted está encargado/a de contar el número de cosas que necesitan para realizar la Feria de la Tecnología. Diga y escriba los números.

MODELO: 112 cajas de papel
           Hay ciento doce cajas de papel.

1. 2.351 lápices   **4.** 1.993 estudiantes
2. 753 sillas   **5.** 5.017 dólares
3. 52 mesas   **6.** 14.556 archivos *(files)*

B. ¡La Feria es más grande!   Hace exactamente un año desde la última Feria y ustedes tienen que contar todo de nuevo. Este año, la Feria es exactamente diez veces más grande que el año pasado. Multiplique todos los números anteriores por diez. Compare los resultados con un/a compañero/a.

MODELO: 112 cajas de papel x10 = ¿?
Este año hay mil ciento veinte cajas de papel.

C. Los premios.   Hay premios para los diez mejores proyectos. Aquí están los resultados. Ponga en orden numérico a los siguientes **ganadores y ganadoras**.

MODELO: **1.** Patricia Ramírez
La primera ganadora es Patricia Ramírez.

1. Roberto González
2. Mariana Rivera
3. Héctor López y Alma Gómez
4. Daniel Russo
5. Beto y Pepe
6. Eduardo Gallegos
7. Alicia Cabrera
8. Iris Vásquez
9. Jorge Román
10. Yolanda Durán

Vocabulario Módulo 1

Sustantivos

el álgebra (f.)	*algebra*	**la línea**	*line*
el/la alumno/a	*student*	**el módulo**	*module*
el año	*year*	**el período**	*period*
el apoyo	*support*	**el planeta**	*planet*
la asistencia	*attendance*	**la preparatoria**	*prep school*
el atletismo	*athletics*	**el procedimiento**	*procedure*
el aula (f.)	*classroom*	**el proceso**	*process*
las bellas artes	*fine arts*	**el proyecto**	*project*
la búsqueda	*search*	**la química**	*chemistry*
el correo	*mail*	**la Red**	*Web*
la cuenta	*bill*	**el requisito**	*requirement*
la distancia	*distance*	**la semana**	*week*
la elección	*choice*	**el servicio**	*service*
la física	*physics*	**el sorteo**	*drawing*
el gasto	*expense*	**el tema**	*theme*
la gente	*people*	**el tiempo**	*weather*
la librería	*bookstore*	**el transporte**	*transportation*

Verbos

acabar de + inf.	*to have just*	**mencionar**	*to mention*
acceder	*to gain access to*	**navegar**	*to navigate*
charlar	*to chat*	**opinar**	*to express an opinion*
cumplir	*to fulfill*		
descubrir	*to discover*	**reemplazar**	*to replace*
eliminar	*to eliminate*	**requerir (ie)**	*to require*
escoger (j)	*to choose*	**seleccionar**	*to select*
gustar	*to like*	**terminar**	*to end*
investigar	*to investigate*		

Adjetivos

abierto/a	*open*	**igual**	*equal*
alternativo/a	*alternative*	**innovador/a**	*innovative*
animado/a	*lively*	**mismo/a**	*same*
aquel/la	*that*	**particular**	*private*
avanzado/a	*advanced*	**pasado/a**	*past, last*
brillante	*brilliant*	**prolongado/a**	*lengthy*
electrónico/a	*electronic*	**siguiente**	*following*
étnico/a	*ethnic*	**unificado/a**	*unified*

Otras expresiones

a través de	*through*	**ayer**	*yesterday*
al azar	*at random*	**en vez de**	*in place of*
al revés	*in reverse*	**mientras**	*meanwhile*
anoche	*last night*	**¡Qué lástima!**	*What a shame!*
anteayer	*day before yesterday*		

Módulo 2

Sustantivos

el alimentador	*feeder*	**la contraseña**	*password*
el altavoz	*speaker*	**los datos**	*data, information*
el ámbito	*sphere, field*	**el disco duro**	*hard drive*
la bandeja	*tray*	**el enlace**	*link*
el bolsillo	*pocket*	**la envidia**	*envy*
la calculadora	*calculator*	**la feria**	*fair*
la cámara	*camera*	**el foro**	*forum*
la capital	*capital*	**la frontera**	*border*
la cerveza	*beer*	**la fuente**	*source*
el ciberespacio	*cyberspace*	**la imagen**	*image*
el cine	*theater, cinema*	**la impresora**	*printer*
el/la comprador/a	*buyer*	**el/la lector/a**	*reader*

la libra	*pound*	el procesador	*processor*
la librería	*bookstore*	la publicidad	*advertising*
el/la librero/a	*bookseller*	el puerto	*port*
el manejo	*use*	el ratón	*mouse*
el manguito	*sleeve*	el regalo	*gift*
el mercado	*market*	el reproductor	*player*
el módem	*modem*	la revista	*magazine*
el modo	*way, manner*	el servidor	*server*
la moneda	*coin*	la subasta	*auction*
el museo	*museum*	la tienda	*store*
la novedad	*innovation*	la tonelada	*ton*
el papá	*dad*	el usuario	*user*
la parte	*part*	la velocidad	*speed*
la potencia	*power*		

Verbos

ahorrar	*to save*	olvidarse de	*to forget about*
comprometer	*to compromise*	realizar	*to carry out*
cortar	*to cut*	reunirse	*to get together*
dejar	*to let, allow*	satisfacer (g)	*to satisfy*
desaparecer (zc)	*to disappear*	sugerir (ie)	*to suggest*
enviar	*to send*	transmitir	*to transmit*
imprimir	*to print*	verificar	*to verify*

Adjetivos

clave	*key*	octavo/a	*eighth*
décimo/a	*tenth*	perezoso/a	*lazy*
encantado/a	*delighted*	plano/a	*flat*
fabuloso/a	*fabulous*	portátil	*portable*
inalámbrico/a	*wireless*	propio/a	*own*
instantáneo/a	*instantaneous*	séptimo/a	*seventh*
maravilloso/a	*marvelous*	tercer/o/a	*third*
noveno/a	*ninth*	vivo/a	*alive*

Otras expresiones

alrededor de	*around, about*	aunque	*even though*

¡OJO! Es importante estudiar los números al final del Módulo 2.

Síntesis

A escuchar

Escuche esta conversación y después conteste las preguntas poniendo un círculo alrededor de la respuesta correcta.

Hoy es el cumpleaños de Pepe. Está muy contento con el regalo que recibe de sus padres y en este momento está llamando a su mejor amigo, Beto, con las noticias. Escuche la conversación.

I. Pepe acaba de recibir su nueva computadora:
 a. mañana   **b.** hace cinco minutos   **c.** el año pasado

2. La computadora tiene una velocidad de:
 a. ciento setenta GHz   **b** uno punto siete GHz   **c.** once mil GHz

3. El disco duro tiene capacidad de:
 a. 80 Gigabytes   **b.** 800 Gigabytes   **c.** 8000 Gigabytes

4. En la clase de Pepe y Beto, ¿cuántos estudiantes tienen su propia computadora?
 a. uno   **b.** dos   **c.** tres

A conversar

Los maestros siempre buscan información para sus clases. Hablen de las posibilidades para usar la tecnología para apoyar las lecciones.

MODELO: *Las enciclopedias de la biblioteca son del año 1990—los estudiantes pueden buscar datos de HOY en Internet.*

A leer

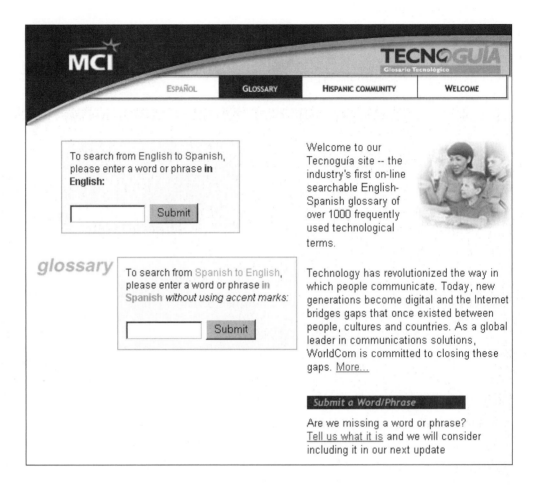

¿Comprende usted? La tecnología creó (*created*) un nuevo vocabulario para todo el mundo. Busque estas palabras en el diccionario en línea de Tecnoguía.

1. cookie   **4.** spam

2. burner   **5.** password

3. DVD

A escribir

El glosario de Tecnoguía no tiene todas las palabras que busca. Escriba cinco que no pudo encontrar, como *ai, abend, bandwidth, e-zine, kernel*, y cree su propio vocabulario en español. ¿Está preparado/a para sugerir sus ideas a Tecnoguía?

Algo más

Ventana cultural

To reinforce multicultural values in the classroom we need to study CUL-TURE. This trivia game celebrating Hispanic Heritage Month is a good way to test your knowledge about Latin American countries.

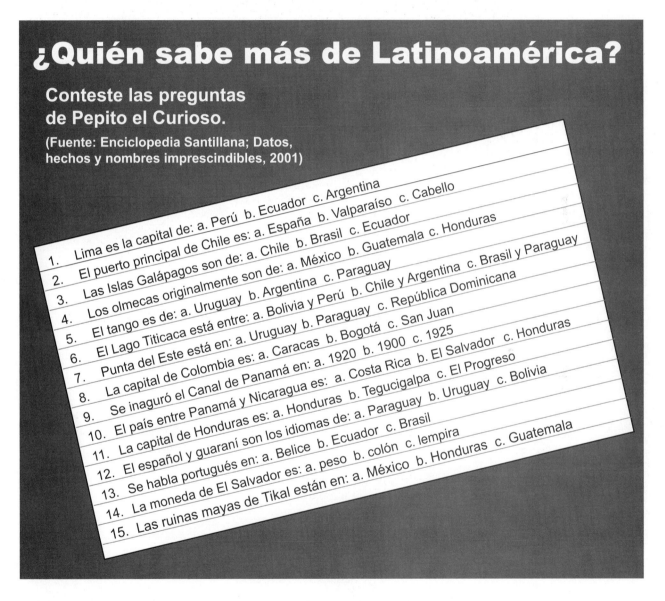

¿Quién sabe más de Latinoamérica?

Conteste las preguntas de Pepito el Curioso.

(Fuente: Enciclopedia Santillana; Datos, hechos y nombres imprescindibles, 2001)

1. Lima es la capital de: a. Perú b. Ecuador c. Argentina
2. El puerto principal de Chile es: a. España b. Valparaíso c. Cabello
3. Las Islas Galápagos son de: a. Chile b. Brasil c. Ecuador
4. Los olmecas originalmente son de: a. México b. Guatemala c. Honduras
5. El tango es de: a. Uruguay b. Argentina c. Paraguay
6. El Lago Titicaca está entre: a. Bolivia y Perú b. Chile y Argentina c. Brasil y Paraguay
7. Punta del Este está en: a. Uruguay b. Paraguay c. República Dominicana
8. La capital de Colombia es: a. Caracas b. Bogotá c. San Juan
9. Se inaguró el Canal de Panamá en: a. 1920 b. 1900 c. 1925
10. El país entre Panamá y Nicaragua es: a. Costa Rica b. El Salvador c. Honduras
11. La capital de Honduras es: a. Honduras b. Tegucigalpa c. El Progreso
12. El español y guaraní son los idiomas de: a. Paraguay b. Uruguay c. Bolivia
13. Se habla portugués en: a. Belice b. Ecuador c. Brasil
14. La moneda de El Salvador es: a. peso b. colón c. lempira
15. Las ruinas mayas de Tikal están en: a. México b. Honduras c. Guatemala

En mis propias palabras.   No se puede enseñar lo que no se sabe. Conteste las preguntas de arriba y compare sus respuestas con las de un/a compañero/a. ¿Necesitan buscar información? ¡No se olviden de usar Internet!★

★Respuestas: 1. a; 2. b; 3. c; 4. a; 5. b; 6. a; 7. a 8. b; 9. a; 10. a; 11. b; 12. a, 13. c; 14. b; 15. c

A buscar

Busque sitios en Internet que ofrecen material para preparar lecciones de Geografía o Ciencias o... Traiga su lista de por lo menos cinco sitios para compartir con sus compañeros. Es buena idea imprimir su página principal.

A conocer www.SuperOnda.com

A los estudiantes les gusta leer de temas de interés para ELLOS—artículos sobre jóvenes en deportes, música, cine, y de sus problemas y vida en general. SúperOnda es una revista que se describe como «La revista para los jóvenes con determinación». Visítela en www.SuperOnda.com

LECCIÓN 8

La escuela secundaria

Módulo 1
- Los deportes
- Describing daily routines: *Los verbos reflexivos*
- Nos ayudamos
- More on reflexive verbs: *Los verbos recíprocos*

Módulo 2
- Necesito saber un poco de todo
- Expressing knowledge and familiarity: **Saber** *y* **conocer**
- Servicio a la comunidad
- Receiving the action of a verb: *El objeto directo*

Síntesis
- A escuchar
- A conversar
- A leer
- A escribir

Algo más
- Ventana cultural: La educación de estudiantes migrantes
- A buscar
- A conocer: César Chávez

Módulo I

Los deportes

los trofeos

el gimnasio

el fútbol americano

el béisbol

el básquetbol

el fútbol

la natación

el entrenador

la animadora

el vestuario

el espejo

peinarse

lavarse

ducharse

la ducha

vestirse

el armario

el atleta

A. ¿Cómo se dice?   Escriba la palabra que corresponda a cada una de las definiciones.

1.   Un complejo atlético donde los atletas practican es un _____.

2.   La sección del gimnasio donde los atletas y estudiantes pueden cambiarse de ropa y guardar sus artículos personales es el_____.

3.   Para limpiarse el cuerpo entero, se usa la_____.

4.   Un _____ es el premio que gana el mejor equipo o jugador de una región.

B. Acciones. Busque el verbo que mejor identifique estas acciones. Use la memoria para recordar verbos de lecciones anteriores.

1.	_____ lavarse	**a.**	cerrar los ojos y descansar
2.	_____ ducharse/bañarse	**b.**	limpiarse partes del cuerpo
3.	_____ peinarse	**c.**	ponerse ropa
4.	_____ vestirse	**d.**	limpiarse todo el cuerpo bajo una "cascada" de agua
5.	_____ dormir	**e.**	arreglarse el pelo

¡El nuevo gimnasio es increíble!

Antonio Marino es el jefe del Departamento de educación física y el entrenador de fútbol de un colegio muy moderno. Hoy acompaña a un grupo de atletas jóvenes que sueñan con ser "héroes futbolistas" en un "tour" del gimnasio nuevo. Van a saber que el programa atlético también es un programa académico muy riguroso.

ANTONIO: Y ahora saben ustedes que las prácticas, el entrenamiento y los partidos de fútbol van a ser la parte más fácil de su programa. Lo difícil es hacer todo esto y mantener excelencia en las clases académicas. Recuerden: son estudiantes primero. ¿Hay preguntas?

JUGADORES: (silencio)

ANTONIO: Excelente. Los miembros de nuestro equipo tienen un horario muy estricto. Se levantan a las 6 de la mañana y se acuestan a las 10. Tienen horas obligatorias para estudiar, para comer, para practicar y para entrenar. Allí está el nuevo salón de pesas donde entrenamos dos horas diarias. Y aquí tenemos el nuevo vestuario para hombres. Es donde se duchan antes y después de cada práctica, se visten con los uniformes y guardan su ropa personal.

JOVEN: El jugador que ahora se admira en el espejo, ¿no es el capitán del equipo?

ANTONIO: Sí, es Ricardo. Tiene que arreglarse y peinarse con perfección ahora: en dos minutos va a ponerse el uniforme y el casco y va a ver a su novia, la capitana de las animadoras.

C. ¿Comprende usted? Conteste las preguntas según la información del diálogo.

1. ¿Hay algo más importante que el atletismo en este colegio?
2. ¿Cómo es el horario de los atletas?
3. ¿Cuánto tiempo pasan cada día en el salón de pesas?
4. ¿Qué hacen los atletas en el vestuario?

D. Campamento de fútbol. El fútbol es una epidemia nacional en Estados Unidos ahora. Lea la publicidad de esta escuela y termine la actividad.

Campamento de verano 2004

Niños de 6 a 12 años y jóvenes de 13 a 20 años. Ambos sexos.

Del 3 al 28 de junio—Club de fútbol Atascadero

El fútbol es un deporte de origen inglés que se juega con dos porterías y un balón entre veintidós jugadores con un árbitro y dos jueces de línea.

El fútbol está atrayendo cada día más aficionados en Estados Unidos. Desde hace 10 años el Club de fútbol Atascadero realiza su escuela de fútbol, bajo la dirección de Antonio Gómez, entrenador de divisiones menores, que implementa un método de enseñanza efectivo y divertido. El club es seguro y supervisado; cuatro semanas de aprendizaje intenso. El club recibe a más de 350 chicos que se dividen por edad y destreza con 10 niños por entrenador. Los turnos se dividen en dos: de 8:00 a.m. a 12:00 p.m. y de 1:00 p.m. a 5:00 p.m.

Costo de la temporada: $250.00. Incluye dos camisetas con el logo de Soccer School, merienda y equipo deportivo (bolas, conos, porterías, etc.)

1. ¿Cuáles son las divisiones de edad de los dos grupos?
2. ¿Qué pueden esperar los participantes?
3. ¿Por cuántas semanas es el campamento y a qué horas?
4. ¿Cuánto cuesta y qué incluye?

E. Los deportes de hoy. Hable con tres compañeros de los deportes más populares de hoy, como el polo acuático, el golf, el tenis, el boxeo, la lucha libre... ¿En cuáles participa usted? ¿Hay más posibilidades para mujeres hoy?

MODELO: *Mi hija juega al polo acuático—un equipo para mujeres es una adición nueva en su secundaria.*

Estructuras   *Describing daily routines: Los verbos reflexivos*

- Reflexive verbs express actions that people do *to* or *for* themselves.

- Reflexive verbs are preceded by reflexive pronouns. The pronoun **se** attached to the end of the infinitive indicates that the verb is reflexive (bañar**se**). **Se** is modified to *reflect* the same person as the subject. The verb itself is conjugated normally.

bañarse *to bathe (oneself)*			
yo	me	baño	*I bathe (myself)*
tú	te	bañas	*you bathe (yourself)*
usted/él/ella	se	baña	*you/he/she bathe(s) (your/him/herself)*
nosotros	nos	bañamos	*we bathe ourselves*
ustedes/ellos/ellas	se	bañan	*you/they bathe (your/themselves)*

Reflexive pronouns

- Reflexive verbs can be used to describe changes in state of mind.

Los entrenadores **se enojan** cuando los atletas no estudian.

The coaches get angry when the athletes don't study.

- When a reflexive verb is used as an *infinitive,* a *present participle* **(–ando** or **–iendo),** or an *affirmative command,* the reflexive pronoun that matches the subject may be attached to the end.
- **¡OJO!** When attaching the pronoun to a present participle, remember to write an accent on the vowel before the **–ndo** ending. When attaching the pronoun to an affirmative command, write an accent on the third vowel from the right—after the new syllable is attached.

Yo quiero lavar**me** el pelo después del partido.

I want to wash my hair after the game.

Rosario está lav**á**ndo**se** las manos ahora.

Rosario is washing her hands now.

Cecilia, l**á**ve**se** las manos ahora.

Cecilia, wash your hands now.

- Other reflexive verbs are:

(handwritten: Verbos Reflexivos)

(handwritten: Final exam)

acostarse (ue)	*to go to bed*	**llevarse mal**	*to not get along*
calmarse	*to calm down*	**ponerse** + adj.	*to become or to put on*
cuidarse	*to take care of oneself*	**preocuparse**	*to worry*
despertarse (ie)	*to wake up*	**quitarse**	*to take off*
dormirse (ue)	*to fall asleep*	**secarse**	*to dry oneself*
enojarse	*to get angry*	**sentarse (ie)**	*to sit down*
levantarse	*to get up*	**sentirse (ie)**	*to feel*
llevarse bien	*to get along well*	**vestirse (i)**	*to get dressed*

Para practicar

A. La mamá del jugador.   La rutina de la mamá de Carlos va a cambiar mucho ahora que su hijo es una estrella del equipo de fútbol. Complete las descripciones de su día con el pronombre indicado, si es una actividad reflexiva. ¡OJO! Todas las actividades no son reflexivas.

MODELO: A las seis y media yo _____ despierto y después yo _____ despierto a mi hijo.
*A las seis, yo **me** despierto y después yo _x_ despierto a mi hijo.*

1. A las siete, Carlos_____ lava las manos y la cara y yo _____ lavo su uniforme.

2. Carlos _____ peina por mucho tiempo porque _____ pone muy nervioso antes del partido.

3. Antes de empezar la práctica, los jugadores _____ duchan y _____ secan.

4. Entonces _____ visten con el equipo de protección.

5. Después de jugar, Carlos y sus compañeros _____ bañan y _____ lavan el pelo otra vez.

6. Cuando regresa a casa, Carlos siempre está cansado y _____ duerme rápidamente.

B. Consejos para un nuevo miembro del equipo.   Ricardo, el capitán, habla con un grupo de compañeros del equipo de sus rutinas. Forme oraciones completas para ayudarlos.

MODELO: A veces yo/levantarse a las cinco de la mañana para estudiar
A veces yo me levanto a las cinco de la mañana para estudiar.

1. Después de la práctica, Eduardo/sentarse en el sofá y no puede/levantarse
2. A veces los entrenadores/enojarse sin razón
3. Yo/preocuparse mucho por la parte académica de mi carrera
4. Nosotros/acostarse a las nueve todas las noches
5. Normalmente nosotros/dormirse inmediatamente
6. Por la mañana, yo/despertarse a las seis, pero no/levantarse hasta las siete

C. ¡Fantasía!   Carlos acaba de recibir el trofeo por ser el mejor jugador de su equipo de fútbol. Conteste estas preguntas de los reporteros imaginando que usted es Carlos.

MODELO: ¿Cómo se siente?
Me siento contento y nervioso.

1.   ¿Se duerme fácilmente por la noche?
2.   ¿Se lleva bien con sus compañeros del equipo y con los entrenadores?
3.   ¿Se pone ropa especial para trabajar?
4.   ¿Se preocupa mucho por el futuro?
5.   ¿Es un equipo unido o se pelean mucho los miembros?
6.   ¿Los entrenadores y los jugadores se respetan?

Módulo I

Nos ayudamos

los equipos

el grito

los aficionados

abrazarse

ganar el campeonato

el héroe, Ricardo

la reportera

perder el partido

A. ¿Cómo se dice?   Escriba la palabra que corresponda a cada una de las definiciones.

1. Un grupo de jugadores que forman una unidad para ganar partidos es un

_____.

2. Un _____ puede ser para animar a los aficionados durante un partido o puede ser para demostrar que una persona está furiosa.

3. Un _____ es una persona que trabaja con los periódicos o la televisión y escribe informes de las noticias.

4. Una _____ es una conversación profesional entre dos personas. Normalmente una persona hace muchas preguntas sobre la vida o circunstancias de la otra.

B. Acciones.   Busque los pares lógicos usando los verbos nuevos y los anteriores.

1. _____ apoyarse   **a.** poner los brazos alrededor de una persona con cariño

2. _____ enojarse   **b.** tener discusiones violentas

3. _____ pelearse   **c.** ponerse furioso

4. _____ abrazarse   **d.** ayudarse unos a otros

Aquí no hay estrellas

Es el partido final del año y Ricardo, el capitán del equipo de Mission High School, acaba de demostrar todo su talento al triunfar para ganar el campeonato del estado. Cuando recibe el premio para el Jugador Más Valioso del partido, todos los reporteros le piden una entrevista. Mientras los otros jugadores se abrazan y se tiran agua fría, Ricardo está contento de hablarles. Tal vez uno de los reclutadores (recruiters) de una universidad importante esté mirando.

REPORTERA: ¡Felicidades, Ricardo! Tu carrera en la escuela secundaria termina hoy y todos los aficionados y los entrenadores están de acuerdo: esta noche sales de esta escuela en una nota de gloria. Dime cómo te sientes después de tu triunfo de esta noche.

RICARDO: ¡No lo creo! Estoy muy contento. Pero no es mi triunfo. Yo no hago nada sólo. Soy parte de un equipo estupendo. Es el triunfo de todos nosotros: los jugadores, los entrenadores—y claro, los aficionados también.

REPORTERA: ¿Los aficionados?

RICARDO:	Claro: nos animamos. Ellos nos animan con sus gritos. Nosotros los animamos con más puntos: ¡nos ayudamos mutuamente!
REPORTERA:	Así es, Ricardo. ¿Y qué recuerdos te vas a llevar de los entrenadores? ¿Es verdad que no se llevan muy bien los entrenadores y los jugadores?
RICARDO:	Al contrario. Nos llevamos muy bien. Es un grupo estupendo. Mire: nos vemos todos los días; estudiamos juntos; comemos juntos; practicamos juntos. De vez en cuando nos peleamos— como es normal. Pero, en realidad, nos comprendemos bien. La primera regla del equipo es ésta: Si nos ponemos enojados por cualquier razón, nos reunimos inmediatamente y nos hablamos. A veces no hay admiración mutua. Pero siempre nos respetamos.
REPORTERA:	¡Gracias, Ricardo! Se acabó el tiempo. Otra vez felicidades. ¿Y que vas a hacer ahora?
RICARDO:	¡Primero quiero ver mi trofeo! Después quiero ir a Disneylandia.

C. ¿Comprende usted?　　Conteste las preguntas según la información del diálogo.

1. ¿Por qué está Ricardo muy contento esta noche?

2. ¿Con quién habla?

3. Explique—en sus propias palabras—por qué son importantes los aficionados.

4. ¿Qué va a hacer primero Ricardo?

D. Como deportista la nutrición es muy importante. Los jugadores siempre reciben instrucciones de los entrenadores en cuanto al mejor plan de preparación, incluyendo una dieta saludable. Estudie la "caja" de Milagro's Campeoncitas y anote seis ingredientes buenos o malos para determinar si es un buen desayuno. Hable con su compañero/a de sus conclusiones.

MODELO: *Tiene poco colesterol. Tiene bastante sodio. ¡Tiene azúcar! Un cereal natural es mejor.*

El Cereal de Triunfo: Milagro's Campeoncitas

Hojas de avena fortalecidas con vitaminas
¡Da Fuerzas!
Campeoncitas alimenta tu ánimo
Contenido neto 20 oz. (567 g)
Información nutricional
Tamaño de porción $^3/_4$ taza
Porciones en la caja aproximadamente 18

Cantidad por porción	Cereal	Cereal con $^1/_2$ taza de leche descremada
Calorías	140	180
Calorías de grasa	28	28
	% Valor diario	
Grasa total 3 g	5%	5%
Colesterol < de 5 mg	1%	1%
Sodio 137 mg	6%	9%
Potasio 291 mg	8%	13%
Carbohidratos disponibles 11 g	4%	6%
Fibra 1g	4%	6%
Sacarosa y otros azúcares 6 g		
Proteínas 18 g		
Vitamina A	25%	30%
Vitamina C	50%	50%
Calcio	10%	25%
Hierro	11%	14%
Vitamina D	10%	25%
Vitamina B2	50%	60%
Niacina	50%	50%
Vitamina B6	35%	35%
Ácido fólico	35%	35%
Vitamina B12	35%	45%

La avena utilizada en este producto contiene rastros de soya.

E. Una buena dieta.   Según la pirámide de comida nutritiva, se deben comer 6–11 porciones de tortillas, panes, granos y cereales diariamente, 3–5 porciones de verduras, 2–4 porciones de frutas, 2–3 porciones de alimentos con proteína, 3-4 porciones de productos lácteos y 1–2 porciones de grasas, aceites y dulces. Con un/compañero/a hable de comida en cada categoría.

MODELO: *Las uvas (grapes) son una fruta.*

Estructuras   *More on reflexive verbs: Los verbos recíprocos*

- Reciprocal verbs are conjugated in the same way as reflexive verbs. They are used to express that two or more people are doing something *to* or *for* each other.

Nosotros siempre **nos** ayudamos.	*We always help each other.*
Marco y el entrenador **se** respetan mucho.	*Mark and the coach respect each other a lot.*
Los miembros del equipo saben apoyar**se** a cada paso.	*The members of the team know to support one another at each step.*

- Many verbs not usually used as reflexive verbs can be made reciprocal by using the appropriate reflexive pronoun: **se** or **nos.**

Los entrenadores **se** consultan cada día.	*The coaches consult each other every day.*
Nos escribimos notas.	*We write each other memos.*

Para practicar

A. Acciones mutuas.   Indique las acciones recíprocas de las siguientes personas.

MODELO: El capitán del equipo y la capitana de animadoras/mirarse
El capitán del equipo y la capitana de animadoras se miran.

1. Los amigos/comunicarse por correo electrónico todos los días
2. Los entrenadores/consultarse antes de tomar decisiones
3. Tú y yo/comprenderse bien
4. El director de la escuela y los profesores y entrenadores/reunirse todas las semanas
5. Nosotros/apoyarse siempre
6. Nosotros nunca/pelearse

B. ¿Quiénes son?   Escriba el nombre de algunas personas famosas o conocidas para completar estas ideas.

MODELO: Nos queremos mucho.
Mi familia y yo nos queremos muchos.

1. Se pelean con frecuencia.
2. Se divorcian.
3. Nos vemos todos los días.
4. No se hablan nunca.
5. Nos apoyamos mucho.
6. Se adoran.

C. Un romance en el gimnasio.   Amanda y Marco son compañeros de clase y nosotros creemos que su relación es mucho más que una amistad. Describa su romance usando los siguientes verbos. Después de terminar, escríbalo otra vez con la forma **nosotros.**

MODELO: verse por primera vez en la oficina
Se ven por primera vez en la cafetería. (Nosotros nos vemos por primera vez en la cafetería.)

1. mirarse a los ojos
2. hablarse
3. encontrarse cerca de la fuente de agua
4. no poder separarse
5. abrazarse con pasión
6. besarse (*kiss*)
7. enamorarse
8. comprarse billetes de abono (*season tickets*)

Módulo 2

Necesito saber un poco de todo

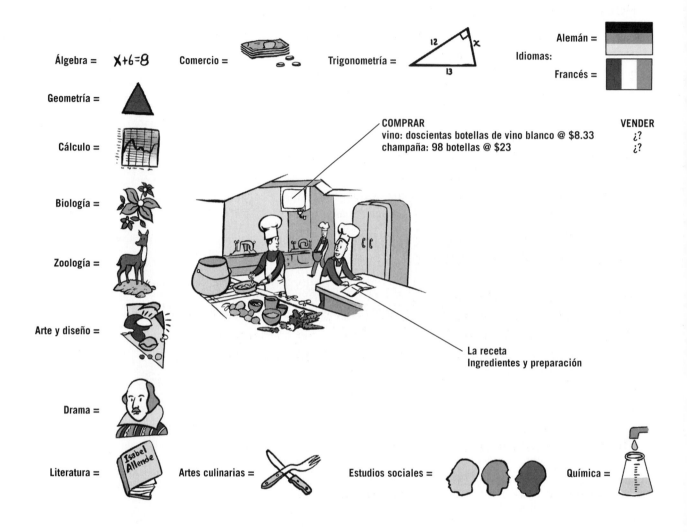

Álgebra = $X+6=8$

Geometría =

Cálculo =

Biología =

Zoología =

Arte y diseño =

Drama =

Literatura =

Comercio =

Artes culinarias =

Trigonometría =

12, 13, x

Estudios sociales =

Idiomas:
Alemán =
Francés =

COMPRAR
vino: doscientas botellas de vino blanco @ $8.33
champaña: 98 botellas @ $23

VENDER
¿?
¿?

La receta
Ingredientes y preparación

Química =

A. ¿Cómo se dice?   Escriba la clase que corresponda a cada una de las definiciones.

1.   Aquí se aprenden fórmulas como Na_2SO_4.
2.   La parte de matemáticas donde se buscan valores desconocidos *(unknown)*.
3.   Estudiamos las ciencias de la vida aquí.
4.   La operación de un restaurante es complicada. En esta clase se combinan las disciplinas de matemáticas, química, comercio, biología y arte.

B. Acciones.   Use la memoria y el dibujo para emparejar este vocabulario con las definiciones correspondientes de la clase de artes culinarias.

1. _____ conocer   **a.** tener información sobre algo

2. _____ saber   **b.** la persona encargada del arte y ciencia de comer

3. _____ receta   **c.** los ingredientes y las instrucciones para preparar platos

4. _____ el/la chef **d.** tener una relación personal con una persona o lugar

Los chefs del futuro

Andrés y Michelle son dos líderes en el Club de Futuros Chefs de América. Ellos sueñan con ser chefs célebres en sus propios restaurantes de cuatro estrellas y con su propio programa de televisión en la Cadena internacional de la comida. Y saben muy bien que no es una profesión fácil: tienen que combinar muchas disciplinas académicas. Ahora, con el club, tienen la oportunidad de asistir a su primera exposición profesional.

ANDRÉS: Michelle, mira este folleto de la Exposición Su Menú. Van a estar aquí en San Francisco el año que viene. ¿Sabes algo de este grupo?

MICHELLE: Sé que es un grupo muy importante en la industria. Siempre predicen las tendencias futuras en los gustos del público, y tienen representantes de los restaurantes más importantes. Si vamos, sé que podemos conocer a muchas personas con influencia en la industria y participar en la Red *(networking)*.

ANDRÉS: Dicen que va a haber muchos chefs célebres.... ¿Conoces a Emeril?

MICHELLE: No, no lo conozco personalmente... pero todo el mundo sabe quién es.

ANDRÉS: ¡Es mi héroe! Vamos a la exposición. ¡Imagínate si lo podemos conocer!

C. ¿Comprende usted?   Conteste las preguntas según la información del diálogo.

1. ¿En qué club son líderes Michelle y Andrés?
2. ¿Qué quieren tener en el futuro?
3. ¿Por qué quiere ir Michelle?
4. ¿A quién quiere conocer Andrés?

D. ¡No me gusta! A su hijo de 13 años no le gusta la comida de la cafetería pero usted no tiene tiempo de prepararle otro almuerzo. Lea el menú de su escuela y separe las posibilidades en dos grupos: 1. Le gusta, 2. No le gusta.

Lunes:	Salchichas/Rebanadas de papa/Rajas de zanahoria/1/2 naranja
Martes:	Emparedado de atún/Gelatina de fruta/Tostaditos de canela/Leche
Miércoles:	Burritos/Ensalada/Duraznos
Jueves:	Tacos/Arroz/Puré de manzana/Queso
Viernes:	Hamburguesas/Lechuga con pepino/Peras/Galletas

E. ¡Mi receta favorita! Escriba su receta favorita con mandatos formales de la Lección 5. Cambie de receta con un/a compañero/a. ¿Su receta es sabrosa? Puede usar un diccionario para buscar más palabras de comida.

MODELO: *Ensalada de lechuga y tomate: Primero, lave la lechuga y los tomates. Corte los tomates en cubitos. Corte la lechuga en trozos. Mezcle. Sirva con aderezo de aceite y vinagre, sal y pimienta.*

Estructuras   *Expressing knowledge and familiarity:*
Saber y conocer

- Spanish has two verbs to express different aspects of the English verb *to know.*

saber			
yo	**sé**	nosotros	**sabemos**
tú	**sabes**		
Ud./él/ella	**sabe**	Uds./ellos/ellas	**saben**

- Use **saber** to say that someone knows information or facts. When followed by an infinitive, **saber** means *to know how to do something.*

Sé que las ensaladas son saludables.	*I know that salads are healthy.*
Emeril **sabe** preparar y presentar	*Emeril knows how to prepare and present*
sus recetas ante el público.	*his recipes to the public.*

conocer			
yo	**conozco**	nosotros/as	**conocemos**
tú	**conoces**		
Ud./él/ella	**conoce**	Uds./ellos/ellas	**conocen**

- Use **conocer** to indicate that someone is personally *acquainted with* or *familiar with* a person or place.

Conozco al chef de aquí. Es amigo mío.	*I know the chef here. He's a friend of mine.*
Andrés y Michelle **conocen** bien el restaurante. Trabajan allí.	*Andrés y Michelle are well acquainted with the restaurant. They work there.*

Para practicar

A. ¿Quién sabe hacer...? Usted es un millonario con una nueva cadena de restaurantes de servicio rápido. Quiere llamar a las personas o empresas más expertas—en la actualidad o en el pasado—para hacer lo siguiente:

MODELO: diseñar el arte de los restaurantes familiares
Botero sabe diseñar el arte para los restaurantes familiares.

1. representar los restaurantes con temas deportivos
2. vender hamburguesas
3. diseñar un menú artístico
4. demostrar la preparación de las recetas en los programas de televisión
5. tocar música salsa para bailar
6. preparar las mejores papas fritas

B. ¿Conoce usted...? Un amigo que va a abrir un nuevo restaurante busca a más expertos para ayudarlo. Usted conoce a muchas celebridades en todas las disciplinas. Identifique la celebridad indicada.

MODELO: ¿Conoce usted a un buen chef?
Sí, conozco a Emeril.

1. ¿Conoce usted a un buen artista para diseñar el menú?
2. ¿Conoce usted a un músico famoso para la inauguración del restaurante?
3. ¿Conoce a un experto en la tecnología para instalar las computadoras?
4. ¿Conoce a un/a maravilloso/a profesor/a de español para traducir el menú?
5. ¿Conoce usted a un experto en nutrición?

C. ¿Saber o conocer? El Club de Futuros Chefs de América va a organizar una fiesta enorme para el fin del año escolar. Como presidente de la organización, usted tiene la responsabilidad de confirmar que ellos saben sus tareas y conocen a las personas importantes. Complete las preguntas con la forma **usted** de **saber** o **conocer.**

MODELO: ¿_____ el número de teléfono para llamar en caso de emergencia médica?
¿Sabe el número de teléfono para llamar en caso de emergencia médica?

1. ¿_____ al director de la escuela?

2. ¿_____ explicar las recetas a los cocineros que preparan la comida?

3. ¿_____ el supermercado donde compramos los ingredientes frescos?

4. ¿_____ supervisar a los meseros?

5. ¿_____ preparar ensaladas?

6. ¿_____ a un buen instructor de artes culinarias?

Módulo 2

Servicio a la comunidad

¿Qué tiempo hace hoy?

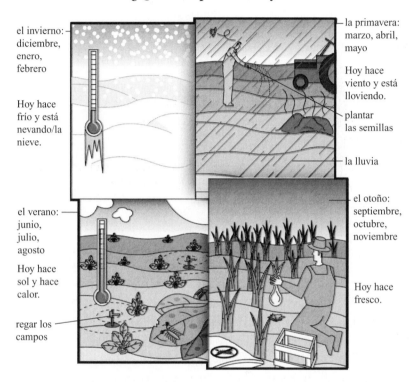

el invierno: diciembre, enero, febrero

Hoy hace frío y está nevando/la nieve.

el verano: junio, julio, agosto

Hoy hace sol y hace calor.

regar los campos

la primavera: marzo, abril, mayo

Hoy hace viento y está lloviendo.

plantar las semillas

la lluvia

el otoño: septiembre, octubre, noviembre

Hoy hace fresco.

A. ¿Cómo se dice?   Escoja la palabra que corresponda a cada una de las definiciones.

a. la lluvia   b. el invierno   c. el tractor   d. las semillas

1. _____ la parte de la planta que ponemos en la tierra para cultivar

2. _____ el agua que cae del cielo *(sky)*

3. _____ la parte del año cuando hace mucho frío

4. _____ una máquina grande que se usa para preparar los campos y la tierra

B. Acciones.   Busque la definición más lógica para cada verbo.

1. _____ regar   **a.**   criatura que come las plantas

2. _____ plantar   **b.**   dar nutrientes

3. _____ el insecto   **c.**   poner las semillas en la tierra

4. _____ alimentar   **d.**   poner agua en las plantas

La lección

Muchos de los Juniors de nuestro colegio están pensando en las oportunidades futuras para ir a la universidad y después trabajar en su profesión ideal. Saben que las notas excelentes, los ensayos personales y las recomendaciones de sus maestros sólo son una parte del proceso de admisión. Necesitan también demostrar su interés en la comunidad. Ernesto es un miembro de los Futuros Maestros de América y Sara es miembro de los Futuros Agricultores de América. Ellos tienen un proyecto de servicio a la comunidad que combina los intereses de los dos cuando hablan a una clase de Kinder.

ERNESTO: *(con un pedazo de papa en la mano)* ¿Saben qué es esto?

ESTUDIANTES: ¿Parte de una papa?

ERNESTO: ¿De dónde vienen las papas?

ESTUDIANTES: Del supermercado... de McDonald's...

ERNESTO: Las papas vienen de esta parte: la semilla. ¿Quién sabe lo que hacemos con las semillas?

ESTUDIANTES: Las plantamos en la tierra.

ERNESTO: Muy bien. ¿Y qué más hacemos?

UN ESTUDIANTE: ¿Las regamos con agua?

ERNESTO: Claro. ¿Y cómo alimentamos las plantas?

OTRO ESTUDIANTE: No sé.

ERNESTO: Las alimentamos con fertilizantes.

ESTUDIANTE: ¿Y entonces tenemos papas?

ERNESTO: Las papas necesitan unos cuatro meses para crecer. Necesitan sol y lluvia. Y mientras crecen, tenemos que cuidarlas bien y protegerlas contra los insectos. Aquí hay uno de los insectos más peligrosos para la papa. ¿Lo ven?

ESTUDIANTES: ¡Uy! ¡Fuchi! ¡Feo!

ERNESTO: Hay muchos insectos. Los matamos para proteger las papas. Pronto las papas están listas para ir al supermercado.

ESTUDIANTES: ¡Y a McDonald's!

C. ¿Comprende usted?   Lea las siguientes oraciones y determine si
probablemente son **Ciertas (C)** o **Falsas (F).** Si son falsas, corríjalas, por favor.

1. _____ Ernesto es miembro de sólo un club.

2. _____ Los niños de Kinder no comprenden el proceso de cultivo.

3. _____ Ernesto les explica el proceso para cultivar los insectos.

4. _____ A los niños les gusta el insecto.

D. Planes para el futuro. Los padres necesitan ayudar a sus hijos a tomar decisiones para sus estudios en el futuro. Conteste las preguntas de esta encuesta como el papá o la mamá de un/a estudiante.

¡ENCUESTA PARA PADRES DE ADELANTE!

Las siguientes son preguntas sobre usted y su hijo/a con opción para participar en ADELANTE (en el 6º o 7º grado). Favor de contestar estas frases marcando la respuesta que mejor refleja su opinión.

He hablado con alguien sobre la inscripción de estudiantes en una escuela más avanzada que la preparatoria. No   Sí

Sé cómo preparar a mi hijo/a para ir a la universidad o escuela técnica después de terminar su bachillerato. No   Sí

La educación más avanzada que espero que mi hijo reciba es (escoja uno):

Menos que la preparatoria   Bachillerato

Certificado de una escuela de negocios, técnica o vocacional

Nivel de escuela comunitaria (2 años)   Nivel licenciatura (4 años)   Maestría o superior

La razón principal por que mi hijo/a no estudiaría más, después de terminar su bachillerato, sería: Sí, lo va a hacer. Es demasiado caro. Quiere trabajar. Tiene malas notas.

No está interesado/a. Quiere estar en el ejército. Tenemos problemas familiares. Otra

Estoy familiarizado/a con los requisitos de entrada en una escuela técnica, vocacional o de negocios y en una universidad de dos o cuatro años.   No   Sí

He hablado con mi hijo/a sobre los estudios después de su bachillerato.   No   Sí

He hablado con alguien sobre becas y ayuda financiera para ir a una escuela más

avanzada que la preparatoria. No   Sí

Sé cuánto va a costar que mi hijo/a vaya a una universidad pública de 4 años.

Claro que no   Lo dudo   No lo sé   A lo mejor   Claro que sí

¡Gracias por contestar esta encuesta!

E. ¿Cuál me interesa? Hay muchos clubes en las escuelas: Futuros maestros de América, Club de ciencia, Trabajos de paz, Organización de estudiantes americanos e internacionales, Club de español, Oratoria y debate, Consejo estudiantil, Jóvenes y adultos en conección, La hermandad cristiana de atletas, Futuros granjeros *(farmers)*... Hable con su compañero/a de sus intereses.

MODELO: *Mis padres tienen una finca muy grande; por eso me interesa el grupo de Futuros granjeros.*

Estructuras *Receiving the action of a verb: El objeto directo*

- Direct objects are people or things that are acted on by the subject of a sentence or question. The following sentences have their direct objects highlighted in bold type. Human direct objects have an **a** in front of them.

El maestro invita **a los niños.**	*The teacher invites the children.*
Los niños plantan **las semillas.**	*The children plant the seeds.*
Riegan **las plantas.**	*They water/irrigate the plants.*

- The following pronouns will replace nouns that function as direct objects.

Direct object pronouns

me	*me*	**nos**	*us*
te	*you (fam. sing.)*		
lo	*him, it, you (form. sing., m.)*	**los**	*them, you (pl., m.)*
la	*her, it, you (form. sing., f.)*	**las**	*them, you (pl., f.)*

- In Spanish, direct object pronouns are placed before a conjugated verb.

El niño examina **las semillas.**	*The child examines the seeds.*
El niño **las** examina.	*The child examines them.*
La maestra invita **al agricultor**.	*The teacher invites the farmer.*
La maestra **lo** invita.	*The teacher invites him.*
¿El agricultor conoce **a los maestros**?	*Does the farmer know the teachers?*
Sí, **nos** conoce bien.	*Yes, he knows us well.*

- If an infinitive follows the conjugated verb and shares the same subject, the pronoun may be placed before the conjugated verb or it may be attached to the end of the infinitive.

Voy a regar **las plantas**.	→	**Las** voy a regar.
		Voy a regar**las.**
Vamos a invitar **a niños**.	→	**Los** vamos a invitar.
		Vamos a invitar**los.**

- In the present progressive, the direct object pronoun may be placed before the conjugation of the verb **estar** or it may be attached to the end of the participle ending in **–ndo.** When attaching the pronoun to the end of the participle form, remember to add an accent to the second-to-last syllable of the *original participle.*

Estoy examinando **las hojas**.   →   Estoy examin**ándolas**.
Las estoy examinando.

Estamos buscando **insectos**.   →   Estamos busc**ándolos**.
Los estamos buscando.

- When using direct object pronouns with command forms of the verb, the pronoun is *always* attached to the end of an affirmative command and is *always* placed before a negative command. When attaching the pronoun to the end of the command, remember to place an accent on the second-to-last syllable of the *original* command form.

¿Planto **las semillas** ahora?   →   Sí, plánte**las** ahora.
No, no **las plante** ahora.

Para practicar

A. El voluntario.   Usted es un voluntario en una escuela primaria. Hoy, usted está demostrando el cuidado del jardín que acaban de plantar. Todos los niños tienen muchas preguntas. Conteste estas preguntas con pronombres de objeto directo.

MODELO: NIÑO: *¿Preparan ustedes la tierra ahora?*
USTED: *Sí, la preparamos.*

1. ¿Ponen el alimento ahora?
2. ¿Usan ustedes pesticidas?
3. ¿Necesitan ustedes ayuda?
4. ¿Las plantas tienen muchos insectos?
5. ¿Las plantas necesitan más agua?
6. ¿Conducen ustedes los tractores?

B. Más servicio a la comunidad.   Ernesto también es voluntario en la industria agrícola de su comunidad. Su supervisor llama por teléfono para saber si todas las tareas han sido completadas. Dígale que los empleados están haciendo lo que pide. Use el presente progresivo y los pronombres de objeto directo.

MODELO: llamar a los trabajadores para confirmar el horario
Estamos llamándolos ahora. o *Los estamos llamando ahora.*

1. preparar los pesticidas
2. lavar los tractores
3. buscar insectos
4. proteger las plantas contra el frío
5. invitar a los estudiantes de la maestra Susana a la finca

C. Los niños.   Hoy Luis ayuda a los niños a plantar sus propias semillas. Conteste sus preguntas con mandatos formales (**ustedes**) y un pronombre directo.

MODELO: ¿Cubrimos las plantas tiernas?
                Sí, cúbranlas.

1.   ¿Preparamos la tierra?
2.   ¿Regamos la tierra?
3.   ¿Usamos abonos?
4.   ¿Plantamos las semillas ahora?
5.   ¿Miramos el pronóstico del tiempo (*weather report*)?
6.   ¿Buscamos más semillas?

Vocabulario Módulo 1

Sustantivos

el aceite	*oil*	**la hoja**	*leaf*
el/la aficionado/a	*fan*	**el horario**	*schedule*
la amistad	*friendship*	**el/la juez/a**	*judge*
el/la animador/a	*cheerleader*	**la lucha libre**	*wrestling*
el/la árbitro	*referee*	**el maíz**	*corn*
el/la atleta	*athlete*	**la natación**	*swimming*
el/la azúcar	*sugar*	**el/la novio/a**	*boy/girlfriend*
el balón	*ball*	**el pan**	*bread*
la camiseta	*T-shirt*	**el partido**	*game, match*
el campeonato	*championship*	**el pedazo**	*piece*
el/la capitán/ana	*captain*	**las pesas**	*weights*
la carrera	*career*	**la portería**	*goal (sports)*
el casco	*helmet*	**el recuerdo**	*memory*
la destreza	*skill*	**el/la reportero/a**	*reporter*
la ducha	*shower*	**el tamaño**	*size*
el espejo	*mirror*	**la taza**	*cup*
la estrella	*star*	**el trofeo**	*trophy*
la fuente	*fountain*	**el turno**	*shift*
el fútbol americano	*football*	**la verdura**	*vegetable*
la grasa	*fat*		

Verbos

abrazarse	*to embrace*	**enojarse**	*to get angry*
acabar	*to end*	**lavarse**	*to wash*
alimentar	*to feed*	**llevarse bien, mal**	*to get along*
arreglar	*to arrange, to*		*well, not at all*
	fix	**peinarse**	*to comb one's*
bañarse	*to bathe*		*hair*
calmarse	*to calm down*	**secarse**	*to dry off*
cambiar	*to change*	**sentarse (ie)**	*to sit down*
cuidarse	*to take care of*	**soñar (ue)**	*to dream*
	(oneself)	**tirar**	*to throw*
despertarse (ie)	*to wake up*	**vestirse (i)**	*to get dressed*
ducharse	*to shower*		

Adjetivos

dulce	*sweet*	**estricto/a**	*strict*
entero/a	*whole*	**rico/a**	*rich*

Otras expresiones

estar de acuerdo	*to agree*

Vocabulario Módulo 2

Sustantivos

el aderezo	*dressing*	**el ensayo**	*essay*
el alemán	*German*	**la entrada**	*entry*
el arroz	*rice*	**el folleto**	*pamphlet*
las artes culinarias	*culinary arts*	**el francés**	*French*
el atún	*tuna*	**la fruta**	*fruit*
la banda	*band*	**la gelatina**	*gelatin*
la beca	*scholarship*	**la geometría**	*geometry*
la biología	*biology*	**la hamburguesa**	*hamburger*
la botella	*bottle*	**el hogar**	*home*
la cadena	*chain*	**la huelga**	*strike*
la champaña	*champagne*	**la industria**	*industry*
el comercio	*business*	**la influencia**	*influence*
la cosecha	*harvest*	**el ingrediente**	*ingredient*
el drama	*drama*	**el invierno**	*winter*
el durazno	*peach*	**la lechuga**	*lettuce*
el ejército	*army*	**la literatura**	*literature*
el emparedado	*sandwich*	**la lluvia**	*rain*
la empresa	*enterprise*	**la manzana**	*apple*
la encuesta	*survey*	**el/la mesero/a**	*waiter, waitress*
la ensalada	*salad*	**la meta**	*goal*

la naranja	orange	**la salchicha**	sausage
la nieve	snow	**la semilla**	seed
el/la obrero/a	worker	**el sindicato**	union
el otoño	fall	**el sol**	sun
la paciencia	patience	**el tostadito**	toast
la papa	potato	**la traducción**	translation
el pepino	cucumber	**el triángulo**	triangle
la pera	pear	**la trigonometría**	trigonometry
la pimienta	pepper	**el/la vecino/a**	neighbor
el queso	cheese	**el viento**	wind
la raja	slice	**el vino**	wine
la rebanada	slice	**la zanahoria**	carrot
la sal	salt	**la zoología**	zoology

Verbos

atender (ie)	to assist	**mezclar**	to mix
averiguar	to find out	**nevar (ie)**	to snow
crecer (zc)	to grow	**regar (ie)**	to water
imaginar	to imagine	**sembrar (ie)**	to plant
llover (ue)	to rain		

Adjetivos

caro/a	expensive	**fresco/a**	cool
encargado/a	in charge of	**sabroso/a**	tasty

Otras expresiones

demasiado/a	too	**hoy**	today

Síntesis

A escuchar

María y Consuelo son dos amigas de la escuela. Es la hora del almuerzo.

Complete las siguientes oraciones con la información del diálogo.

1. Antes de ir a la cafetería, Consuelo quiere _____ porque están sucias.

2. María quiere hablarle a Consuelo de su nuevo _____.

3. Consuelo no conoce al nuevo maestro, pero sabe que es

_____.

4. Según María, el nuevo maestro sabe mucho de _____.

5. Por primera vez este año, a María le _____ ir a la escuela.

A conversar

👥👥 Como padre, usted quiere ayudar a su niño a encontrar su vocación para planificar su futuro. Hable con otros padres (sus compañeros) de estrategias para hacerlo.

MODELO: *Hable con el personal de la escuela para averiguar lo que se necesita hacer para asistir a la universidad o a una escuela vocacional.*

A leer

Los sistemas educativos no son iguales.

«Mi hijo va al Colegio Benito Juárez,» dice la mamá mexicana al hablar con su vecina estadounidense. «No es posible—tiene solamente ocho años,» contesta ésta. Bueno, la realidad es diferente de un lugar a otro. En español, **colegio** no significa universidad, como en inglés, sino una escuela de cualquier grado; así un estudiante de ocho años SÍ puede ser estudiante de colegio.

Por lo general, los niños pequeños van a una escuela primaria y entonces a una escuela secundaria. Al terminar la secundaria, para terminar su educación, van a una escuela técnica o empiezan la preparatoria, **prepa,** que les prepara para entrar en la universidad.

👥👥 **¿Comprende usted?** Prepare una tabla de comparación de escuelas en Estados Unidos y en otras naciones con dos o tres compañeros. Puede buscar más información en Internet. No es necesario usar solamente datos de países donde se habla español—¿qué sabe usted de *lycées?*

A escribir

Como el/la consejero/a de actividades en su escuela, usted cree que los estudiantes deben participar en algún club, deporte o actividad como la banda. Prepare un anuncio para el boletín para animarlos a participar.

MODELO: *¿Sabe Ud. escribir bien? El periódico de la escuela lo/la busca para entrevistar a atletas de varios deportes.*

Algo más

Many students move with their families as often as twice a year, changing schools with each new home. For these students, whose families are frequently involved in agriculture and move to follow the crop rotation, the disruption of a new environment causes a lack of continuity in their studies. Furthermore, in homes where so much change is a constant, there is often a shortage of resource materials, from books to computers. The Migrant Education Program is designed to assist them in many ways.

La educación de estudiantes migrantes

La educación migratoria es un programa nacional que proporciona servicios de educación adicional y de apoyo a más de 800.000 niños/as migrantes para ayudar a superar interrupciones e inconveniencias. El programa comenzó *(started)* en 1965. A causa de las necesidades específicas de la niñez migratoria, los niños reciben ayuda y servicios adicionales como tutelaje para complementar la instrucción del salón de clases en las áreas de lectura y redacción en español e inglés, matemáticas y/o materias de contenido principal. La meta de la instrucción adicional es ayudar a los estudiantes a satisfacer o exceder los niveles de contenido y los puntos de referencia a través de instrucción integrada y diferenciada. Además hay servicios tales como médicos de emergencia, dentales y de la vista, visitas al hogar, traducciones y referencia a agencias de servicio local para atender las necesidades del estudiante y de la familia. El programa sirve a niños de edad preescolar hasta el duodécimo *(12th)* grado.

En mis propias palabras. Haga una lista de cinco "faltas" *(shortages)* posibles para un estudiante que cambia de escuela dos a tres veces en un año escolar.

A buscar

Busque información de programas de educación migratoria en distritos en varios estados—en español, claro. Si es posible ir a la oficina central del distrito cerca de su casa, traiga esa información a clase. Si no, imprima por lo menos una página de Internet.

www.cubanet.org/sindical

http://sisargentina.hypermart.net

www.laboreducator.org/famsp.htm

www.labournet.org.uk/spanish

A conocer: César Chávez

Fundador principal del sindicato United Farm Workers, Chávez es un héroe para mucha gente que trabaja en la agricultura. De origen humilde, se dedicó por completo a la protección de los obreros agrícolas. Era el principio de La Causa, una causa apoyada por los grupos obreros, por grupos religiosos organizados, minorías y estudiantes. César Chávez tenía la visión para entrenar a los obreros del sindicato y enviar a muchos de ellos a las ciudades donde actuarían como un arma para organizar un boicot y la huelga contra la cosecha de uvas. Se puede leer la biografía de César Chávez y ver una película sobre él en español en www.ufw.org.

LECCIÓN 9

Consejos útiles

Módulo 1
- Mis padres tienen sueños
- Giving advice and suggestions: *Introducción breve al subjuntivo*
- La educación de adultos
- More on the subjunctive: *Más sobre el subjuntivo*

Módulo 2
- Es importante continuar las clases
- Giving recommendations: *El subjuntivo con expresiones impersonales*
- ¡Qué bueno que empiece la carrera!
- Expressing emotion and doubt: *El subjuntivo con expresiones de emoción y duda*

Consejera

Síntesis
- A escuchar
- A conversar
- A leer
- A escribir

Algo más
- Ventana cultural: Se aprende la cultura por la música
- A buscar
- A conocer: Ernie y Lorie Chapa

Módulo I

Mis padres tienen sueños

Galería de ex-alumnos, Colegio del Norte

soñar con ser maestro

el médico

la abogada

el profesor de
matemáticas

Consejero académico: Roberto Rebolledo
Aquí se exploran:
1. profesiones y carreras
2. universidades
3. $$$ becas y préstamos para los estudios
4. direcciones futuras
Prepárense aquí para el PSAT

A. ¿Cómo se dice?   Busque la definición que mejor identifique las siguientes palabras o frases.

I. _____ becas y préstamos   **a.** profesional de la salud

2. _____ abogada   **b.** un graduado de una institución

3. _____ ex-alumno   **c.** dinero para pagar los estudios

4. _____ médico   **d.** profesional de la justicia

B. Acciones.   Use la memoria, la imaginación y el dibujo para identificar estas acciones.

I. _____ prepararse   **a.** llenar formularios, escribir ensayos personales y pedir recomendaciones

2. _____ aconsejar   **b.** investigar

3. _____ explorar   **c.** guiar y recomendar

4. _____ solicitar admisión   **d.** estudiar mucho para un examen

Una cita con el consejero

El consejero Rebolledo quiere pedir una cita con todos los estudiantes que van a empezar el tercer (Junior) año del colegio. Quiere que los estudiantes le hablen de sus sueños para el futuro. Ahora está hablando con Álvaro Suárez, un buen alumno con muchos intereses.

SEÑOR REBOLLEDO: Hola, Álvaro, y gracias por responder tan rápidamente a mi invitación para pedir una cita. Ahora que entras en el tercer año, es importante planificar el futuro. ¿Tienes planes para después de la graduación?

ÁLVARO: Mis padres quieren que yo siga los estudios en la universidad. Quieren que sea médico o abogado. Pero no sé...

SEÑOR REBOLLEDO: ¿No sabes si quieres seguir los estudios?

ÁLVARO: No es eso. Es que ellos quieren que yo estudie para médico y yo quiero estudiar para maestro de niños. Quieren que vaya a Harvard y yo quiero ir a la universidad del estado o la universidad comunitaria de aquí.

SEÑOR REBOLLEDO: ¿Por qué?

ÁLVARO: Hay muchas razones: soy el primero de mi familia que va a la universidad. No sé si soy capaz. Mis padres no tienen mucho dinero...

SEÑOR REBOLLEDO: Álvaro, quiero que hagamos un plan para explorar varias carreras. Después podemos investigar opciones de universidades y maneras de pagar los estudios con becas y préstamos.

ÁLVARO: Mis padres tienen otro sueño. Espero que usted también pueda ayudarnos a realizarlo. Quieren ser ciudadanos de Estados Unidos. No hablan mucho inglés y quieren aprenderlo antes de empezar más estudios.

SEÑOR REBOLLEDO: Álvaro, quiero que ellos pidan una cita inmediatamente para hablar. Vamos a realizar todos los sueños: tu futuro académico y el futuro de ellos.

C. ¿Comprende usted? Conteste las preguntas según la información del diálogo.

1. ¿Por qué quiere el Sr. Rebolledo hablar con los estudiantes de tercer año?
2. ¿Qué sueño tienen los padres de Álvaro para el futuro de su hijo?
3. ¿Qué quiere ser Álvaro?
4. ¿Qué otro sueño académico puede resolver el consejero?

D. El futuro maestro.   El sueño de Álvaro es ser maestro. Lea esta carta de ánimo para futuros maestros y hable con un/a compañero/a de cinco razones para hacerse maestro.

MODELO: *Se puede cambiar la vida de un niño al abrirle las puertas a la educación.*

Estimado futuro maestro:

En nombre de los maestros de Estados Unidos, queremos que participe en nuestro grupo. Enseñar a los niños y adolescentes abre los corazones y las mentes al aprendizaje y estimula su intelecto.

Esta carta está dirigida a diferentes públicos, con diversos niveles de experiencia e interés, que están considerando ingresar a la carrera de maestro. El importante trabajo de enseñar a las futuras generaciones requiere mucha energía, empeño, creatividad y compromiso. Si disfruta de la compañía de niños y adolescentes y le preocupan los problemas de la educación, infórmese de los pasos a seguir. Ayude a cambiar las cosas.

Enseñe.

Atentamente,

Sonia Del Mar

Directora, Profesora

Estructuras   *Giving advice and suggestions: Introducción breve al subjuntivo*

- In Lección 5 you learned about using command forms to tell people what you would like to see happen. This is the first phase of a grammatical concept called the *subjunctive mood*.
- All of the other verb forms you have learned so far are in the *indicative mood*. The indicative mood is generally used to describe what the speaker assumes to be true.
- The subjunctive mood is used to indicate that the speaker does not consider the statement to be a fact.
- Verbs in the subjunctive mood are used in the subordinate clause (usually the second clause of a sentence) when the main clause (usually the first clause of a sentence) expresses a suggestion, wish, doubt, emotion, or attitude.

Indicative: Álvaro estudia en el colegio. (What *is...*)
Subjunctive: Los padres **quieren que** Álvaro **estudie** en Harvard.
                    (What the parents *want*, but may or may not happen.)

- The formal command forms you previously learned and verbs in the subjunctive mood are derived by using the present tense **yo** form of the verb and changing the final vowel of **-ar** verbs to **-e,** and the final vowel of **-er** and **-ir** verbs to **-a.**

	hablar	comer	vivir
Command			
que yo	habl**e**	com**a**	viv**a**
que tú	habl**es**	com**as**	viv**as**
que él/ella/Ud.	habl**e**	com**a**	viv**a**
que nosotros/as	habl**emos**	com**amos**	viv**amos**
que ellos/ellas/Uds.	habl**en**	com**an**	viv**an**

- The following 5 verbs have irregular subjunctive forms.

	ir	dar	estar	ser	saber
Command					
que yo	vay**a**	d**é**	est**é**	se**a**	sep**a**
que tú	vay**as**	d**es**	est**és**	se**as**	sep**as**
que él/ella/Ud.	vay**a**	d**é**	est**é**	se**a**	sep**a**
que nosotros/as	vay**amos**	d**emos**	est**emos**	se**amos**	sep**amos**
que ellos/ellas/Uds.	vay**an**	d**en**	est**én**	se**an**	sep**an**

- As with formal commands, verbs ending in:

-zar	become	**-ce**	Empie**ce** Ud. a explorar el futuro.
-gar	become	**-gue**	Pa**gue** Ud. los costos de la universidad.
-car	become	**-que**	Bus**que** Ud. la información.

- An **e** in the stem of the **nosotros/as** form of stem-changing **-ir** verbs changes to **-i** and an **-o** changes to **-u** in the subjunctive. Note that this change occurs only with stem-changing **-ir** verbs, not with **-ar** and **-er** verbs.

INFINITIVE		SUBJUNCTIVE
-ar	**cerrar**	**cierre, cierres, cierre,** cerremos, **cierren**
-er	**volver**	**vuelva, vuelvas, vuelva,** volvamos, **vuelvan**

but ¡OJO!

-ir	**sentir**	sienta, sientas, sienta, **sintamos,** sientan
	dormir	duerma, duermas, duerma, **durmamos,** duerman

- The subjunctive of **hay** is **haya.**
- When there is only one subject that wants, hopes, desires, or prefers to do something, the verb is followed by an infinitive.

El estudiante quiere **ser** maestro.　　*The student wants to be a teacher.*
Los estudiantes necesitan　　　　　　*The students need to explore options.*
explorar las opciones.

- When one subject wants, desire, hopes, prefers, etc. that a second subject do something, the two clauses are joined by **que** and the subjunctive is used in the second clause.

El consejero quiere **que el estudiante**　　*The counselor wants the student to*
investigue sus opciones.　　　　　　　　*explore his options.*
El estudiante espera **que el consejero**　　*The student hopes that the counselor*
comprenda los problemas.　　　　　　　　*understands the problems.*

Para practicar

A. ¿El estudiante o yo?　　Usted es un consejero que trabaja con estudiantes que necesitan *mucha* dirección. Lea la siguiente lista de actividades e indique si usted prefiere hacerlas o si prefiere que el estudiante las haga.

MODELO:　　tomar las decisiones finales
　　　　　　　　Yo prefiero tomar las decisiones finales.

1. explorar aptitudes profesionales
2. escribir el ensayo personal para la solicitud a la universidad
3. escribir las recomendaciones académicas
4. buscar becas y préstamos
5. investigar las universidades preferidas
6. estudiar para los exámenes SAT

B. Instrucciones para el día.　　Tiene que dar instrucciones para las actividades del día a los estudiantes y sus maestros. Usted es un consejero muy simpático, así que no da mandatos directos. Empiece las instrucciones con **"Quiero que…"** o **"Prefiero que…"**

MODELO: Juan/ir a la biblioteca con estos libros
Quiero que Juan vaya a la biblioteca con estos libros.

1. los maestros/hablar de la importancia de planificar el futuro
2. los padres/buscar maneras de motivar a sus hijos
3. los estudiantes/sacar buenas notas
4. los estudiantes y sus padres/venir a una reunión en mi oficina mañana
5. los padres/apoyar a los hijos en el proceso
6. los estudiantes/tener éxito

C. El estudiante nuevo. Hay un nuevo estudiante que quiere explorar sus opciones profesionales y académicas. Escriba una lista de cinco cosas que usted quiere que haga.

MODELO: *Quiero que haga una lista de las clases o profesiones interesantes.*

Módulo I

La educación de adultos

Clases de informática avanzada: los lunes de 8–10 de la mañana o los jueves de 7–9 de la tarde

Identifique su sueño profesional: nosotros le podemos ayudar

Educación vocacional y superior

Exploración de carreras: nueva clase esta semana
¿Piensa tomar clases en la Universidad Comunitaria?
Representantes disponibles los martes y jueves
Se solicitan voluntarios para ser tutores de lectura

Educación: el puente a los sueños

Centro de educación para adultos: Nuevas Fronteras

Hello! Welcome! Inglés como segundo idioma: ESL

Educación básica:
ABC: Alfabetización, aprenda a leer y escribir

Inmigración, ciudadanía y naturalización

Preparación básica para adultos

GED: Termine los estudios

A.   ¿Cómo se dice?   Escriba la palabra que corresponda a cada una de las definiciones.

1.   Un adulto que no sabe leer ni escribir necesita clases de

_____.

2.   Las personas que no saben hablar inglés necesitan estudiar

_____.

3.   Una persona que trabaja sin recibir dinero es un _____.

4.   Los inmigrantes que tienen preguntas sobre las visas, deben hablar con las

personas en _____.

B. En mis propias palabras.   ¿Puede usted definir o explicar las siguientes cosas o ideas en sus propias palabras?

1.   centro de educación para adultos
2.   inmigración
3.   la alfabetización
4.   tutor

Ganas y fuerzas

El consejero Rebolledo acaba de reunirse con la familia de Álvaro. ¡Qué buena gente! El padre de Álvaro, Jorge, es el conserje de la escuela Menlo Park. Está tan contento en la escuela trabajando con los niños que él tiene un sueño secreto de ser—algún día—maestro bilingüe en Menlo Park. Alma, la madre de Álvaro, no sabe exactamente lo que quiere estudiar. Pero sabe a ciencia cierta que ella sí tiene muchas ganas de aprender. ¿Son sueños imposibles?

SR. REBOLLEDO: Entonces, Álvaro, tenemos un plan. Recomiendo que pases unas horas cada semana navegando por Internet para visitar una variedad de universidades. Ahora, quiero hablar con tus padres. Puedes regresar a tu clase. (*a los padres*) Ustedes tienen un buen hijo. Es muy inteligente y está tan dedicado a sus estudios...

MADRE: Gracias, Sr. Rebolledo. Álvaro sabe que para nosotros, no hay nada más importante que la educación. Insistimos en que la escuela sea su prioridad y prohibimos que salga antes de completar las tareas. Queremos que tenga todas las oportunidades que nosotros no tenemos por no tener suficiente educación. Por eso exigimos que Álvaro siga con sus estudios.

SR. REBOLLEDO: Con esta pasión que tienen por la educación, voy a recomendar que me acompañen al *Centro de educación para adultos: Nuevas Fronteras.* Tenemos clases de alfabetización y GED. Y clases de naturalización y ciudadanía para ayudar con la inmigración, clases de inglés como segundo idioma... clases vocacionales...

PADRES: ¡Parece un sueño! ¿Cuándo podemos ir?

SR. REBOLLEDO: Trabajo allí esta tarde a las siete. Sugiero que nos reunamos en la recepción a las seis y media. También recomiendo que lleguen preparados para comenzar como nuevos estudiantes esta misma noche.

C. ¿Comprende usted?   Conteste las preguntas según la información del diálogo.

1. ¿Por qué cree el Sr. Rebolledo que Álvaro es muy buen estudiante?

2. Para los padres, ¿cuál es la prioridad para su hijo?

3. ¿Dónde trabaja ahora el padre?

4. Mencione tres clases que ofrece el *Centro de educación para adultos.*

D. Escoja horticultura ambiental.   Los colegios de la comunidad ofrecen muchísimos programas vocacionales. Lea este folleto y escriba un resumen breve de lo que es esta carrera—cuatro frases.

Qu es la horticultura ambiental?

La horticultura ambiental es un trabajo del medio ambiente. Los hombres y mujeres que trabajan en horticultura comparten su entusiasmo trabajando al aire libre, mejorando la tierra y embelleciendo jardines. Entre las industrias de m s r pido crecimiento en Estados Unidos, la horticultura ambiental proporciona un futuro din mico. Los trabajos son variados y las vacantes est n aumentando con buenos salarios y beneficios. Es una carrera en la cual personas con habilidad cultivan plantas, encuentran mercados para ellas, las instalan y las cuidan. Este proceso incluye la venta al por mayor y al por menor en los negocios de producci n en invernaderos de flores y macetas y servicios de arreglos florales. Tambi n abarca toda la industria de jardines y c sped, la cual dise an , instalan y mantienen til y atractiva .

 E. Mi vocación preferida.   Busque datos de los centros comunitarios o escuelas para adultos de su área en cuanto a sus clases de preparación para carreras, como mecánico, asistente de dentista, bombero, policía, maestro de guardería...Traiga información de dos programas que le interesan y compártala con su compañero/a.

MODELO: *En Ventura College hay un programa de Toyota para ser mecánico.*

Estructuras   *More on the subjunctive: Más sobre el subjuntivo*

- When the following verbs are used in the first clause of a sentence and followed by **que,** the subjunctive form of the verb is always used in the second clause.

aconsejar	*to advise*	**desear**	*to desire/wish*	**esperar**	*to hope/expect*
exigir	*to demand*	**insistir en**	*to insist on*	**pedir (i)**	*to ask for/request*
permitir	*to permit*	**preferir (ie)**	*to prefer*	**prohibir**	*to prohibit*
recomendar (ie)	*to recommend*	**sugerir (ie)**	*to suggest*	**querer (ie)**	*to want*

Su padre **exige** que usted **estudie.**   *Your father demands that you study.*

La ley **prohíbe** que **traiga** armas a la escuela.   *The law prohibits that you bring firearms to school.*

■ Remember if there is only one subject and no **que,** the infinitive form is used.

Prefiero hablar con el consejero.   *I prefer to speak with the counselor.*

Esperan regresar a la escuela pronto.   *They hope to go back to school soon.*

Para practicar

A. El director del colegio.   Usted es el/la director/a de un colegio urbano. Decida si usted **permite, prohíbe** o **insiste en que** los maestros y estudiantes hagan las siguientes actividades.

MODELO: traer cosas ilegales a la escuela
Prohíbo que los estudiantes traigan cosas ilegales a la escuela.

1. planificar el futuro con anticipación

2. ir a la cafetería durante el almuerzo

3. tener todas las tareas completas

4. pasar por los pasillos sin tener permiso

5. hablar respetuosamente a los maestros

6. fumar marihuana en el baño

B. Sugerencias.   Usted y su pareja están trabajando con un consejero académico para volver a la escuela después de muchos años. Usted contesta la llamada telefónica del consejero cuando él llama con la lista de sugerencias y tiene que explicárselas a su pareja.

MODELO: Podemos salir a las siete.
Sugiere que salgamos a las siete.

1. Podemos empezar esta noche.

2. Podemos estudiar inglés.

3. Podemos ir directamente al Centro de Estudios.

4. Podemos conocer a todo el personal del Centro.

5. Podemos almorzar en la cafetería.

6. Podemos visitar unas clases.

C. El consejero.   Usted es un consejero académico en un colegio grande. Haga una lista de cinco recomendaciones que quiere hacerles a sus estudiantes para tener éxito en el futuro.

MODELO: *Recomiendo que busquen (escojan) sus clases con cuidado.*

Módulo 2

Es importante continuar las clases

Oficinas	Función/Servicio
Admisiones y archivos	Admisiones, inscripciones, calificaciones, listas de clases, verificación de estado de residencia
Evaluaciones	Exámenes exploratorios de matemáticas y lectura
Centro de orientación vocacional	Ayuda en la búsqueda de empleo
Guardería	Programa preescolar para niños entre los 18 meses y los 5 años de edad. Se cobra cuota.
Consejeros	Orientación académica, vocacional y personal
Centro de asistencia escolar	Servicios de ayuda y clases especiales para estudiantes con impedimentos físicos o de otro tipo
Ayuda financiera	Donaciones, préstamos, trabajo de media jornada
Fundación	Becas
Centro de reingreso	Ayuda para estudiantes de reingreso y asuntos de mujeres
Centro de salud	Seguro contra accidentes, servicios médicos y psicológicos
Centro de transferencia	Transferencia a otras escuelas
Centro de tutores	Asistencia académica en todas las materias

A. ¿Cómo se dice?   Use la tabla para completar la idea.

1.   Para inscribirme en clases, llevo mi solicitud a _____.

2.   Necesito ayuda en mi clase de literatura; voy al _____.

3.   Los padres que quieren estudiar en el *Centro de educación para adultos* pueden

dejar a sus niños en la _____ durante las clases.

4.   Hay personal médico disponible en la _____.

B. Parejas.   Empareje los siguientes lugares con su pareja más lógica.

1. _____ Centro de asistencia escolar
   a. No sé qué clase de matemáticas necesito.

2. _____ Fundación
   b. Quiero que me den dinero para la escuela.

3. _____ Centro de reingreso
   c. Ando en silla de ruedas.

4. _____ Evaluaciones
   d. ¡No estudio desde hace 10 años!

Los nuevos estudiantes de Nuevas Fronteras

Hoy empieza otro ciclo de clases en el Centro de educación para adultos, Nuevas Fronteras. *Los estudiantes son muy diversos y tienen razones muy diferentes para estar aquí, pero tienen una cosa en común: quieren aprender. El líder del grupo para esta orientación no es otro que nuestro amigo Ricardo Rebolledo.*

RICARDO: Bienvenidos todos a nuestro primer paso en el camino hacia el éxito personal y profesional. No es fácil dejar una vida y empezar otra. Pero con "ganas y fuerzas sí se puede". Yo soy graduado de este programa y ahora soy consejero académico y estudio para el doctorado. Es probable que ésta no sea la primera vez que ustedes piensan en regresar a la escuela. Pero es evidente por su presencia aquí que están motivados. Vamos a conocernos. Por favor, digan su nombre y qué motivo tienen para estar aquí.

ROBERTO: Soy Roberto. Quiero volver a la escuela porque no tengo diploma del colegio. Tengo un buen trabajo que me gusta, pero no tengo futuro con la compañía. Y, con la economía actual, es posible que en unos meses mi compañía ya no exista. Tengo dos hijos y quiero remediar el problema ahora y aprender una profesión—mecánico de autos o técnico de computadoras. Pero primero quiero graduarme de la escuela secundaria.

RICARDO: Mucho gusto en conocerte, Roberto. Es importante tomar el control de nuestra situación económica y empezar a planificar el futuro ahora.

PAULINA: Perdonen. Estoy muy nerviosa. Me llamo Paulina. Estoy aquí porque no sé hablar inglés después de estar tres años en este país. Pero ahora mi hijo está en Kínder y no puedo comunicarme con su maestro ni ayudarlo con su tarea. Ahora es urgente que aprenda inglés inmediatamente—para él.

JORGE: Me llamo Jorge y ésta es mi esposa Alma. Es interesante que todos mencionemos los hijos como la razón principal de estar aquí—para nosotros también. Todos los días le hablamos de la importancia de la educación. Hoy, en una conferencia para planificar su futuro, el Sr.

Ricardo nos dijo: "Es irónico que siempre le digan a Álvaro que la educación es tan importante. Pero ustedes, los padres, son los modelos. ¿Por qué no le dan un ejemplo de la educación en acción?" Alma y yo queremos graduarnos de la universidad con nuestro hijo. Ojalá que sea posible.

RICARDO: Es evidente que ustedes están motivados. ¡Qué bien que estén aquí ahora! Durante la próxima sesión, vamos a explorar más servicios y recursos disponibles para facilitar sus estudios.

C. ¿Comprende usted?   Conteste las preguntas según la información del diálogo.

1. ¿Cómo sabe Ricardo que es difícil dejar una vida para empezar otra?
2. ¿Qué quiere hacer Roberto?
3. ¿Por qué decide Paulina ahora que debe aprender inglés?
4. ¿Qué motivación tienen todos estos estudiantes para volver a la escuela?

D. MESA.   MESA es parte de una iniciativa nacional para promover las oportunidades educativas para estudiantes de grupos minoritarios sub-representados. Después de leer los requisitos para los miembros de este programa, prepare un cartel (*poster*) para atraer a estudiantes—¡trabaje con compañeros!

MESA—Consejos y dinero para ayudar a estudiantes

MESA empezó en 1970 en la Universidad de California, Berkeley. Su enfoque es ayudar a los estudiantes de las escuelas intermedias y secundarias y especialmente a las minorías étnicas, a tener éxito, ofreciéndoles consejos en cuanto a su futura carrera. Las iniciales en inglés representan Mathematics, Engineering, Science Achievement. El programa prepara a estudiantes para sus especialidades en la universidad y para carreras en Matemáticas, Ingeniería y Ciencias. Hay servicio de tutores, estudio independiente, ayuda para escoger una universidad y una carrera, excursiones, competencias, desarrollo de líderes, programas de verano y becas.

Para ser miembro se necesita:

- Calificaciones de 2.0
- Ingresar en clases pre-universitarias de matemáticas, ciencias e inglés
- Asistir a 18 reuniones y 1 de padres
- Recibir tutelaje 12 veces al año
- Una excursión
- Un proyecto de re-pago
- Tomar el examen SAT o ACT como *Senior*

Estructuras

Giving recommendations: El subjuntivo con expresiones impersonales

- In addition to using the subjunctive to express desire for something to happen, it is also used after these expressions to make a subjective comment on the action that follows them.

Es bueno/malo/mejor que...	Es preferible que...
Es común que...	Es raro que...
Es importante que...	Es ridículo que...
Es increíble que...	Es triste que...
Es lógico que...	Es una lástima que...
Es necesario que...	Es urgente que...
Es normal que...	Ojalá que...

Es triste que mi hijo sufra por mí.	*It is sad that my son should suffer because of me.*
Es importante que yo esté aquí.	*It is important that I be here.*
Es una lástima que Justino no esté.	*It is a shame that Justino isn't here.*

- Impersonal expressions may be followed by an infinitive if they refer to generalizations. If they refer to specific people's actions, use the subjunctive:

Es bueno graduarse de la escuela secundaria.	*It is good to graduate from High School.*
Es importante que te gradúes.	*It is important for you to graduate.*

Para practicar

A. Las reglas. Es la primera noche que Alejandro asiste a sus clases en el *Centro de educación para adultos.* Usted es su primer amigo. Explíquele a Alejandro que debe seguir las siguientes reglas.

MODELO: Es importante asistir a todas las clases.
Es importante que asistas a todas las clases.

1. Es necesario hacer todas las tareas cada día.
2. Está prohibido tomar alcohol o drogas en el Centro.
3. Es importante practicar el inglés todos los días.
4. Es urgente hablar con el maestro si tiene problemas.
5. Es bueno conocer a los compañeros.
6. Es importante llegar a tiempo.
7. Es excelente sacar buenas notas.
8. Es necesario buscar ayuda económica.

B. Paulina no está cómoda. La primera vez que una persona está en una nueva situación es natural que sienta emociones confusas. Aconseje a Paulina respondiendo a sus ideas con una de las expresiones impersonales.

Es normal que	Es importante que	Es lógico que
Es preferible que	Es malo que	Es urgente que
Es imposible que	Es ridículo que	Es una lástima que

MODELO: Quiero volver a casa.
Paulina, es mejor que esperes hasta el fin de la clase.

1. No quiero participar en las discusiones hoy.
2. Estoy muy nerviosa aquí.
3. Quiero buscar a mi esposo.
4. Tengo mucho miedo.
5. No quiero hacer la tarea para mañana.
6. Prefiero no hablar con nadie.
7. No me gustan los compañeros.
8. Voy a llorar.

C. ¡Imaginación! Imagine que está aconsejando a un/a estudiante de la secundaria que quiere abandonar la escuela. Escriba cinco recomendaciones positivas (*es bueno* o *importante* o *necesario… que…*) y cinco percepciones negativas (*es malo* o *ridículo* o *estúpido… que…*).

MODELO: *Es necesario que hables con tus padres.*

Módulo 2

¡Qué bueno que empiece la carrera!

A+: estar contenta

Recomendamos que busque apoyo y recursos aquí en el centro. Sugerimos que asista a todas las clases. Es importante que organice su tiempo.

F: tener miedo de que/temer que

tiene dudas

entusiasmo

alegrarse de que...

A. Sinónimos.   Use la memoria, la imaginación y el dibujo para emparejar estas palabras con significados apropiados.

1. _____ recomendar   **a.** estar contento

2. _____ tener miedo   **b.** no estar seguro

3. _____ dudar   **c.** temer

4. _____ alegrarse de que   **d.** sugerir

5. _____ tener entusiasmo   **e.** estar animado

B. Antónimos. Elija la palabra con el significado *contrario* a la palabra o frase a la derecha.

1.	_____ dudar	**a.**	estar triste
2.	_____ alegrarse de	**b.**	creer
3.	_____ tener miedo	**c.**	es bueno
4.	_____ es lástima	**d.**	tener confianza

Consejos para los nuevos estudiantes

En la segunda sesión de la orientación a la escuela, Ricardo habla con los estudiantes de sus sueños y sus miedos. Algunos son muy optimistas y otros son muy pesimistas. Es importante que Ricardo los ayude a ser más realistas.

RICARDO: Aquí están otra vez mis nuevos estudiantes. ¡*Nuevos estudiantes!* Paulina, ¿te gusta tener el título de *nueva estudiante?*

PAULINA: ¡Ay!, no señor. No me gusta que me llame eso.

RICARDO: ¿Por qué?

PAULINA: Temo que para mí, la escuela sea muy difícil. No sé estudiar… Tengo miedo de sacar malas notas.

RICARDO: Me alegro de que hables de eso. Dudo que estés sola con ese miedo. Clase, ¿quién más tiene un poco de miedo de empezar este programa?

TODOS: *(levantan la mano)*

RICARDO: Ves, Paulina, es evidente que todos tienen por lo menos un poco de miedo. Una parte de este curso se llama: "Aprenda a aprender: Habilidades para estudiar". Recomiendo que lo tomen en serio. Es fácil desarrollar buenas costumbres para estudiar. ¿Qué más sienten ustedes en este momento?

TODOS: ¡Nerviosos! ¡Contentos! ¡Emocionados! ¡Impacientes!

RICARDO: Jorge, ¿dices que estás impaciente?

JORGE: Es que ahora que es realidad, no puedo esperar más. Necesito aprender más inglés, matemáticas, ciencias…. Hay tanto que quiero hacer. Y la verdad es que ya soy cada día más viejo…

RICARDO: Me encanta que tengas tanto entusiasmo. Pero hay que ser realista. Además de las clases que van a tomar, ustedes tienen trabajos y familias y quehaceres en la casa. Es importante que conozcan sus límites de estrés. Siento decirles que no sean todos super-hombres. ¡Pero yo sí creo que van a ser ¡super-estudiantes!

C. ¿Comprende usted?   Conteste las preguntas según la información del diálogo.

1.   ¿Cuál es el nuevo título que tienen los miembros del grupo?

2.   ¿A Paulina le gusta?

3.   ¿Cómo está Jorge en este momento?

4.   ¿Por qué no quiere Jorge que los estudiantes sean super-hombres?

D. La escuela pide documentación.   El señor Hernández trata de cumplir con los requisitos legales para recibir su permiso legal para quedarse en Estados Unidos, pero ya tiene un problema. No puede matricularse en clases sin tener su documentación oficial. Lea la carta y termine la actividad.

Immigration Services of Santa Paula, Inc.

Accredited by the Board of Immigration Appeals, U.S. Department of Justice

1341 Beverly, Santa Paula CA 91340   Phone: (818) 995-4432   Fax: (818) 838-5599

11 de abril de 2003

Tomás Hernández Castillo

Caso: 90956

Estimado Sr. Hernández:

El abogado Hugo Reséndez ya no está asociado con Servicios de Inmigración de Santa Paula. No tenemos abogado de leyes y hemos cancelado la unidad de servicios legales. Su archivo del caso legal aquí también se le devuelve. Su próxima cita de corte es para el 28 de septiembre de 2003 a las 8:30 de la mañana con el juez Fong.

Se debe notificar a la corte de inmigración si ha cambiado de domicilio para que la correspondencia se le envíe a su residencia actual.

El abogado Reséndez sigue con la obligación legal de ofrecerle representación ante la corte de inmigración en su caso. Usted puede comunicarse con su abogado en su nueva dirección:

Abogado Hugo Reséndez
No. de Licencia de Abogado: 00791564
704 W. Arthur St.
Cayucos, CA 90301
Teléfono: (310) 671-6715

Atentamente,

Jesús Morales
Jesús Morales
Director

---

1. El nombre del inmigrante es _____.

2. Su abogado se llama _____.

3. Tiene cita con el juez Fong el _____ a las _____.

4. El director de *Immigration Services* of Santa Paula es _____.

ійій **E. Asuntos de la inmigración.** Busque información de un aspecto de la inmigración—legislación, inmigración ilegal, el envío de dinero por parte de los inmigrantes a sus familias en el extranjero... Hable con sus compañeros sobre lo que encuentre.

MODELO: *En www.zacatecanos.com dice que hay un programa "tres por uno" en el que el gobierno federal, estatal y municipal de México pone un dólar por cada dólar enviado por los inmigrantes que viven en EE.UU. El programa paga por proyectos de construcción y educación, incluyendo un centro de computadoras, clínicas de salud, caminos y presas. Desde su comienzo ha pagado por 326 proyectos con un total de $18 millones.*

Estructuras   *Expressing emotion and doubt: El subjuntivo con expresiones de emoción y duda*

■ The subjunctive can be used to express the way someone feels about what someone else is doing or about what is happening to someone else. Here are some verbs of emotion that are commonly followed by the subjunctive.

me (te, le...) gusta que	me (te, le...) molesta que...
me (te, le...) encanta que	me (te, le...) sorprende que...
alegrarse de que...	sentir que...
estar contento/a de que...	temer que...
estar triste de que...	tener miedo de que...

Me alegro de que estén aquí.
Siento que las clases **sean** difíciles.
¿Le gusta que su esposa **vuelva** a la escuela?
¿Teme que no **reciban** buenas notas?

I'm glad you're all here.
I'm sorry that classes are difficult.
Do you like it that your wife is going back to school?
Are you afraid they won't receive good grades?

■ The subjunctive is also used to question the truth about something. It is used after verbs and expressions of doubt or uncertainty.

VERBS	EXPRESSIONS OF DOUBT
dudar que...	es dudoso que...
no creer que...	es posible/imposible que...
no estar seguro/a de que...	es probable/improbable que...
no es cierto que...	no es verdad que...

Dudo que haya tiempo para comer.   *I doubt there's time to eat.*
Es posible que tengan un tarea.   *It is possible that they have the homework.*

■ Since **creer que, estar seguro de que, es cierto que,** and **es verdad que** indicate that the speaker considers his or her assumptions to be true, they take the indicative in affirmative statements. When these expressions are used negatively, doubt is implied and the verb is in the subjunctive.

Creo que ella **va** al bufete.   *I believe she is going to the law office.*
No creo que ella **tenga** su visa.   *I don't believe she has her visa.*

■ When these expressions are used in a question, they take the indicative if the speaker is merely seeking information, but use the subjunctive if the speaker is expressing doubt as to the answer.

—**¿Es verdad que tú vas** a la escuela?   *Is it true you are going to school?*
—Sí, **creo que empiezo** en mayo.   *Yes, I think I'm starting in May.*
—**¿Cree que sea** fácil?   *Do you think it will be easy?*
—**No creo que sea** fácil.   *I don't think it will be easy.*

■ Use **quizás** or **tal vez** to say *maybe, perhaps*. The subjunctive is used after these expressions, unless the speaker feels quite sure that the assertion is true.

Quizás llegue el estudiante hoy.   *Perhaps the student might arrive today.*
El estudiante **llega** hoy, **quizás.**   *The student will arrive today, maybe.*

Para practicar

A. Las noticias. El hermano de su amigo está estudiando en un centro para adultos. Diga la reacción que usted tiene ante esta serie de noticias. Use frases de esta lista:

| Me alegro de que… | Siento que… | Me sorprende que… |

1. A mi hermano le gustan mucho las clases.

2. No pasa mucho tiempo con su familia.

3. Las clases en el centro son gratis.

4. Es muy difícil sacar buenas notas.

5. Estudia con una maestra excelente.

6. También trabaja en un almacén.

B. Los maestros. Los maestros del *Centro de educación para adultos* se consultan sobre algunos de sus estudiantes. Cada uno tiene una opinión diferente. Complete las ideas de los maestros usando la forma del verbo indicado en el subjuntivo o el indicativo.

MODELO: Dudo que Beto _____ (recibir) buenas notas.
Dudo que Beto reciba buenas notas.

1. Es verdad que el examen _____ (ser) complicado.

2. Dudo que él _____ (ser) de Venezuela.

3. Es posible que ellos _____ (decidir) tomar la clase otra vez.

4. No creo que _____ (haber) problemas pidiendo una extensión.

5. Es obvio que los estudiantes dedicados _____ (ir) a tener mucho éxito.

6. Me molesta mucho que ellos no _____ (estar) contentos aquí.

7. Es evidente que ellos _____ (estar) nerviosos.

8. No me gusta que ellos no _____ (venir) a la clase.

C. ¿Conoce usted a un nuevo estudiante? ¿Tiene usted algún pariente o amigo/a que quiera volver a la escuela? Haga una lista de sus opiniones y sugerencias sobre sus acciones. Use expresiones como: *creo que…, es importante que…, dudo que…, no es bueno que…, me molesta mucho que…, me gusta mucho que…*

MODELO: *Es bueno que mi primo quiera volver a la escuela.*

Vocabulario Módulo 1

Sustantivos

el/la abogado/a	*attorney*	**la informática**	*computer science*
la alfabetización	*literacy*	**el medio ambiente**	*environment*
el césped	*grass*	**la pareja**	*pair*
la ciudadanía	*citizenship*	**el préstamo**	*loan*
el crecimiento	*growth*	**el puente**	*bridge*
el empeño	*determination*	**el/la representante**	*representative*
la fuerza	*force*	**la vacante**	*vacancy*
la habilidad	*skill*		

Verbos

aconsejar	*to advise*	**fortalecer (zc)**	*to fortify*
desear	*to wish*	**permitir**	*to permit*
disfrutar	*to have fun*	**planificar**	*to plan*
estimular	*to stimulate*	**prohibir**	*to prohibit*
exigir	*to require*	**proporcionar**	*to provide*
explorar	*to explore*	**solicitar**	*to apply*

Adjetivos

ambiental	*environmental*	**útil**	*useful*
comunitario/a	*community*	**variado/a**	*varied*
dirigido/a	*directed, supervised*		

Otras expresiones

a ciencia cierta	*for sure*	**al por menor**	*retail*
al aire libre	*open air*	**atentamente**	*sincerely*
al por mayor	*wholesale*		

Módulo 2

Sustantivos

el asunto	*matter*	**la duda**	*doubt*
el bufete	*law firm*	**el/la dueño/a**	*owner*
la calificación	*grade*	**el enfoque**	*focus*
el clima	*climate*	**las estadísticas**	*statistics*
la competencia	*competition*	**el estrés**	*stress*
la computación	*computing*	**el/la fundador/a**	*founder*
la conciencia	*conscience*	**el/la guía**	*guide*
el/la contratista	*contractor*	**la herencia**	*heritage*
la cultura	*culture*	**la imprenta**	*printing press*
el desafío	*challenge*	**la ingeniería**	*engineering*
el diploma	*diploma*	**el instituto**	*institute*

la lástima	*pity*	**el recurso**	*resource*
el pago	*payment*	**el reingreso**	*readmit*
el párrafo	*paragraph*	**el/la técnico/a**	*technician*
el porcentaje	*percentage*	**el título**	*title, degree*
el quehacer	*chore*	**el/la viajero/a**	*traveler*

Verbos

alegrarse de que	*to be happy about*	**inscribir**	*to enroll*
		instalar	*to install*
apuntar	*to note*	**molestar**	*to bother*
cobrar	*to charge*	**organizar**	*to organize*
devolver (ue)	*to return (something)*	**reparar**	*to repair*
		respetar	*to respect*
dudar	*to doubt*	**sorprender**	*to surprise*
encantar	*to delight*	**temer**	*to fear*
graduarse	*to graduate*	**viajar**	*to travel*

Adjetivos

cierto/a	*certain*	**emocionado/a**	*emotional*
dudoso/a	*doubtful*	**enfocado/a**	*focused*

Otras expresiones

ojalá	*I hope, Let's hope, May Allah grant*	**quizás**	*perhaps*
		tal vez	*perhaps*

Síntesis

A escuchar

El Centro de educación para adultos, Nuevas Fronteras, *tiene un excelente sistema de orientación por el cual un estudiante nuevo recibe la ayuda de un estudiante con experiencia en el programa.*

Escuche el diálogo e indique si las siguientes declaraciones son **Ciertas (C)** o **Falsas (F)**. Si son falsas, corríjalas.

1. _____ Marisa es una estudiante nueva en *Nuevas Fronteras.*

2. _____ Elena está muy nerviosa y tiene miedo de hacer preguntas.

3. _____ La librería, la guardería y los tutores están en el Centro de computación.

4. _____ Marisa sugiere que Elena tome clases de computación por razones intelectuales.

A conversar

▟▟▟▟ ¿Conoce a alguien que continúe su educación después de no asistir a la escuela por muchos años? Hable con sus compañeros de estos amigos o familiares.

MODELO: *Nuestro jardinero acaba de terminar su licencia de contratista y va a abrir su propio vivero.*

A leer

Yo sí puedo
Iniciativa para la excelencia en la educación de los hispanoamericanos

Leslie Sánchez, directora de la iniciativa de la Casa Blanca, viaja por Estados Unidos en un tour nacional enfocado en programas de educación para hispanos. El Presidente George W. Bush empezó este programa hace un año porque, según las estadísticas, uno de cada tres estudiantes latinos no termina la secundaria. El viaje de Sánchez tiene como objetivo buscar escuelas y programas como modelos para presentarlos ante el Presidente. «Quiero saber qué es lo que hacen, cómo lo empiezan y con quiénes tienen una asociación.»

En Oxnard College, con un 56% de estudiantes hispanos, hay una variedad de programas que cumplen con el sueño de Bush de mejorar la educación para los latinos. Uno es la Academia regional de Cisco Networking, en la cual los estudiantes se gradúan después de hacer un examen para recibir certificación como técnicos de instalación y reparación de redes de computadoras.

¿Comprende usted?

1. ¿Cómo se llama este programa federal?
2. ¿Quién es la directora?
3. ¿Por qué existe esta iniciativa?
4. ¿Cuál es uno de los programas de Oxnard College?

A escribir

Investigue un programa de ayuda de su colegio/universidad local y escriba un párrafo explicando qué ofrece, a quiénes está dirigido, etc.

MODELO: *La fundación de Ventura College acepta solicitudes para becas...*

Algo más

Ventana cultural

Se aprende la cultura por la música

El Centro Inlakech de Artes Culturales en Oxnard ofrece entrenamiento para los músicos del futuro, contando con unos 300 a 400 alumnos cada año, y a la vez un programa de educación y conciencia cultural. Javier Gómez, el fundador y director artístico, dice que el programa de mariachis es un ejemplo de cómo ver lo mejor de los jóvenes, apoyarles y darles atención.

«Les da a los niños de la comunidad la oportunidad de explorar y desarrollar sus talentos y enseñárselos al público de la comunidad. Hay buenas cosas que pasan aquí y este programa es un ejemplo perfecto.» Las lecciones de música mariachi, canciones, bailes folclóricos y drama son una asociación entre Inlakech y Mariachi Fletes de Cocula, Jalisco, México.

Cómo aprender la cultura. ¿Por qué es importante respetar nuestra herencia por medio de la cultura? Apunte cuatro cosas que representan la cultura para usted—¿la comida?, ¿la religión?, ¿la familia?

A buscar

Vaya al sitio web de la *Iniciativa para la excelencia en la educación de los hispanoamericanos* (www.yosipuedo.gov/postsecondary/picking.html) y busque datos de qué está pasando HOY en ese programa.

A conocer: Ernie y Lorie Chapa

Ellos creen que su educación jugó *(played)* un papel decisivo al prepararlos para los desafíos de empezar su empresa y llevarla al éxito. Son dueños de *Pacific Partner,* un negocio de artes gráficas y comunicación fundado en 1999. Trabajan con computadoras, cámaras, imprentas y diseño. Empezaron un programa de becas para ayudar a estudiantes de EOP (Programa de oportunidad igual) para decirles: «Tenemos confianza en lo que pueden hacer en la Universidad de Cal Poly. Les ayudamos con el primer paso y los guiamos al próximo.»

LECCIÓN 10

Consejera

La universidad

Módulo I
- La solicitud de admisión
- Discussing past activities: *Introducción al pretérito*
- Becas, préstamos y otros programas
- More on the preterite: *Verbos irregulares*

Módulo 2
- ¡Cuánto tuve que estudiar!
- Relating past activities: *Verbos en –ir con cambios en el pretérito*
- Ya me gradué
- More past activities: *Usos del pretérito*

Síntesis
- A escuchar
- A conversar
- A leer
- A escribir

Algo más
- Ventana cultural: Latinos—la vuelta a las raíces
- A buscar
- A conocer: Dr. Robert Flores

Módulo I

La solicitud de admisión

Mi plan para solicitar entrada en mi universidad preferida

Sophomore: Grado 10 (hace dos años)	**Junior: Grado 11**(el año pasado)	**Senior: Grado 12** (ahora)
Planificar clases	Reunirse con orientador	Visitar universidades
Participar en clubes	Explorar carreras y profesiones	Organizar recomendaciones
Mantener buenas calificaciones	Investigar universidades por Internet	Exámenes estandarizados
(A+)	Practicar exámenes estandarizados	SAT/ACT/AP
	(PSAT)	Hacer solicitudes de admisión
	Investigar becas	Escribir el ensayo personal
	Pensar en el ensayo personal	Entrevistas
		Solicitar becas
		Preparar documentos para obtener ayuda económica $$$$
		Mandar la documentación con las calificaciones
		¡Esperar!

Ensayo personal

Mis sueños futuros

A. ¿Cómo se dice? Escriba la palabra que corresponda a cada una de las definiciones.

1. PSAT, SAT y ACT son ejemplos de _____.

2. En la _____ de admisión, incluyo los datos personales y académicos para asistir a cierta universidad.

3. Con el _____ yo puedo mostrar mi personalidad e individualidad ante el comité de admisiones.

4. Durante la _____ miembros del comité de admisiones pueden hacerme preguntas y tengo la oportunidad de preguntarles sobre la universidad.

B. El tiempo es relativo. Escriba la palabra necesaria para completar cada una de las siguientes oraciones.

1. En el grado _____ es importante escoger clases con la idea de entrar en la universidad.

2. Hay que tomar las prácticas de los exámenes estandarizados en el grado _____.

3. Si estamos en el año 2005, el año hace dos años fue _____.

4. Si estamos en el año 2006, el año pasado fue _____.

Buenos consejos

El consejero Rebolledo sabe que los estudiantes prestan más atención a los consejos de otros estudiantes que a los consejos de los padres, maestros y consejeros. Rebolledo tiene un programa excelente en que los "seniors" que tienen experiencia con el proceso de solicitar admisión a las universidades ayudan a los "sophomores" y "juniors". Álvaro, que acaba de terminar sus solicitudes, habla con dos jóvenes que acaban de empezar.

ÁLVARO: El proceso empezó para mí cuando mis padres decidieron que debía ir a Harvard. Hablé con el Sr. Rebolledo, y él me ayudó a organizar todo y habló con mis padres.

ENRIQUE: ¿Tú vas a Harvard?

ÁLVARO: Ojalá yo vaya a Harvard. Quiero ir, pero dudo que me acepten. También solicité admisión en cuatro universidades más.

ÉRICA: Hay tantas universidades. ¿Cómo decidiste elegir esas cinco? Yo estoy tan confundida.

ÁLVARO: Al principio, mis padres insistieron en Harvard, pero yo no tuve interés. Pero después, unos amigos de Boston me invitaron a visitar el campus. Pasé un fin de semana allí y ahora es mi favorita. Las visitas a las universidades me ayudaron mucho con las decisiones.

ENRIQUE: ¿Cuántas visitaste?

ÁLVARO: ¡Cientos!—por Internet, primero. El año pasado el Sr. Rebolledo y yo empezamos a hablar de mis sueños y ambiciones. Él me dio una lista de universidades para explorar con "tours virtuales". Escribí a más de treinta para pedir más información. Tengo un archivo lleno de folletos de universidades si quieren verlos.

ÉRICA: ¡Yo, sí! ¿Tienen información sobre los requisitos y lo que buscan?

ÁLVARO: Un poco. Casi todos quieren la puntuación de los exámenes estandarizados. Estudié y practiqué mucho para el SAT. Recibí una calificación combinada de 1503.

ÉRICA: Es excelente. Debes recibir muchas becas así.

ÁLVARO: También empecé a solicitar becas del estado y de fundaciones particulares. Mi abuelo es miembro de un grupo fraternal que ofrece muchas becas. Solicité fondos de ellos.

ÉRICA: A ver: sacaste buenas notas; participaste en deportes y clubes, llenaste las solicitudes para admisión y becas, organizaste las recomendaciones; mandaste las calificaciones; hiciste el SAT y el ACT con buenos resultados... ¿Qué haces ahora?

ÁLVARO: ¡Ay! Ésta es la peor parte. Sólo puedo esperar. Es una agonía.

SR. REBOLLEDO: Álvaro, no quiero interrumpir tu reunión, pero llamó tu madre. Hace cinco minutos recibió un sobre *(envelope)* de Harvard...

C. ¿Comprende usted? Conteste las preguntas según la información del diálogo.

1. ¿A qué universidad quiere ir Álvaro?
2. Nombre tres pasos en el proceso de solicitar admisión a la universidad.
3. ¿Sacó Álvaro buenas o malas calificaciones en el SAT?
4. ¿Qué recibió la mamá de Álvaro?

D. FAFSA. La Solicitud gratuita de ayuda federal para estudiantes es un formulario que muchos conocen muy bien. Presentamos aquí solamente parte del formulario que es necesario enviar para solicitar becas estudiantiles federales y estatales, trabajo-estudio y préstamos. Se puede encontrar el formulario completo en www.fafsa.ed.gov. Termine éste con su información.

FAFSA

1-3. Nombre completo

1. Apellido

2. Nombre

3. Inicial

4-7. Dirección postal permanente

4. Número y calle

5. Ciudad

6. Estado

7. Código postal

8. Número de Seguro Social

9. Fecha de nacimiento

10. Número de teléfono permanente

( )

11-12. Número de licencia de conducir y estado

13. ¿Es usted ciudadano/a de EE. UU.? Escoja uno.

a. Sí, soy ciudadano/a de EE. UU.. ◯
b. No, pero soy extranjero/a con permiso oficial.................... ◯
c. No, no soy ciudadano/a o extranjero/a con permiso oficial. ◯

14. Número de registro de extranjero

15. ¿Cuál es su estado civil actual?

Marque si usted cursará estudios a tiempo completo, 3/4 de tiempo, tiempo parcial, menos de tiempo parcial o si no asistirá a clases.

Verano	Tiempo completo/indeciso(a) ◯	3/4 de tiempo ◯	Medio tiempo ◯	Menos de medio tiempo ◯ No asistirá ◯
Otoño	Tiempo completo/indeciso(a) ◯	3/4 de tiempo ◯	Medio tiempo ◯	Menos de medio tiempo ◯ No asistirá ◯
Invierno	Tiempo completo/indeciso(a) ◯	3/4 de tiempo ◯	Medio tiempo ◯	Menos de medio tiempo ◯ No asistirá ◯
Primavera	Tiempo completo/indeciso(a) ◯	3/4 de tiempo ◯	Medio tiempo ◯	Menos de medio tiempo ◯ No asistirá ◯

¿Cuál es su estado de residencia legal?   Si usted es varón, ¿está inscrito en el Servicio Selectivo? Sí ◯ No ◯

¿Ha sido declarado/a culpable por posesión o venta ilegal de drogas? Sí ◯ No ◯

Segundo paso: Declare sus ingresos y bienes.

Tercer paso: Díganos qué universidades deben recibir esta información. _____

Cuarto paso: Firme. _____

Estructuras   *Discussing past activities: Introducción al pretérito*

- To tell what you did at a specific moment in the past, use the preterite tense.
- The regular forms of **-ar, -er,** and **-ir** verbs follow. Note that the **nosotros/as** forms of **-ar** and **-ir** verbs are the same in the present and preterite tenses.

	hablar	comer	vivir
yo	hablé	comí	viví
tú	hablaste	comiste	viviste
él/ella/Ud.	habló	comió	vivió
nosotros	hablamos	comimos	vivimos
ellos/ellas/Uds.	hablaron	comieron	vivieron

—¿**Habló** con el consejero?   *Did you talk to the advisor?*

—Sí, ya **hablé** con el consejero.   *Yes, I already spoke to the advisor.*

—¿Cuándo **comió** Ud.?   *When did you eat?*

—**Comí** hace una hora.   *I ate an hour ago.*

—¿**Vivieron** Uds. en Boston?   *Did you live in Boston?*

—No, **vivimos** en Texas.   *No, we lived in Texas.*

- **Cambios ortográficos:** In the preterite, **-ar** verbs ending in **-car, -gar,** and **-zar** have spelling changes in the **yo** form.

buscar   →   **busqué,** buscaste, buscó, buscamos, buscaron

investigar   →   **investigué,** investigaste, investigó, investigamos, investigaron

empezar   →   **empecé,** empezaste, empezó, empezamos, empezaron

- There are no stem changes in the preterite for **-ar** or **-er** verbs.
- The verb **dar** uses **-er** endings in the preterite.

dar   →   **di, diste, dio, dimos, dieron**

- In the preterite tense, infinitives ending in **-er** or **-ir** whose stems end in a vowel will follow the spelling rule that says that an unaccented **i** will change to a **y** when it appears between two vowels:

leer   →   leí, leíste, **leyó,** leímos, **leyeron**

oír   →   oí, oíste, **oyó,** oímos, **oyeron**

- **Hace** + a time expression + **que** + a verb in the preterite tells *how long ago* something happened.

Hace dos semanas que hablé con ellos.   *I spoke to them two weeks ago.*

Hace un año que él empezó el proceso de solicitar admisión.   *He began the application process a year ago.*

- Omit **que** when starting the sentence with the verb rather than with the time expression.

Hablé con Érica **hace dos semanas.**   *I spoke with Érica two weeks ago.*

Tomé el examen **hace una semana.**   *I took the test a week ago.*

Para practicar

A. La visita a una universidad.   Usted es un estudiante de visita en una universidad para decidir si es su sueño académico. Tiene que pasar el día con un estudiante de allí y repetir todas sus acciones. Explique qué hizo ayer.

MODELO: El estudiante asistió a tres clases.
Yo asistí a tres clases.

El estudiante. . .

1.   habló con los profesores.
2.   escribió muchas notas.
3.   buscó información por Internet.
4.   sacó buenas notas.
5.   comió en el comedor de la residencia estudiantil.
6.   empezó a escribir un informe para su clase de historia.
7.   leyó los requisitos para admisión.
8.   comprendió la importancia de la decisión.

B. ¿Cuándo?   El consejero con quien usted trabaja tiene una lista de instrucciones para los estudiantes que hacen sus solicitudes de admisión a la universidad. Explíquele que cada persona ya terminó su tarea.

MODELO: María tiene que pasar por mi oficina por los documentos.
Ya pasó por la oficina.

1.   Ricardo tiene que investigar información sobre las universidades en Hawaii.
2.   Los estudiantes de la clase del Sr. Molina tienen que preparar sus ensayos personales.
3.   Andrés tiene que empezar a buscar becas.
4.   Los miembros de *Futuros Maestros de América* tienen que leer sus ensayos.
5.   Los maestros tienen que escribir las cartas de recomendación.
6.   María tiene que hablar con el director.

C. ¿Cuánto tiempo hace que...?   Conteste las siguientes preguntas indicando la última vez que hizo (*did*) estas actividades. Después, hágale las mismas preguntas a un/a compañero/a.

MODELO: ¿Cuánto tiempo hace que usted... estudió?
Estudié hace dos horas.

¿Cuánto tiempo hace que usted...

1.   investigar un tópico en Internet?
2.   leer un artículo en el periódico?
3.   solicitar ayuda económica para las clases?
4.   buscar información en la biblioteca?
5.   comer?
6.   estudiar español?

Módulo I

Becas, préstamos y otros programas

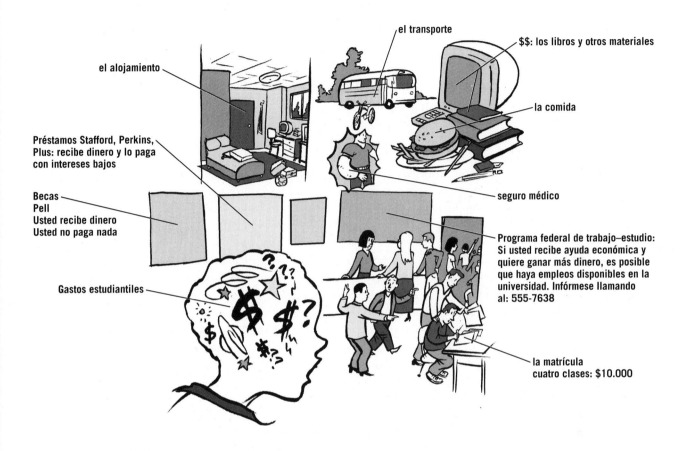

el transporte

$$: los libros y otros materiales

el alojamiento

la comida

Préstamos Stafford, Perkins, Plus: recibe dinero y lo paga con intereses bajos

seguro médico

Becas
Pell
Usted recibe dinero
Usted no paga nada

Programa federal de trabajo–estudio: Si usted recibe ayuda económica y quiere ganar más dinero, es posible que haya empleos disponibles en la universidad. Infórmese llamando al: 555-7638

Gastos estudiantiles

la matrícula
cuatro clases: $10.000

A. ¿Cómo se dice?   Identifique la palabra o frase de la derecha que mejor explique la palabra de la izquierda.

1. _____ beca

a. el dinero que se paga por los costos de la vida

2. _____ préstamo

b. dinero para los estudios que no se tiene que pagar

3. _____ programa federal de Trabajo–Estudio

c. dinero para los estudios que se tiene que pagar después

4. _____ gastos

d. un empleo dentro de la institución académica

B. En sus propias palabras.   Describa estos términos en sus propias palabras.

1. alojamiento
2. transporte
3. gastos
4. materiales académicos

Un testimonio

Honorables Miembros del Congreso:

Ayer supe que, por razones económicas, ustedes están considerando la posibilidad de reducir los fondos disponibles para los programas federales de becas y préstamos para la educación superior. Antes de tomar una decisión, yo quiero que escuchen mi historia.

Me llamo Alicia Mendoza y yo fui la primera persona de mi familia en asistir a la universidad. Es más, fui la primera persona de mi pueblo que asistió a la universidad.

En mi primer año de la escuela secundaria, vino a mi pueblo un maestro joven—recién graduado de la universidad. Yo estaba muy entusiasmada con mis lecciones en esos días y él resultó ser un maestro excelente—inteligente y simpático. Me habló mucho del valor de una educación y me dio muchas ganas de ir a la universidad. El problema fue que mis padres tuvieron muchos gastos médicos y a veces no podían pagar el alquiler. ¡Pagar los costos altísimos de una educación era imposible!

Mi maestro me habló de todos los programas federales de becas y préstamos y me ayudó a buscar unas becas particulares para aumentar los fondos para el alojamiento, la comida y los libros. Después de cuatro años me gradué Magna Cum Laude con título de maestra. Hoy, durante el día, soy maestra en mi pueblo nativo, animando a los niños desde una edad temprana a apreciar la educación. De noche, soy profesora en la Universidad Comunitaria de la región trabajando con otros estudiantes que decidieron mejorar su vida, la vida de su familia y la vida de la comunidad por medio de la educación. Anoche tuvimos la última clase. Gracias al apoyo federal y la ayuda económica, los estudiantes de mi clase pudieron realizar su sueño de ser graduados también. Estos programas son el futuro y la esperanza de millones que no tienen otras oportunidades. Por favor, ¡protejan los sueños!

Sinceramente,

Alicia Mendoza

Alicia Mendoza

C. ¿Comprende usted?   Conteste las preguntas según la información del diálogo.

1.   ¿Quién es Alicia Mendoza?
2.   ¿A quiénes escribió ella la carta? ¿Por qué?
3.   ¿Quién inspiró a Alicia a seguir sus estudios?
4.   ¿Qué hace Alicia ahora?

D. Hispanic Scholarship Fund.   Lea las becas de este grupo y escriba cuatro oraciones con la información más importante de su misión.

Quiénes somos y qué hacemos

Hispanic Scholarship Fund es la organización hispana más grande de la nación para la entrega de becas. La organización HSF reconoce y premia a estudiantes universitarios hispanos sobresalientes en Estados Unidos, Puerto Rico y las Islas Vírgenes estadounidenses. Tras su fundación en 1975, la HSF ha otorgado cerca de 61 mil becas por valor de más de $115 millones de dólares.

El desafío que enfrentamos

Los hispanos ahora son la mayor minoría de Estados Unidos. A medida que la población continúa su dramático crecimiento, la educación se convierte en un tema clave. Aunque muchos hispanos alcanzan niveles educativos excelentes, los datos de la Oficina del Censo revelan una discrepancia sorprendente entre el logro educativo de los hispanos en comparación a otros grupos de la población. Con ese objetivo, HSF adoptó en 1996 una nueva misión: duplicar la tasa de hispanos con diploma universitario en un 18 por ciento para el año 2010.

El proceso de la beca

Los candidatos exitosos se eligen sobre la base de logros académicos, potencial personal, capacidad de liderazgo y necesidades financieras. La selección de becarios se realiza con la asistencia del Educational Testing Service y de lectores regionales.

Universidades con inscripción hispana

Estas universidades son las primeras cinco en cuanto a su inscripción hispana:
1.   Florida International University
2.   The University of Texas, Pan America
3.   The University of Texas, El Paso
4.   California State University, Los Angeles
5.   The University of Texas, San Antonio

E. Ayuda para mí.   ¿Usted recibió ayuda económica para terminar su carrera universitaria? ¿Becas? ¿Préstamos? ¿Sus padres pagaron sus estudios? ¿Trabajó? Hable con sus compañeros de su estrategia para pagar los gastos de la universidad.

Estructuras   *More on the preterite: Verbos irregulares*

- In the preterite tense, the following verbs have irregular stems and irregular endings. The endings for all of these verbs are the same (**-e, -iste, -o, -imos, -ieron**).

Infinitive	Stem	Conjugation
venir	**vin**	vine, vin**iste**, vino, vin**imos**, vin**ieron**
saber	**sup**	supe, sup**iste**, supo, sup**imos**, sup**ieron**
poner	**pus**	puse, pus**iste**, puso, pus**imos**, pus**ieron**
poder	**pud**	pud**e**, pud**iste**, pud**o**, pud**imos**, pud**ieron**
querer	**quis**	quise, quis**iste**, quiso, quis**imos**, quis**ieron**
hacer	**hic***	hice, hic**iste**, hizo*, hic**imos**, hic**ieron**
tener	**tuv**	tuve, tuv**iste**, tuvo, tuv**imos**, tuv**ieron**
estar	**estuv**	estuve, estuv**iste**, estuvo, estuv**imos**

***¡OJO!** Note that only the third person singular form of **hacer** replaces the **-c** with a **-z** to preserve the pronunciation.

Ayer **supe**★ que recibí una beca.	*I found out yesterday that I received a scholarship.*
No **pudimos**★ contener la alegría.	*We could not contain our joy.*
Hicieron muchas solicitudes para becas.	*They did many scholarship applications.*
Quisieron★ eliminar a otros gastos.	*They wanted to eliminate other expenses.*

★**¡OJO!** Refer to *Lección 11, Módulo 1, Estados mentales, físicos y más* for more information on the differences in translation between the preterite and the imperfect.

- The preterite forms of the verbs **ir** and **ser** are also irregular. Note that they have identical conjugations and their meaning must be derived from the context.

ir/ser   fui, fuiste, fue, fuimos, fueron

—¿Quién **fue** el ganador de la beca?	*Who was the winner of the scholarship?*
—**Fue** Gerardo Campos.	*It was Gerardo Campos.*
—¿Adónde **fue** para sus clases?	*Where did he go for his classes?*
—**Fue** a una universidad en Puerto Rico.	*He went to a school in Puerto Rico.*

Para practicar

A. La búsqueda de dinero.   Usted es un estudiante que necesita ayuda económica. Explique lo que hizo para conseguir sus becas y préstamos.

MODELO: hacer citas con representantes de varias universidades
        Hice citas con representantes de varias universidades.

1. buscar información por Internet
2. tener problemas con las solicitudes
3. saber los nombres de las personas con influencia
4. ir a las entrevistas
5. poner las solicitudes en el correo
6. estar en mi casa cuando recibí noticias de la beca
7. tener una gran fiesta
8. hacer mucho trabajo

B. Las decisiones académicas.   Usted es un/a "super-estudiante" y muchas universidades quieren que les presten atención. ¿Qué hicieron estos reclutadores (*recruiters*) académicos para atraerlo/a a su institución?

MODELO: llamarme por teléfono
        Me llamaron por teléfono.

1. invitarme a recepciones	4. hacerme promesas de muchas becas
2. escribirme cartas	5. ponerme en una lista de estudiantes aceptados
3. venir a visitarme	6. querer aceptarme

C. ¿Y usted?   Escriba una lista de cinco cosas que hizo para estar informado/a sobre las becas y préstamos disponibles para sus estudios. Si no recibió ayuda económica, use la imaginación para inventar los pasos.

MODELO: *Leí muchos artículos sobre los temas importantes en el periódico.*

Módulo 2

¡Cuánto tuve que estudiar!

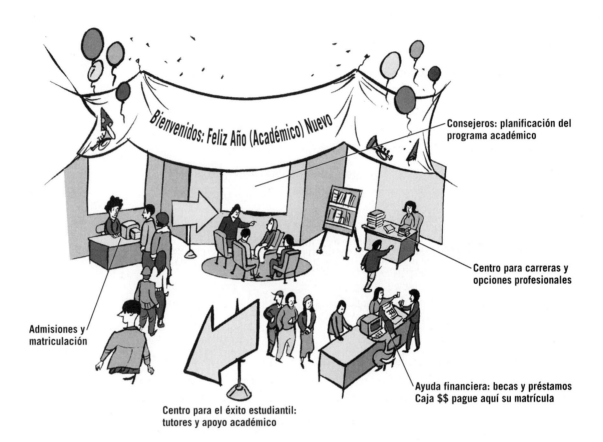

Bienvenidos: Feliz Año (Académico) Nuevo

Consejeros: planificación del programa académico

Centro para carreras y opciones profesionales

Admisiones y matriculación

Ayuda financiera: becas y préstamos
Caja $$ pague aquí su matrícula

Centro para el éxito estudiantil:
tutores y apoyo académico

A. ¿Cómo se dice?   Busque la definición que mejor identifique las siguientes palabras o frases.

I. _____ matriculación

a. dinero dedicado a ayudar económicamente a los estudiantes

2. _____ ayuda financiera

b. departamento dedicado al apoyo académico de los estudiantes

3. _____ éxito estudiantil

c. el proceso de inscribirse en una universidad

4. _____ tutor

d. una persona paraprofesional que ayuda a los estudiantes con la materia

B. ¿Adónde voy?   Diga adónde tiene que ir el estudiante que necesita hacer las siguientes cosas.

1. _____ pagar la matrícula

2. _____ determinar una dirección profesional

3. _____ pedir ayuda con la planificación del semestre

4. _____ pedir ayuda con una clase difícil

¡Cuánto tuve que estudiar!

Roberto es un estudiante muy inteligente que tuvo que aprender a estudiar. Ahora habla con un grupo de estudiantes nuevos en una clase de "Éxito estudiantil".

ROBERTO: El primer semestre que yo estuve aquí, saqué notas horribles. Tuve dos **F,** dos **D** y una **A**—en la clase de Golf por un crédito. Perdí mi beca y repetí mis requisitos y clases fundamentales de inglés, Biología y Álgebra.

ELISA: ¿Fuiste a muchas fiestas?

ROBERTO: ¡Ni eso! Dediqué muchas horas al estudio, pero no sabía cómo estudiar, ni seguía ningún método. Antes de empezar el semestre siguiente, fui a mi profesora de español—que es muy buena persona—y le pedí ayuda. Ella me dio un plan.

HERIBERTO: ¿Qué hizo?

ROBERTO: Primero pidió mi cuaderno de su clase. Leyó mis notas y me dijo que entendía por qué tuve problemas. Ni ella pudo comprender sus propias lecciones. Entonces, me dio una lista de recomendaciones para crear buenas costumbres de estudio y las implementé inmediatamente. Organicé mis notas y mi tiempo. Completé todas mis tareas y anoté las cosas que no entendía. Hice muchas preguntas en las clases. Cuando los profesores repitieron conceptos, los marqué y estudié mucho. Apagué el televisor y el radio durante las horas del estudio y organicé sesiones de estudio fuera de clase con mis compañeros. El segundo semestre, obtuve un GPA de 4.0; me dieron mis becas y empecé a trabajar aquí con las clases de *Éxito estudiantil.*

C. ¿Comprende usted?   Conteste las preguntas según la información del artículo.

1. ¿Qué notas sacó Roberto el primer semestre?

2. ¿Con quién habló para pedir ayuda?

3. Describa tres cosas que hizo para mejorar su manera de estudiar.

4. ¿Cómo fue su GPA el segundo semestre?

D. ¿Es el dinero? Después de leer el artículo de los factores que causan que los estudiantes latinos dejen sus estudios, escriba la información adecuada para terminar cada una de las oraciones.

Hay muchos factores que reducen el número de latinos en la universidad.

Muchos latinos siguen sus estudios universitarios, pero este grupo étnico tiene menos representación que los afroamericanos y los caucásicos en cuanto a los títulos de licenciatura.

Pew Hispanic Center (www.pewhispanic.org) encontró que hay más hispanos matriculados en universidades, en cuanto al porcentaje, pero que hay menos que terminan la carrera. La razón principal: dinero. Muchos se matriculan en universidades comunitarias de dos años para quedarse en casa y así ahorrar dinero—y asisten a clases a tiempo parcial—un factor de riesgo. El 16% de los latinos reciben su licenciatura al final de los estudios, en comparación con el 21% de los afroamericanos y el 37% de los caucásicos.

La diferencia es aún más notable en los estudios posgraduados: el 3.8% de los caucásicos que terminaron la secundaria siguen programas de títulos avanzados; frente a solamente el 1.9% de los latinos.

---

1. La razón principal por la cual algunos latinos no terminan su educación es

_____ .

2. Un factor de riesgo para el estudiante latino es que hay más que asisten

_____ .

3. El porcentaje de latinos que ganan su licenciatura es_____ en

comparación con _____ de los afroamericanos y

_____ de los caucásicos.

4. Los porcentajes de latinos y caucásicos que cursan estudios posgraduados

son _____ y _____ .

▟▟▟▟ **E. Lluvia de ideas.** Apunte sus ideas—por lo menos cinco—sobre por qué algunos estudiantes no terminan sus carreras universitarias. Compare su lista con la de tres compañeros.

MODELO: *Algunos estudiantes no tienen suficiente dinero y no ven la posibilidad de trabajar y solicitar becas y préstamos.*

Estructuras   *Relating past activities: Verbos en -ir con cambios en el pretérito*

- The **-ar** and **-er** verbs that have stem changes in the present tense do not have them in the preterite. Use the regular infinitive stem to form the preterite.

El estudiante **empezó** a sacar buenas notas.	*The student began to earn good grades.*
La profesora **entendió** a su estudiante.	*The professor understood her student.*

- Only **-ir** verbs have stem changes in the preterite tense. In stem-changing **-ir** verbs, **e** becomes **i** and **o** becomes **u** only in the third person (**él, ella, usted, ellos, ellas, ustedes**) preterite forms.

pedir → pedí, pediste, p**i**dió, pedimos, p**i**dieron
dormir → dormí, dormiste, d**u**rmió, dormimos, d**u**rmieron

Pedí ayuda de los tutores.	*I asked the tutors for help.*
Los tutores no **pidieron** dinero.	*The tutors did not ask for money.*
No **dormí** antes del examen.	*I did not sleep before the exam.*
El estudiante no **durmió** antes del examen.	*The student did not sleep before the exam.*

- Additional verbs that follow this pattern are:

e → i   **servir, repetir, preferir, seguir, mentir, elegir, sentir**
o → u   **morir**

- Verbs ending in **-cir** have a spelling change to **j.** Note that **decir** changes **e → i** in the stem. The verb **traer** also has this change to **j.** Use the following endings with these verbs.

-e, -iste, -o, -imos, -eron

traducir *(to translate)*	traduje, tradujiste, tradujo, tradujimos, tradujeron
decir *(to say or tell)*	dije, dijiste, dijo, dijimos, dijeron
traer *(to bring)*	traje, trajiste, trajo, trajimos, trajeron

Para practicar

A. En la universidad.   Usted es un estudiante nuevo en una universidad grande. Diga si usted (**Yo**) o los profesores (**Ellos**) hicieron las siguientes cosas.

MODELO: sentirse nervioso antes del examen
Yo me sentí nervioso/a antes del examen.

1.   repetir las instrucciones tres veces
2.   preferir dar exámenes analíticos
3.   seguir estudiando hasta las tres de la mañana
4.   no dormir ni un momento por el miedo
5.   pedir ayuda con los conceptos difíciles
6.   traer notas a clase

B. El mejor profesor del año.   Usted ganó el premio por ser el mejor profesor de español del año. Usando el tiempo pretérito, explique cómo creó la magia en su clase.

MODELO: decir cosas para animar a los estudiantes
Dije cosas para animar a los estudiantes.

1.   no traducir el vocabulario al inglés
2.   traer ropa y comida típicas a la clase
3.   estar disponible para contestar las preguntas por e-mail
4.   explicar bien la materia
5.   tener buen sentido de humor
6.   nunca ponerme furioso con los estudiantes

C. Los profesores excelentes.   Con un/a compañero/a, invente a un profesor de español excelente y después escriba seis cosas que esa persona hizo por los estudiantes.

MODELO: *El profesor Ferrán es excelente.*
El leyó poesía española a la clase.

Módulo 2

¡Ya me gradué!

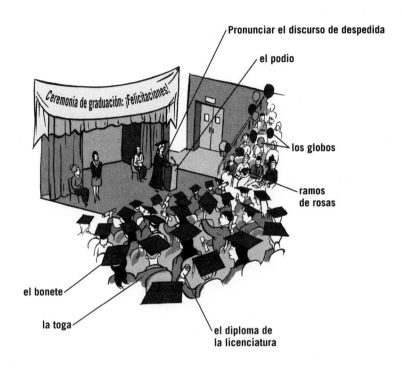

Pronunciar el discurso de despedida

el podio

los globos

ramos de rosas

el bonete

la toga

el diploma de la licenciatura

Ceremonia de graduación: ¡Felicitaciones!

A. ¿Cómo se dice? Busque la definición que mejor identifique las siguientes palabras o frases.

I. _____ licenciatura

2. _____ requisito

3. _____ toga y bonete

4. _____ discurso de despedida

a. curso obligatorio

b. ropa especial para la ceremonia de graduación

c. palabras estudiantiles en la ceremonia de graduación

d. el título oficial de Bachelor's

B. En sus propias palabras. Escriba una definición original de las siguientes palabras.

I. la graduación   **3.** un comité

2. el consejero   **4.** los globos

¿Hay problemas?

En nuestra universidad, un estudiante que se prepara para la graduación tiene que llenar una solicitud y mandarla al Comité de Revisión de la Graduación *para confirmar que todos los requisitos están en orden. Esta mañana Álvaro recibió una llamada del decano del comité pidiendo una cita inmediata en persona. ¡Pobre Álvaro!*

DECANO: ¡Álvaro! Pasa. Quiero hablar contigo. Siéntate.

ÁLVARO: ¿Hay algún problema? Cuando recibí su llamada, me puse tan nervioso que corrí para acá.

DECANO: Álvaro, ¿cuándo fue la última vez que consultaste con tu consejero?

ÁLVARO: Hace un par de meses que le hablé. No sé cuál es el problema. Cumplí con todos los requisitos básicos que él me dio en la lista: revisé los cursos que tomé y él me dijo que todo está en orden; verifiqué con la cajera que no debo dinero; hice el plan de estudios para este semestre y el semestre que viene. Tengo todo listo para la graduación en diciembre del año que viene. ¡Ya me midieron para la toga y el bonete! ¡Ay, Decano! Si perdí un paso y no puedo graduarme el semestre que viene, no sé qué voy a hacer.

DECANO: Álvaro, es que el comité y yo pusimos mucha atención a tu caso y encontramos que...

ÁLVARO: El semestre pasado llevé 21 créditos para poder graduarme a tiempo y repetí una clase de español para mejorar mi nota.

DECANO: ¡Álvaro! Un momento, por favor. Lo que quise decirte es que prestamos mucha atención a tu solicitud para la graduación y notamos dos cosas importantes: con las clases que completaste este semestre, ya tienes bastantes créditos para graduarte ahora en mayo. No tienes que esperar hasta el año que viene. Y con el record de excelencia que mantuviste aquí, queremos invitarte a pronunciar el discurso de despedida en la ceremonia de la graduación. ¡Muchas felicidades, hijo!

C. ¿Comprende usted? Conteste las preguntas según la información del diálogo.

1. ¿Quién llamó a Álvaro para pedir una cita?
2. ¿Por qué corrió Álvaro a verlo?
3. ¿Por qué se puso nervioso?
4. ¿Son buenas o malas las noticias del decano? ¿Qué son?

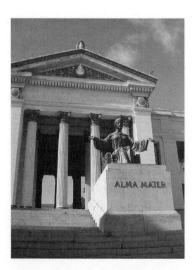

D. La primera universidad virtual en español. Lea el anuncio de esta universidad y termine la actividad. Si las declaraciones son **Ciertas**, escriba una **C**; si son **Falsas**, escriba una **F** y haga las correcciones necesarias.

El comienzo de la primera universidad virtual en español en EE. UU.

Se fundó la primera universidad virtual en español en EE. UU. en diciembre de 2002 con un acuerdo entre AAMA, la Asociación para el fomento de mexicoamericanos, basada en Houston, y el Instituto tecnológico de estudios superiores en Monterrey, Nuevo León, México (Monterrey Tec). AAMA es una organización hispana sin fines de lucro—número nueve en tamaño—en esta nación.

Monterrey Tec ya tuvo programas para latinos en EE. UU. de alfabetización, inglés e informática por Internet y a través de sus Centros comunitarios de aprendizaje en Houston, Dallas y Miami. Ahora ofrecen servicios educativos avanzados vía satélite e Internet para hispanohablantes en EE. UU.

Los inmigrantes latinos vienen a EE. UU. para trabajar y ayudar a sus familias a alcanzar "el sueño americano", pero muchos no tienen la oportunidad de desarrollarse académicamente y mejorar su empleo y sueldo.

La mayoría de los programas ofrecidos están acreditados por SACS (Southwest Association of Colleges and Schools), incluyendo la Maestría en Administración, Finanzas, Mercadotecnia, Informática, Educación y más.

---

1. _____ Esta universidad es el resultado de un acuerdo entre la Universidad de Texas en San Antonio y UNAM (Universidad Nacional Autónoma de México).

2. _____ AAMA es una organización hispana sin fines de lucro.

3. _____ La meta de esta universidad es el desarrollo académico de los inmigrantes latinos para que aumenten sus oportunidades de empleo y sueldo.

4. _____ Los títulos que se ofrecen son solamente en el campo de Informática.

Estructuras   *More past activities: Usos del pretérito*

Spanish, like English, has more than one tense to describe an action in the past. Use the preterite tense to:

- Describe single events in the past that are considered complete.

El decano **firmó** el permiso.   *The dean signed the permission.*
El estudiante **pagó** la deuda.   *The student paid the debt.*

- Describe events that took place a specific number of times.

Yolanda **llamó** al profesor tres veces.   *Yolanda called her teacher three times.*
La estudiante **estuvo** en la oficina del   *The student was in the advisor's office*
consejero dos veces.   *twice.*

- Express the beginning or end of an action.

El problema **empezó** hace dos meses.   *The problem began two months ago.*
Los miembros del comité **entraron** a la   *The committee members went into*
reunión a las nueve y **salieron** a las siete.   *the meeting at nine and left at seven.*

- Narrate a series of events.

Los profesores **identificaron** el problema,   *The faculty identified the problem,*
lo **discutieron** y lo **resolvieron**.   *argued about it, and resolved it.*
El director **nominó** al estudiante   *The director nominated the student*
y el comité lo **aceptó.**   *and the committee accepted him.*

- Describe mental or emotional reactions in the past.

Álvaro **se preocupó** cuando oyó las   *Álvaro got worried when he heard*
noticias.   *the news.*
Nos **pusimos** enojados cuando   *We got mad when we found out the*
supimos la verdad.   *truth.*

Para practicar

A. El reportero.   Usted es un/a fotógrafo/a que está tomando fotos de las actividades del presidente de la clase de graduados antes de la ceremonia. Escriba un titular *(caption)* para las siguientes fotos.

MODELO: despertarse a las ocho
El presidente se despertó a las ocho.

1. leer sus notas para el discurso de despedida
2. ver las noticias por televisión
3. ir al sitio de la ceremonia muy temprano para ensayar *(rehearse)*
4. participar en el banquete de celebración
5. vestirse con su toga y bonete
6. recibir su diploma

B. ¿Y usted?   Su jefe, el fotógrafo principal, quiere saber lo que hizo usted ayer. Escriba la lista de sus actividades en el pretérito.

MODELO: desayunar a las cinco
Desayuné a las cinco.

1. seguir al presidente al sitio de la ceremonia
2. sacar muchas fotos del grupo de amigos
3. organizar el archivo
4. buscar más información para el artículo
5. hacer llamadas telefónicas a su familia
6. empezar a escribir el artículo

C. Ya me gradué.   ¡Felicidades! Usted y su compañero/a se graduaron hoy. Hagan una lista de diez actividades que ustedes hicieron para realizar este sueño.

MODELO: *Seleccionamos las clases y los profesores con mucho cuidado.*

Vocabulario Módulo 1

Sustantivos

el alojamiento	lodging	el impuesto	tax
el alquiler	rent	el ingreso	income
los bienes	goods	el interés	interest
el censo	census	el paso	step
el/la ciudadano/a	citizen	la promesa	promise
el club	club	la puntuación	score, grade
la custodia	custody	el registro	registry
el/la dependiente/a	dependent	el saldo	balance
		la tasa	rate
el/la extranjero/a	foreigner	el testimonio	proof, testimony
las Fuerzas Armadas	Armed Forces	el varón	male
		la venta	sale
el/la huérfano/a	orphan	el/la veterano/a	veteran

Verbos

alcanzar	to reach	nacer (zc)	to be born
cursar	to take a course	otorgar	to award
enfrentar	to face		

Adjetivos

ajustado/a	adjusted	culpable	guilty
bruto/a	gross (income)		

Otras expresiones

mañana	tomorrow

Módulo 2

Sustantivos

el acuerdo	agreement	el globo	balloon
la agricultura	agriculture	la licenciatura	Bachelor's degree
el banquete	banquet		
el bonete	cap	la llamada	call
la caja	cash drawer	la maestría	Master's degree
el/la cajero/a	cashier	la milla	mile
el centavo	cent	el permiso	permission
la ceremonia	ceremony	el ramo	bouquet
el crédito	credit	el riesgo	risk
el decano	dean	el semestre	semester
la despedida	farewell	el sueldo	salary
la deuda	debt	el talento	talent
la fundación	foundation	la toga	gown

Verbos

abandonar	*to abandon*	**identificar**	*to identify*
amar	*to love*	**pronunciar**	*to deliver*
anotar	*to make note of*		*(speech)*
anticipar	*to anticipate*	**reírse de (i)**	*to laugh about*

Adjetivos

agrícola	*agricultural*	**único/a**	*unique, only*
básico/a	*basic*		

Otras expresiones

acá	*here*	**¡Felicitaciones!**	*Congratulations!*
contigo	*with you*	**sin fines de lucro**	*non-profit*
en orden	*in order*		

Síntesis

A escuchar

Escuche el siguiente diálogo y conteste estas preguntas. *Margarita y Esteban están hablando en la cafetería. Es obvio que Margarita está muy preocupada.*

1. ¿Por qué está triste y preocupada Margarita?
2. ¿Qué dijo su tío?
3. ¿Qué hizo Esteban en circunstancias semejantes?
4. ¿Qué recomendó Esteban?

A conversar

¿Tuvo usted una experiencia única durante su carrera universitaria? ¿Cambió de especialidad? ¿Dejó una clase por problemas con un profesor? ¿Sacó mala nota en alguna clase? ¿Vio a estudiantes copiando *(cheating)* en los exámenes? Hable con sus compañeros de un ejemplo memorable.

MODELO: *Tuve problemas con un profesor porque él quiso ayudarme con mis lecciones—¡en su apartamento!*

A leer

Universidad Internacional

El Centro para estudios bilingües multiculturales
Programa intensivo en español para maestros bilingües
Aprenda, viva y ame el lenguaje español en Cuernavaca, México

Nuestro programa aumenta y perfecciona las destrezas lingüísticas en español de maestros que trabajan con estudiantes cuyo lenguaje materno es el español. Además hay un enfoque en el vocabulario relacionado con el aula y la escuela.

La participación va de un mínimo de dos semanas hasta un máximo de cuatro. Cada estudiante vive con una familia mexicana en Cuernavaca, la capital del estado de Morelos, 50 millas al sur de la ciudad de México. Se le llama "la Ciudad de la primavera eterna" con temperaturas de 75º todo el año. Hay excursiones a sitios arqueológicos y museos.

Los maestros reciben 4 o 8 créditos transferibles (15 horas de instrucción por cada crédito)—y el precio es de $100.00 por cada crédito.

Universidad Internacional
Presidente: Ing. Javier Espinosa Romero

Apartado postal 1520
Cuernavaca, Morelos, México C.P. 62000
Tel: 011 (52-777) 3171087
Fax: 011 (52-777) 3170533
EE. UU. 1 (800) 932 2068

Para obtener más información, visite www.spanish.com.mx

¿Comprende usted?

1. ¿Para quiénes es este programa?
2. ¿Por cuánto tiempo es?
3. ¿Dónde es?
4. ¿Cuánto cuesta?

A escribir

Apunte cinco cosas importantes que debe considerar un estudiante con ganas de estudiar en el extranjero. ¡OJO! Quizás sea necesario investigar algunos programas en Internet.

Algo más

Ventana cultural

Latinos, once so anxious to join the American mainstream, have rediscovered a passion for their heritage. When Latinos read about the popularity of all things Hispanic on the covers of magazines such as Newsweek and Time, there's often a roll of the eyes and an exasperated, "Duh! Didn't we already know this?"

by Christine Granados

Se dice que "para saber adónde vamos, es imprescindible saber de dónde venimos". En estos momentos Latinos de todas las regiones tienen una sed insaciable para re-descubrir sus raíces y llevarlas al futuro. Aquí tienen una cita de Christine Granados de *Hispanic* magazine.

Es obvio—los hispanos forman una parte importante de Estados Unidos. Estos latinos muestran un orgullo que tiene su origen en el movimiento de derechos civiles y el de los chicanos.

Yolanda McDonald, una mexicoamericana, se acuerda de los niños que se reían de ella cuando estaba en la escuela. "Mis compañeros decían que yo era diferente, porque era morena", dice Yolanda. "Soy una ciudadana de Estados Unidos y estoy muy orgullosa de mi país" continúa Yolanda, "pero quiero mantener mi herencia cultural y así aportar algo único a mi América."

Las investigaciones sobre este tema indican que para los estudiantes hispanos de segunda y tercera generación, es decir, que tienen ascendencia hispana a pesar de ser ciudadanos estadounidenses, es importante establecer la conexión con su propia cultura. Ricardo Castillo, un abogado en Phoenix, encontró sus raíces en la universidad. "No sabía mucho de mi cultura cuando era estudiante pero me hice amigo de otros hispanos y empecé a redescubrir de dónde vine. Asistí a algunas clases sobre la cultura chicana para aprender más sobre mi pasado, y ¡hasta aprendí a hablar español! Mis padres sólo me hablaban en inglés cuando yo era niño, porque pensaban que era mejor para mí" dice Ricardo, "pero yo creo que para desarrollarme completamente necesito conocer mis raíces y aceptarlas con orgullo".

Hoy en día, la popularidad de figuras del mundo del cine y de la canción, como Ricky Martin, Jennifer López, Enrique Iglesias y otros ayuda a conectar a los jóvenes latinos con su cultura, promoviendo un acercamiento entre la cultura popular actual en Estados Unidos, y aquélla que estos hispanos aún llevan en sus venas.

Latinos—la vuelta a las raíces

Christine Granados

En mis propias palabras. Ya sabemos que la población hispana en Estados Unidos es más grande ahora y tiene cada día más importancia en la vida política, económica y cultural. ¿Dónde ve usted la influencia hispana? Escriba sobre su papel en el gobierno, en el campo político, en el mundo de los deportes, la música, las películas, la arquitectura, la comida, en. . .

A buscar

¿Cuál es el porcentaje de hispanos en SU distrito escolar? Busque datos demográficos en cuanto a la población hispana de su escuela, el distrito y/o la ciudad, el condado y el estado.

A conocer: Dr. Robert Flores

El Doctor Robert Flores es el Director del Departamento de educación agrícola y comunicación de California Polytecnic University en San Luis Obispo. Es miembro del departamento desde hace 19 años y participó en el desarrollo de EARTH University en Costa Rica. Además fue Director del Programa multicultural de agricultura en Cal Poly y Coordinador de Currículum para California Agricultural Leadership Program.

LECCIÓN 11

Entonces y ahora

Módulo 1
- Así era
- Describing past situations: *El imperfecto*
- Entrevistas
- More on the imperfect: *Estados mentales, físicos y más*

Módulo 2
- La historia oral
- Narrating in the past: *El pretérito y el imperfecto*
- La historia del futuro
- Contrasting past tenses: *El pretérito y el imperfecto*

Consejera

Síntesis
- A escuchar
- A conversar
- A leer
- A escribir

Algo más
- Ventana cultural: El festival latino de libros y familia
- A buscar
- A conocer: Francisco Jiménez

Módulo I

Así era

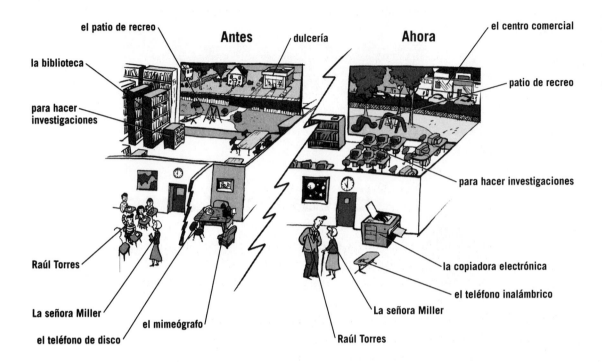

el patio de recreo

Antes

dulcería

Ahora

el centro comercial

la biblioteca

patio de recreo

para hacer investigaciones

para hacer investigaciones

Raúl Torres

la copiadora electrónica

La señora Miller

el teléfono inalámbrico

el mimeógrafo

La señora Miller

el teléfono de disco

Raúl Torres

A. ¿Cómo se dice?   Usando el dibujo, la imaginación y la memoria, compare y contraste el equipo de **antes** y **ahora**.

MODELO: hacer investigaciones

Antes	*Ahora*
la biblioteca y los libros	*las computadoras y la Red*

Antes	**Ahora**

1.   sacar copias

2.   jugar en el patio de recreo

3.   hacer llamadas

4.   comprar dulces, chocolates y refrescos

B. En sus propias palabras.   Dé una definición o ejemplo de estas palabras y frases.

1.   el patio de recreo   **3.**   las investigaciones

2.   la biblioteca   **4.**   motor de búsqueda o buscador

Así era

Raúl Torres es un estudiante de pedagogía que va a graduarse muy pronto de la universidad. Pero, primero tiene que cumplir con las obligaciones de la clase final de su carrera: "maestro en prácticas". Entre todas las escuelas posibles, ¡qué suerte!, van a mandarlo a Menlo Park—su propia escuela primaria. ¡Qué sorpresa para él y para el Director!

DIRECTOR: Bienvenido, Raúl, a Menlo Park. Espero que le vaya a gustar su estancia en nuestra escuela. Primero, vamos a hacer un tour de las instalaciones y después hablamos un poco de la clase que va a enseñar.

RAÚL: Sr. Director, yo puedo ser el guía del tour. Por aquí está la cafetería y allí debe estar el gimnasio.

DIRECTOR: ¿Conoce nuestra escuela?

RAÚL: Era mi escuela. Asistía a Menlo Park de niño. Vivía a unas dos cuadras de aquí en este mismo barrio. Mis abuelos tenían una dulcería adonde todos íbamos después de las clases. Todos los días comíamos chocolates, tomábamos sodas y jugábamos a los juegos de vídeo. Era una tradición. Toda mi familia asistía a Menlo Park. Y todos los amigos durante muchas generaciones visitaban la tienda de mis abuelos.

DIRECTOR: ¡No me diga! ¿Y todavía viven aquí usted y su familia?

RAÚL: Mucha parte de mi familia, sí. Mi abuela, mis padres, dos de mis hermanos y muchos tíos, primos y primas. Yo viví en Chile un tiempo, que es donde estudiaba educación bilingüe. Cuando decidí que quería volver con mi familia y trabajar aquí, ¡no sabía que iba a tener la suerte de volver a Menlo Park! Estoy muy emocionado.

DIRECTOR: Yo también. Por dos razones. Nos hacía falta un maestro bilingüe joven con energía. Y precisamente ayer su nueva supervisora aquí, la maestra Miller, y yo estábamos pensando en la posibilidad de...

RAÚL: ¡No puede ser! ¿La maestra Miller? ¿Nancy Miller? Era mi maestra favorita aquí—y fue la inspiración de mi carrera de maestro. ¿Dónde está? Tengo que verla y darle un abrazo.

C. ¿Comprende usted? Conteste las preguntas según la información del diálogo.

1. ¿Por qué conoce Raúl Menlo Park?
2. ¿Dónde vivía?
3. ¿Quiénes tenían la dulcería?
4. ¿Por qué quiere ver a la maestra Miller?

D. Programador analista. La vida cambia. Armando cursó estudios hace menos de 20 años para ser programador analista, pero sus cursos ya no existen. Con un/a compañero/a, diseñe un programa de estudios de HOY para trabajar en el mundo de informática.

Centro de Computación Herman Hollerith, S. C.

Registro en S.E.P. T-85215

Certifica

Que según constancia que obra en el archivo del plantel el/la alumno/a
Armando García Martínez
....

cursó durante el año escolar........................ 1987/1988 ....

las materias que se indican, las cuales forman parte del Plan de
Estudios de................ Programador analista ....

habiendo obtenido las calificaciones siguientes:

Materias	Calificación
Principios	80
Organización de archivos	80
Diagramación	80
Lenguaje COBOL	90
Lenguaje R.P.G.	100
Lenguaje BASIC	90
Análisis	90
Promedio general	87

La escala de calificaciones va de 0 a 100. La calificación mínima para ser aprobado es de 70 puntos.

José de la Luz Navarro	*Francisco Ramírez Aguirrre*	*J. Jaime García Jiméne*
José de la Luz Navarro	Francisco Ramírez Aguirrre	J. Jaime García Jiménez
Supervisor	Director	Coordinador

MODELO: *Hoy un puesto con Microsoft como técnico es suficiente; no se necesitan BASIC/COBOL. Hay que saber arreglar problemas con software.*

E. ¡Adelante, mujeres! Para ver cómo era la vida de mujeres antes, en su motor de búsqueda, escriba "Adelante, mujeres". Hable con compañeros de lo que encuentra. Además, hay un vídeo, de *National Women's History Project*, que se enfoca en cinco siglos de la historia de mujeres mexicoamericanas/chicanas. Trate de verlo.

Estructuras   *Describing past situations:*
El imperfecto

- To talk about things that *used to be,* use the imperfect tense. While the preterite is used to describe the completed aspect of an event, the imperfect is used to indicate the habitual, repeated, or ongoing nature of events or actions in the past.

- The formation of the imperfect tense is simple:

	tomar	comer	vivir
yo	tom**aba**	com**ía**	viv**ía**
tú	tom**abas**	com**ías**	viv**ías**
él/ella/usted	tom**aba**	com**ía**	viv**ía**
nosotros/as	tom**ábamos**	com**íamos**	viv**íamos**
ellos/ellas/ustedes	tom**aban**	com**ían**	viv**ían**

- The only three irregular verbs in the imperfect are:

	ir	ser	ver
yo	**iba**	**era**	**veía**
tú	**ibas**	**eras**	**veías**
él/ella/usted	**iba**	**era**	**veía**
nosotros/as	**íbamos**	**éramos**	**veíamos**
ellos/ellas/ustedes	**iban**	**eran**	**veían**

- The imperfect may be used in a variety of ways in English.

  Habitual actions:

Asistía a Menlo Park todos los días.	*I attended Menlo Park every day.*
	I would attend Menlo Park every day.
	I used to attend Menlo Park every day.
Íbamos a la dulcería.	*We went to the candy store.*
	We would go to the candy store.
	We used to go to the candy store.

- Use the imperfect to express time and age in the past.

Tenía ocho años cuando **estudiaba** allí.	*I was eight years old when I studied there.*
Eran las tres de la tarde.	*It was three in the afternoon.*

Para practicar

A. Cuando era joven. Complete estas oraciones con un verbo en el imperfecto. Después, indique si eran verdad cuando usted era joven. Si la oración no es verdad, corríjala, cambiando la palabra correspondiente.

MODELO: yo/comprar chocolates *en Internet*
No compraba chocolates en Internet. Compraba chocolates en una dulcería.

1. mi familia/tener *una computadora*
2. yo/estudiar *mucho*
3. nosotros/ver películas *en DVD*
4. mis amigos y yo/jugar a juegos *de vídeo*
5. tú/escuchar música en *el reproductor de MP3*
6. yo/ir a la escuela *en camión*

B. Entonces y ahora. La tecnología ha causado muchos cambios en la educación durante los últimos quince años. Indique qué diferencias había en el pasado en comparación con estas descripciones de la educación de hoy.

MODELO: Hoy muchas familias tienen más de una computadora en casa.
Antes, nadie tenía una computadora en casa.

1. Hoy puedo pedir ayuda con la tarea por Internet.
2. Ahora muchos profesores tienen su propio sitio web.
3. Ahora busco información económica en Internet.
4. Ahora recibo cartas electrónicas en un instante.
5. Hoy voy de compras sin salir de casa.
6. Hoy soy aficionado de la tecnología.

C. ¿Y usted? Piense en los días de su niñez y conteste estas preguntas. Después, entreviste a un/a amigo/a con las mismas preguntas.

MODELO: ¿Qué hacías los sábados?
Iba al cine.

1. ¿Qué profesión quería tener de adulto?
2. ¿Cómo celebraba su cumpleaños?
3. ¿Adónde iba de vacaciones?
4. ¿Cuál era su comida favorita?
5. ¿Cómo se llamaban sus mejores amigos?
6. ¿Qué programas de televisión miraba?

Módulo I

Entrevistas

El barrio viejo

el baile maratón — el soldado

mi abuela: — hierbas
mi antepasado

remedio casero

A. ¿Cómo se dice?   Escoja la palabra o frase más lógica para completar estas oraciones.

a. remedio   **b.** soldado   **c.** antepasados   **d.** maratón

1.   Mis _____ son miembros de mi familia de las generaciones anteriores.

2.   Un _____ casero es una medicina preparada en casa.

3.   Un _____ es un baile prolongado para ver quién resiste más.

4.   Un _____ es un militar que defiende a su nación.

B. En sus propias palabras: Defina estas palabras o frases usando sus propias palabras.

1.   el barrio
2.   la historia oral
3.   una entrevista
4.   la generación

Entrevistas

¡Qué emoción! La primera reunión entre la maestra Miller y su estudiante inolvidable, Raúl, fue una celebración mágica de recuerdos de personas, épocas y de momentos históricos de la escuela y del barrio. Estaban tan contentos que Raúl dijo: "debemos escribir nuestra historia para los niños y sus familias". La maestra le contestó: "Aún mejor—debemos pedir su participación: vamos a hacer un proyecto de 'historia oral' de nuestro barrio." Aquí hay algunas de las entrevistas que los estudiantes hicieron con los familiares y otros residentes para su proyecto: Así era Menlo Park.

Cuando mi mamá y sus hermanos se enfermaban, mi abuelita les daba diferentes tipos de hierbas. Cuando les dolía el estómago, tenían que tomar un té que se llama manzanilla—creo que es *chamomile* en inglés. Cuando yo era muy chiquito, me caía mucho. Siempre me dolían las rodillas y codos. Mi mamá me ponía un remedio preparado de una flor que se llama árnica. Siempre me sentía mucho mejor. (Conrado, 5to grado)

El salón de bailes Casino Riverside en realidad no era salón ni casino. Era un patio al lado del río. Había muchos bailes allí. Nuestra tía bailaba allí durante la Segunda Guerra Mundial. Durante los concursos de "maratón", bailaban y bailaban hasta que no podían bailar más. Después de bailar, todos iban a la taquería donde comían tacos y menudo.
(Berta, 3er grado y Nicolás, 4to grado)

Mi abuelo nació en 1911. Asistía a Menlo Park en 1918. Nos hablaba de todos los amigos que tenía en el barrio y decía que la escuela era muy difícil porque los maestros eran tan estrictos. Los estudiantes tenían que completar la tarea. Y si mi abuelo no estaba preparado, se ponía muy nervioso. Le encantaba la escuela. No había cafetería: los niños traían burritos y galletas y fruta. Les gustaba mucho jugar al béisbol y al básquetbol.
(Alice, 5to grado)

Antes de la Navidad, mi bisabuela *(great-grandmother)*, mi abuela, mis tías y mi mamá hacían tamales y hallacas. Todos íbamos a la casa de mi abuela para jugar y bailar. Nos divertíamos mucho.
(Conrad, 5to grado)

El padre de mi mamá—mi abuelo—vivía aquí en 1905, en este barrio. El tenía un caballo, una vaca y muchas gallinas. Pero, Sra. Miller, ¡NO TENÍA ELEFANTES!
(John, grado 4to)

C. ¿Comprende usted?   Conteste las preguntas según la información del diálogo.

I.   ¿Por qué hacen entrevistas los niños?

2.   ¿Qué tomaban la mamá y los tíos de Conrado si les dolía el estómago?

3.   En realidad, ¿qué era el salón de bailes Casino Riverside?

4.   ¿Qué animales tenía la familia de John? ¿Qué animales *no* tenía su familia? ¿Por qué le dice esto a la Sra. Miller?

D. La eficiencia del maestro.   ¿Cómo era su experiencia en esta clase? Termine la encuesta.

Reacción estudiantil a la eficiencia del maestro en la enseñanza

Fecha

Título del curso:

¡OJO! Use sólo un lápiz número 2 llenando completamente cada óvalo.

Favor de responder a las preguntas respecto a su profesor.

		ALTO				BAJO
1.	Tenía buen dominio del contenido de la materia.	⑤	④	③	②	①
2.	Definió claramente los requisitos del curso.	⑤	④	③	②	①
3.	Estaba bien preparado para la clase.	⑤	④	③	②	①
4.	Animaba la participación del estudiante.	⑤	④	③	②	①
5.	Trataba a los hombres y a las mujeres igual.	⑤	④	③	②	①
6.	Los exámenes eran justos.	⑤	④	③	②	①
7.	Las tareas eran propias del curso.	⑤	④	③	②	①
8.	Estaba abierto a otras opiniones.	⑤	④	③	②	①
9.	Las técnicas de la enseñanza eran eficientes.	⑤	④	③	②	①
10.	Usaba la hora de la clase eficientemente.	⑤	④	③	②	①
11.	Me gustaría tomar otra clase de este profesor.	⑤	④	③	②	①
12.	En total, ¿cómo era la clase con este profesor?	⑤	④	③	②	①

Estructuras   *More on the imperfect:*
Estados mentales, físicos y más

- Use the imperfect to describe physical or mental states in the past.

No **sabía** que tenía parientes famosos.	*I didn't know I had famous relatives.*
Estaba nerviosa la primera vez que fui a la escuela Menlo Park.	*I was nervous the first time I went to Menlo Park School.*

■ The imperfect is used to indicate two activities in the past that were in progress at the same time. These two activities are often joined by **mientras** *(while)*.

Escuchaban la música **mientras bailaban** los maratones.
listening → while dancing

They listened to music while they danced the marathons.

El abuelo **hablaba** mientras su nieta **tomaba** notas.
speaking → while taking notes

The grandfather talked while his granddaughter took notes.

■ Use the imperfect to indicate that an action in the past was interrupted by another event (often in the preterite) or was never completed.

Íbamos a la escuela cuando encontramos la pelota.

We were going to school when we found the ball.

Raúl **visitaba** a la maestra Miller cuando tuvo una inspiración.

Raúl was visiting with Mrs. Miller when he had an inspiration.

■ In the imperfect, the verbs **conocer, saber, querer,** and **poder** have English equivalents with slightly different implications.

conocer—**Conocí** implies that you met someone.
         Conocía implies that you knew him.

saber—**Supe** implies that you found something out.
       Sabía implies that you knew it.

querer—**Quise** implies that you tried to do something.
        Quería implies that you wanted to.

poder—**Pude** implies that you managed to do something.
       Podía implies that you tried.

Para practicar

A. ¡Se apagaron las luces! ¿Qué hacían estas personas cuando se apagaron las luces? *(the lights went out)*

MODELO: la maestra
           La maestra enseñaba matemáticas cuando se apagaron las luces.

1. la secretaria de la escuela
2. el conserje de la escuela
3. la directora de la escuela
4. la abuela de la niña enferma
5. los niños en el patio de recreo
6. el maestro de Educación física

B. A la vez...   Después de escuchar las historias que trajeron los estudiantes a la escuela, Raúl hace un ejercicio de imaginación. Diga que más pasaba en el momento en que ocurrían estos eventos.

MODELO: Mientras los niños caminaban a la escuela...
Mientras los niños caminaban a la escuela, hablaban del partido de béisbol.

1.   Mientras los maestros enseñaban Matemáticas, los niños...
2.   Mientras teníamos una pelea de agua, nosotros...
3.   Mientras la maestra escribía en la pizarra, algunos niños...
4.   Mientras mi mamá preparaba el desayuno, yo...
5.   Mientras teníamos una pelea de agua, los maestros...
6.   Mientras los niños jugaban en el patio de recreo, los monitores...

C. ¿Qué hacía usted?   ¿Recuerda el primer día de la escuela o de una clase nueva? Describa cómo se sentía, qué pensaba y qué más hacía mientras esperaba al maestro o profesor.

MODELO: *Me sentía nervioso/a porque quería aprender mucho. Tenía miedo de no poder comprender. Tomaba soda mientras esperaba al maestro.*

Módulo 2

La historia oral

Proyecto de la historia oral

Descripción: Proyecto para enseñar la historia personal y de la comunidad de los estudiantes mientras usan las modalidades de *escuchar, escribir, hablar*. El proyecto incorpora la Biografía, los Estudios sociales, Lengua e Historia.

Las técnicas:

1. **Escuchar:** identificar a personas para preguntar; escuchar críticamente.

2. **Escribir:** describir, informar y entretener al público. Organizar información.

3. **Hablar:** presentar información oralmente. Métodos para comunicación verbal y no-verbal.

OBJETIVO: Usar todas las técnicas verbales para demostrar cómo cambian las comunidades, instituciones, familias e individuos a lo largo del tiempo.

Titulares del periódico

Pancho Villa y la Revolución Mexicana llegan a Columbus
Columbus, New Mexico, 9 de marzo, 1916

Vuelan los hermanos Wright: Kitty Hawk
N. C. 17 de diciembre, 1903

¡TERMINA LA SEGUNDA GUERRA MUNDIAL!
¡VIVA LA PAZ!
Washington, DC, 14 de agosto, 1945

EL HOMBRE EN LA LUNA: ¡Llegan los astronautas!
La Luna, 16 de julio, 1969

A. ¿Cómo se dice?   Llene el espacio con una palabra o frase lógica.

1. Un satélite del planeta Tierra es la _____.

2. Un _____ es una persona especializada en la exploración del espacio.

3. La ausencia de la guerra es la _____.

4. Una frase que identifica una noticia en el periódico es un

    _____.

B. Empareje.   Identifique la palabra de la columna **B** que mejor represente la palabra de la columna **A**.

A		**B**
1. _____ revolución	**a.**	persona que lucha contra un enemigo
2. _____ vuelan	**b.**	explorador del espacio
3. _____ astronauta	**c.**	viajar por el aire
4. _____ soldado	**d.**	guerra

La historia oral

Raúl estaba tan conmovido por los resultados del proyecto que hicieron los niños de Menlo Park que decidió presentar el proyecto como parte de su tesis. Aquí hay un pasaje de la tarea de una de las niñas más tímidas que él usó como ilustración del impacto del proyecto.

Una mañana mientras yo me vestía para ir a la escuela, estaba pensando en mis antepasados—en si algunos de ellos eran famosos o si trabajaban con personas famosas.

Cuando llegué a la escuela esa mañana, vi en la Agenda del Día que íbamos a tener una presentación especial. Entonces le pregunté a mi maestro quién iba a hablar con nosotros. Él me explicó que tenía que ver con este proyecto. Íbamos a escribir de nuestra familia y de nuestro barrio.

Entonces, en una de las tareas que nos pidió, tuvimos que escribir sobre un antepasado importante. Cuando llegué a casa, le pregunté a mi nana si teníamos a alguien importante en la familia. No sabía mucho pero sí me dijo que uno de mis bisabuelos era un soldado de Pancho Villa. Yo me quedé muy sorprendida cuando supe que tenía un pariente importante.

Entonces, escribí un ensayo sobre mi bisabuelo y al día siguiente le conté la historia a la clase. Yo pensaba que era muy, muy importante tener un bisabuelo que era soldado de Pancho Villa. Me sentí muy orgullosa. Con este proyecto, aprendí algo muy importante de mi familia. Después, mi abuela me llevó a la biblioteca para buscar libros sobre Pancho Villa y sus soldados y también los investigué por Internet. También decidí que en el futuro quiero ser maestra de historia.

C. ¿Comprende usted?   Conteste las preguntas según la información del diálogo.

1. ¿Cuál era la presentación especial?
2. ¿Qué supo la niña de su nana?
3. ¿Qué hizo con la información que le dio su nana?
4. ¿Qué decidió la niña sobre su futuro?

D. El seminario y colegio de Saint John's. Su padre fue a Saint John's y quiere que usted vaya también. Después de leer el boletín, hable con su papá (su compañero/a) de cómo era la escuela cuando él asistía y cómo es ahora.

MODELO: E1: *St. John's pone atención especial al enriquecimiento de una vida personal de fe.*
E2: *Siempre podía hablar con mis profesores de mis preocupaciones y dudas.*

El seminario y colegio de Saint John's

¿Eres un católico que piensa en desempeñar un papel de líder en el siglo XXI?

Tenemos una misión

Nuestra misión principal consiste en preparar a los estudiantes para el acceso a estudios teológicos superiores en calidad de individuos maduros educados liberalmente dentro de la tradición intelectual católica.

Reunámonos

Tres residencias proporcionan alojamientos con amplias habitaciones dobles para todos los estudiantes. Las instalaciones incluyen campos de deporte, piscina, salas de gimnasio, salas de recreo con billares, tenis de mesa y una tienda para los estudiantes.

David y Goliat

St. Johns' ofrece las ventajas de un colegio pequeño: clases reducidas con una proporción óptima entre estudiantes y profesores, con la posibilidad de graduarse de una o más de las cuatro especialidades siguientes: inglés, filosofía, español y estudios religiosos.

Estructuras

Narrating in the past: El pretérito y el imperfecto

- While the preterite and the imperfect are both aspects of the past tense, they are not interchangeable. Each gives a different message about time frames.
- The preterite is often used to describe an action that is "perfectly complete" within the sentence and captures an instant of time, like a photograph.

Compré una computadora.	*I bought a computer.*
El profesor **entró** en la clase.	*The professor entered the class.*

- The imperfect is often described in terms of a video camera. The focus is on the progression of action through time, rather than on the completeness of the action. In fact, use of the imperfect sometimes means that the action may have been abandoned before completion. (The action is *imperfectly* complete in the sentence.)

La niña **pensaba** en su abuelo entró el maestro.	*The girl was thinking about her grandfather when the teacher entered.*
Navegaba por la Red cuando vi la foto de mi abuelo famoso.	*I was surfing the Web when I saw the photo of my famous grandfather.*

- Compare the following sentences and tell why the imperfect or preterite was used.

*Mientras **explicaba** el proyecto, el maestro nos **hizo** unas preguntas.*

*Mientras **explicaba** el proyecto, me **escuchaban** atentamente.*

Para practicar

A. ¿Por qué?   Explique las circunstancias que causaron estas acciones.

MODELO: Compré el libro de historia...
Compré el libro de historia porque quería aprender más historia.

1. El maestro explicó el proyecto otra vez porque...
2. Busqué información en Internet porque...
3. Mi abuela se puso nostálgica porque...
4. Mis abuelos no se escribieron por e-mail porque...
5. Los niños comieron mucho porque...
6. La maestra no vino a la escuela porque...

B. Ahora y entonces.   Diga si usted hacía estas cosas cuando era niño/a y diga si hizo lo mismo la semana pasada.

MODELO: jugar a Pac Man
Jugaba a Pac Man cuando era niña. No jugué a Pac Man la semana pasada.

1. hacer investigación para informes para la escuela por Internet
2. escribir los reportes a mano
3. hacer investigaciones sobre la historia de mi familia
4. comunicarse con su familia por e-mail
5. mirar Barney en la tele
6. comer sándwiches de crema de cacahuate y mermelada (*peanut butter and jelly*)

C. Cambios.   Con un/a compañero/a haga una lista de cinco cambios en la vida que resultaron de la revolución electrónica.

MODELO: *Antes tenía que ir a la biblioteca para investigar un tema para un informe. Ahora navego por la Red.*

Módulo 2

La historia del futuro

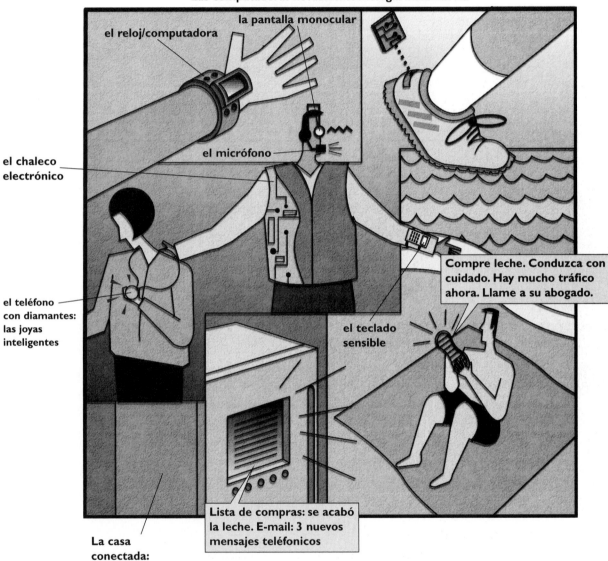

Ropa para el profesional bien conectado:
Las computadoras llevables: tecnología inalámbrica

A. ¿Cómo se dice?   Escriba la palabra que corresponda a cada una de las definiciones.

I.   Un ejemplo de la ropa inteligente es el _____.

2.   Otras computadoras llevables se encuentran en los _____ y las

_____.

3.   Un ejemplo de un electrodoméstico inteligente es _____.

4.   Tres servicios que ofrece la pantalleradora son _____,

_____ y _____.

B. En sus propias palabras.   Escriba una definición de estas palabras.

I.   la pantalla monocular
2.   las joyas inteligentes
3.   el teclado sensible
4.   la casa inteligente

La historia del futuro

La reacción al Proyecto de la historia oral *fue tan positiva por todos lados que Raúl y la maestra Miller decidieron llevarlo a otro paso. Ahora, en vez de mirar para atrás para documentar la historia, los niños tenían que mirar hacia el futuro e inventar la historia tecnológica. ¡Qué divertido! Aquí publicamos el resultado del proyecto que hicieron Edith y María Patricia en forma de una escena teatral.*

EDITH: ¿Viste la sección de "Las llevables"? ¡No creía lo que veía! Ya inventaron ropa con computadoras. Había relojes con microchips, chalecos con microchips. . . zapatos con microchips. . .

MARÍA PATRICIA: Sabía que la tecnología inalámbrica estaba cada día más avanzada, pero lo que vimos es increíble. Para mí el teléfono digital con acceso a Internet es impresionante. Cuando le pregunté al vendedor de los zapatos con microchips cómo se usan, me contó del apretón de manos electrónico. ¿Oíste lo que me dijo?

EDITH: No lo oí. En ese momento jugaba con el monocular digital con pantalla de una pulgada que imita a una pantalla de seis pulgadas. ¿Qué te dijo?

MARÍA PATRICIA: Me explicó que implantaron microchips en los zapatos que funcionan con la energía generada por el cuerpo humano. Él vio una demostración donde dos hombres de negocios estaban corriendo en el parque e intercambiaron sus tarjetas de negocios con un simple apretón de manos. El microchip en los zapatos procesó y almacenó la información. ¡Increíble!

EDITH: A mí me gustó más la sección de la casa inteligente. El momento en que vi la Pantallafrigeradora la quería. El refrigerador tenía una computadora con pantalla en la puerta—¡muchos refrigeradores entregan agua por la puerta: imagínate, éste te entrega tus mensajes! Cuando se acabó la leche, el aparato lo anotó en la lista de compras. Después llamó al supermercado para registrar la lista de compras para la semana. Mientras miraba CNN en el refrigerador, tuve una visión: estaba en el patio de recreo mirando una película en el monocular cuando me llamó mi refrigerador, me dejó una lista de mensajes y e-mails y me dijo que la casa estaba limpia. ¡Qué sueño!

MARÍA PATRICIA: Y tuve otro sueño cuando vi las computadoras llevables. Estaba aquí en el centro comercial buscando ropa nueva. Cuando vi el vestido que quería, no elegí la talla "chica, mediana o grande"; ¡elegí el tamaño 1 Ghz, 2 Ghz, o 3 Ghz!

C. ¿Comprende usted?   Conteste las preguntas según la información del diálogo.

1.   ¿Cuáles son las llevables que vieron María Patricia y Edith?
2.   ¿Qué energía usan los zapatos con microchip?
3.   ¿Qué hizo el refrigerador inteligente?
4.   ¿Qué le impresionó más a Edith? ¿Qué visión tuvo?

D. eLearning—la educación del futuro.   Como "futurista" y miembro de un comité federal de planificación, usted participó en la creación de directrices para implementación en los próximos diez años. Lea las decisiones ya tomadas y

eLearning—la educación del futuro

1. Objetivo: Movilizar a las comunidades educativas

2. Contenido: La iniciativa eLearning forma parte de la estrategia nacional—"convertirse en la economía basada en el conocimiento más competitiva y dinámica del mundo—una sociedad de la información para todos". En el futuro, el nivel económico y social de las sociedades estará determinado por el modo en que los ciudadanos pueden aprovechar las posibilidades de estas nuevas tecnologías.

3. Objetivos:
   - todas las escuelas con acceso a Internet; una Red de muy alta capacidad para las comunicaciones científicas que conectará los centros de investigación, las universidades, las bibliotecas y las escuelas entre sí
   - dotar a cada ciudadano de las competencias necesarias para vivir y trabajar en la nueva sociedad de la información
   - un número suficiente de profesores para que puedan utilizar Internet y los recursos de multimedia

termine la actividad.

1. El objetivo es _____.

2. La estrategia nacional es _____.

3. Todas las escuelas necesitan _____.

4. Los profesores deben poder _____.

E. La educación del futuro. Hablen en grupos de tres de lo que ven para el futuro, mencionando los cambios posibles en la entrega de lecciones por medio de la tecnología. Contraste con lo que había en el pasado.

MODELO: E1: *Veo aulas sin maestros en las cuales la lección se presenta en pantalla grande desde todas las partes del mundo. Antes había un profesor en cada salón.*

Estructuras   *Contrasting past tenses: El pretérito y el imperfecto*

- When you tell a story in the past, you will often use both the preterite and the imperfect aspects of the past, even in the same sentence.
- Use the preterite to describe events that took place in sequence.

Fuimos al centro comercial, **vimos** la exposición de tecnología y **tomamos** una soda.	*We went to the mall, saw the technology show, and had a soda.*

- Use the imperfect to set the scene, giving background information against which the action takes place.

Era un día normal. **Brillaba** el sol. **Hacía** calor. **Preparaba** las lecciones de clase en el salón de maestros.	*It was a normal day. The sun was shining. It was hot. I was preparing the lesson plan in the teachers' lounge.*

- Note that in the preceding scene, nothing has happened, but the stage has been set for the action to happen against.

De repente, mi secretaria **abrió** la puerta del salón. Me **dijo** algo que no **comprendí.** Cuando **se calmó** me **explicó** que había una llamada urgente de mi refrigerador.
Suddenly, my secretary opened the door to the lounge. She said something that I didn't understand. When she calmed down, she explained that there was an urgent call from my refrigerator.

- Remember that it is sometimes helpful to think of the imperfect as an activity or state that goes on through time, and the preterite as an action that is over and done with in an instant.

Para practicar

A. Caperucita Roja.   Use la forma correcta del verbo en paréntesis en el pretérito o el imperfecto para terminar esta versión moderna de Caperucita Roja. *(Little Red Riding Hood)*

Érase una vez (1) _____ (haber) una muchacha que

(2) _____ (ser) muy bonita y que (3) _____

(llamarse) Caperucita Roja. Ella y su mamá (4) _____ (vivir) en una casa muy vieja en el desierto. Todos los días, Caperucita Roja

(5) _____ (caminar) por el desierto. Allí ella

(6) _____ (jugar) con los animales y siempre

(7) _____ (buscar) hierbas y otros productos naturales para usar en los remedios caseros de su nana. Un día, su mamá le

(8) _____ (decir): "Caperucita Roja, hace dos minutos yo

(9) _____ (saber) que tu nana (10) _____ (enfermarse) mientras (11) _____ (trabajar) en su nueva computadora. Ella necesita completar las tareas para su clase de Pedagogía. Por favor, quiero que le lleves esta sopa de pollo que yo le

(12) _____ (hacer) y que le ayudes con los problemas que tiene con la computadora." Caperucita Roja (13) _____ (ponerse) sus nuevos zapatos de tenis Nike con microchip y

(14) _____ (ir) inmediatamente en dirección a la casa de la abuela. En el camino, ella (15) _____ (ver) al amigo lobo. Ella, que claramente no (16) _____ (saber) que sería peligroso hablarle, le (17) _____ (decir): "Voy a la casa de mi nana enferma para llevarle esta sopa de pollo y este té de manzanilla que mi madre le (18) _____ (hacer)". Cuando Caperucita Roja

(19) _____ (llegar) a la casa de su abuela, ya

(20) _____ (haber) muchos soldados que tenían al lobo en esposas *(handcuffs)*. Parece que la casa inteligente de la nana

(21) _____ (tener) un sistema de seguridad electrónico.

Mientras el lobo (22) _____ (entrar) por la ventana, la casa inteligente (23) _____ (llamar) a las fuerzas armadas. ¡Y todos vivieron felices para siempre—menos el lobo!

▮▮▮▮ B. ¿Y usted? Con cinco oraciones o menos, narre la acción principal de un cuento tradicional de niños, sin dar los nombres de los personajes. Después, sus compañeros deben identificar el cuento. ¡Es mejor si tiene tema académico!

Vocabulario Módulo 1

Sustantivos

el análisis	analysis	la hierba	herb
el antepasado	ancestor	la máquina	machine
el baile	dance	el/la maratón	marathon
el caballo	horse	el menudo	tripe stew
el centro comercial	shopping center	la Navidad	Christmas
el codo	elbow	el/la pariente	relative
el concurso	competition	la pedagogía	pedagogy, teaching
el contenido	content		
la cuadra	block	el principio	principle, concept
el curso	course		
el dominio	control	la reacción	reaction
la dulcería	candy store	el remedio	remedy
la eficiencia	efficiency	el río	river
el elefante	elephant	la rodilla	knee
la energía	energy	el soldado	soldier
la escala	scale	el/la supervisor/a	supervisor
la estancia	stay	la taquería	taco stand
la gallina	chicken, hen	la vaca	cow
la hallaca	cornmeal with meat, vegetables wrapped in banana leaf		

Adjetivos

casero/a	homemade

Otras expresiones

antes	before

Módulo 2

Sustantivos

el apretón de manos	handshake	la estrategia	strategy
el/la astronauta	astronaut	el festival	festival
el billar	billiards, pool	la frase	phrase
la biografía	biography	la guerra	war
el/la bisabuelo/a	great-grandparent	la habitación	room
		la iniciativa	iniciative
el chaleco	vest	la joya	jewel
el diamante	diamond	la luna	moon
la directriz	directive	la modalidad	mode, method
el electrodoméstico	appliance	la nana	grandma

el objetivo	objective	la sociedad	society
el pasaje	passage	la talla	size
el pasatiempo	hobby	el teclado	keyboard
el/la patrocinador/a	sponsor	la técnica	technique
la piscina	swimming pool	el titular	headline
la pulgada	inch	la tradición	tradition
el seminario	seminary		

Verbos

desempeñar	to carry out, to perform	movilizar	to mobilize
		narrar	to narrate
dotar	to provide	resumir	to summarize
incorporar	to incorporate		

Adjetivos

		llevable	wearable
amplio/a	ample	maduro/a	mature
anciano/a	elderly	sensible	sensitive
católico/a	Catholic	suave	smooth, great
competitivo/a	competitive	teológico/a	theological
conmovido/a	moved		
dinámico/a	dynamic		

Otras expresiones

atrás	back

Síntesis

A escuchar

Conteste las siguientes preguntas según la información que escucha en esta llamada telefónica. *Edith y María Patricia tienen más planes.*

1. ¿Qué hacía Edith cuando la llamó María Patricia?
2. ¿Qué hizo María Patricia esta tarde?
3. ¿Quiénes invitaron a María Patricia a comer?
4. ¿Por qué necesita aprender a hacer tamales?

A conversar

Entreviste a un/a anciano/a (puede ser su compañero/a) sobre su niñez—hágale cuatro o cinco preguntas en cuanto a dónde vivió, cómo eran su escuela y su casa, cuáles eran las rutinas familiares...

A leer

Los latinos se conectan

Los hispanos son el grupo étnico con mayor aumento en cuanto a su crecimiento en el uso de Internet en EE. UU.; lo usan para conectarse con sus raíces, sus amigos y familias y sus pueblos nativos en el extranjero. Y cada día hay más contenido con relevancia cultural en línea.

Se están creando plazas típicas, pero virtuales, de pueblos con fotos, noticias y mensajes.

Los jóvenes son los que corren más a usar la tecnología. De la población entre 18–24 años, el 17% usa Internet, pero un 30% de hispanos. Entre los de 25–34 años, los latinos representan el 31% en comparación con el 24% de la población general. (Fuente: Pew Internet and American Life Project 2000 Tracking Survey)

¿Comprende usted?   Escriba dos oraciones para resumir la importancia de la conexión hispana por Internet. Una de sus frases puede ser pura opinión personal. ¿Cómo se conectaban antes?

MODELO: *Los latinos usan la tecnología de email/Internet para comunicarse con sus seres queridos. Antes no había tanta comunicación.*

A escribir

Narre la historia de su niñez—escriba sobre un evento especial como unas vacaciones inolvidables o algo que hacía muchas veces, tal vez un pasatiempo favorito. Lea su cuento en clase.

Algo más

Ventana cultural

El festival latino de libros y familia

Edward James Olmos es el productor del festival latino de libros y familia que comenzó en 1997 en Los Ángeles, California. Ese año había unos 14.000 visitantes; en 1998 casi el doble. En 2000 el número creció a más de 50.000 y en 2002 había una representación de más de 200 compañías y 600 puestos *(booths)*. La entrada es gratis gracias a la participación de patrocinadores y a la publicidad.

Según las estadísticas de los festivales del 97 y 98, el 85% de los visitantes hablan español bien y el 91% hablan inglés bien. El 90% son hispanos y el 79% viajaron a México en los últimos tres años.

El festival se separa en pueblos: El pueblo de libros, el de cultura, el de salud, el de carreras y educación, el de "Mi casita", el de tecnología y el de recreo y viajes. Las casas editoriales de libros latinos generan $450 millones al año, el doble que hace 10 años.

El programa de 2003 incluye un tour del festival en Phoenix, San Diego, Los Ángeles, Houston, Chicago e Inland Empire del sur de California.

En mis propias palabras. Imagínese que es Edward James Olmos. ¿Por qué le importa dedicarse a este festival? Apunte cinco razones para su participación. Hable del pasado del festival y de su futuro. Quizás sea necesario buscar más datos en el sitio web: www.latinobookfestival.com.

MODELO: *En 2000 en Los Ángeles, había 55.000 personas en el festival, pero en 1997 sólo asistieron 14.000.*

A buscar

¿Cómo va a ser la educación del futuro, especialmente en comparación con la del pasado? En su motor de búsqueda escriba ese tema y mire los resultados. Hay un enlace ya en www.prenhall.com/rush.

A conocer: Francisco Jiménez

Francisco Jiménez es el director del *Programa de estudios étnicos* de la Universidad de Santa Clara en California. En sus clases de conversación en español, los estudiantes participan en agencias sin fines de lucro que sirven a la comunidad hispana. Jiménez también creó un programa con una escuela secundaria en su área para animar a estudiantes de minorías a ser maestros.

LECCIÓN 12

Repaso II

Lección 7: La educación alternativa
- Expressing generalizations, expectations and passive voice: *Se impersonal*
- The recent past: *Acabar de* + *infinitivo*
- Expressing likes and dislikes: *Gustar*
- Numbers: *De cien a millones; los números ordinales*

Lección 8: La escuela secundaria
- Describing daily routines: *Los verbos reflexivos*
- More on reflexive verbs: *Los verbos recíprocos*
- Expressing knowledge and familiarity: *Saber y conocer*
- Receiving the action of a verb: *El objeto directo*

Consejera

Lección 9: Consejos útiles
- Giving advice and suggestions: *Introducción breve al subjuntivo*
- More on the subjunctive: *Más sobre el subjuntivo*
- Giving recommendations: *El subjuntivo con expresiones impersonales*
- Expressing emotion and doubt: *El subjuntivo con expresiones de emoción y duda*

Lección 10: La universidad
- Discussing past activities: *Introducción al pretérito*
- More on the preterite: *Verbos irregulares*
- Relating past activities: *Verbos en –ir con cambios en el pretérito*
- More past activities: *Usos del pretérito*

Lección 11: Entonces y ahora
- Describing past situations: *El imperfecto*
- More on the imperfect: *Estados mentales, físicos y más*
- Narrating in the past: *El pretérito y el imperfecto*
- Contrasting past tenses: *El pretérito y el imperfecto*

Lección 7

La educación alternativa

Módulo I

A. Es cuando... Las madres de Beto y Pepe junto con el maestro Porter están explicando sus soluciones a la situación a unos padres y oficiales del distrito que no comprenden bien la tecnología.

Ayúdeles, por favor, escribiendo una frase equivalente a la de la lista—y una definición.

MODELO: salón virtual
Es una clase electrónica. Los estudiantes están en diferentes lugares y se comunican por computadoras.

1. escuela particular
2. la matrícula
3. bellas artes
4. tecnología

B. Los estudiantes ideales. Ahora, el maestro Porter está trabajando con los estudiantes por medio de la tecnología. Él tiene una lista de tareas para ellos, pero son tan dedicados que ya tienen todo bajo control. Dígale que ya completaron las tareas usando **acabar de.**

MODELO: Ustedes necesitan buscar tópicos por Internet.
Acabamos de buscar tópicos por Internet.

1. Susana tiene que hacer su tarea de matemáticas.
2. María y Julio tienen que investigar los dinosaurios.
3. Marco tiene que abrir su correo electrónico.

C. Imaginación. Use la imaginación para adivinar (*guess*) qué acaba de pasarles a estos maestros, padres o estudiantes para evocar estas reacciones.

MODELO: Paquito corre a casa para mostrarle a su mamá su prueba de matemáticas.
Acaba de recibir una "A".

1. El conserje mira el aula y está satisfecho.
2. Una directora ofrece un empleo a un maestro joven.
3. Un monitor del patio de recreo llama al 911.
4. Una madre le dice a otra madre: "Eres brillante".

D. ¿Qué se hace? Escriba una lista de cinco cosas que se hacen en la escuela.

MODELO: *Se aprenden matemáticas.*

Módulo 2

A. El estudiante bien informado.   Hoy los estudiantes del maestro Porter están ayudando a unos niños de Kinder con sus primeras lecciones de computadora. Usted puede ayudarlos transformando estos términos en palabras que puedan comprender fácilmente.

MODELO: correo electrónico
   Una carta que llega a la computadora y no por el servicio postal.

1. contraseña
2. nombre de usuario
3. salón de conversación
4. motor de búsqueda

B. Los gustos.   Diga si a estas personas les gustan o no les gustan estas cosas.

MODELO: un estudiante de Kinder/los juegos de vídeo
   A un estudiante de Kinder le gustan los juegos de vídeo.

1. una persona que trabaja intensamente/mensajes instantáneos
2. usted/recibir correo electrónico
3. un maestro de geografía/visitas virtuales a diferentes regiones
4. los estudiantes dedicados/computadoras que no funcionan

C. Estadísticas del sitio: *aprender.org.*   Esta organización para maestros y niños acaba de publicar una lista de estadísticas sobre el uso de su sitio web. Escriba, por favor, todos los números ¡con letra!

MODELO: Hay un **61**% más de visitantes en el sitio este año que el año pasado.
   Hay un sesenta y un por ciento más de visitantes en el sitio este año.

1. **781.000** estudiantes y maestros ya visitaron el sitio.
2. Pasan un promedio de **11** minutos navegando por el sitio.
3. Se proyecta que necesitan **$2.000.000.**
4. Dentro de **3** semanas, otros **1.5 millones** van a visitar.

D. ¿Y usted?   ¿Qué le gusta de las computadoras y qué no le gusta? Escriba una lista de cinco cosas positivas y cinco cosas negativas.

MODELO: *No me gustan los anuncios "pop-up".*

Lección 8

La escuela secundaria

Módulo 1

A. Solamente hablo un poco de español. Usted es un entrenador deportivo con un grupo de estudiantes muy diverso de diferentes partes del mundo. Una señorita tiene dificultad con el idioma. Ponga la palabra o la frase en español que ella quiere describir.

MODELO: *El complejo deportivo* donde practico en mi país es muy viejo pero las condiciones no son malas.
¿El gimnasio donde practica?

1. Todos los que practican fútbol americano tienen que usar *equipo protector para la cabeza.*
2. *El salón donde nos cambiamos de ropa es muy grande y cómodo.*
3. *La parte del gimnasio donde nos acondicionamos físicamente con máquinas*
4. *La cosa en la pared del baño donde me miro para peinarme*

B. En los vestidores. Explique para qué se usan estos productos que encontramos en el vestidor de un gimnasio moderno.

MODELO: _____ un peine, un cepillo
Se peina el cabello con un peine y un cepillo.

1. _____ el champú y el acondicionador
2. _____ el uniforme
3. _____ el espejo
4. _____ jabón

C. Sugerencias. Mientras hablan de los artículos de higiene personal, uno de los estudiantes extranjeros le pide ayuda. Necesita ir a una farmacia para comprar algunas cosas, pero no conoce las marcas de aquí. Dígale para qué usan estas marcas los miembros de su propia familia.

MODELO: Mis hermanos/productos de Vidal Sassoon
Mis hermanos se peinan con productos de Vidal Sassoon.

1. Mi hermana/champú y acondicionador Pantene
2. Muchas personas/toallas Fieldcrest
3. Mis tíos/uniformes de Nike
4. Muchos estudiantes/radio-reloj RCA

D. Buenos estudiantes—y buenos amigos.　Hay un reportero para el periódico estudiantil que nota que los entrenadores y los miembros del equipo se llevan muy bien. Es obvio que todo es a base del respeto mutuo y la cooperación. Use las siguientes acciones recíprocas para explicar estas circunstancias.

MODELO:　hablar con confianza
Nos hablamos con confianza.

1. consultar con preguntas
2. ayudar con los problemas
3. apoyar los unos a los otros
4. respetar

Módulo 2

A. Por eso.　Como la persona encargada de Club de Futuros Chefs de América, usted tiene que explicarles a los estudiantes la importancia de aprender una variedad de materias para tener éxito en la profesión. En sus propias palabras, explique por qué son importantes estas clases para ellos.

MODELO:　comercio
El comercio es importante para saber cómo ganar dinero en un restaurante.

1. química　**2.** idiomas　**3.** matemáticas

B. Los expertos.　Sus estudiantes están cada vez más convencidos de que usted es el experto más experto del mundo; por eso le hacen tantas preguntas. Termine sus preguntas usando la forma correcta de **saber** o **conocer**.

MODELO:　¿_____ usted dónde puedo encontrar nuevas recetas de comida mexicana?
¿Sabe usted dónde puedo encontrar nuevas recetas de comida mexicana?

1. ¿_____ usted a Emeril, el cocinero más famoso del mundo?

2. ¿_____ usted una universidad donde podemos estudiar más?

3. ¿_____ usted cuánto cuesta un boleto de avión de aquí a París para visitar los restaurantes famosos?

4. ¿_____ usted preparar una buena paella?

C. Más preguntas. Un grupo de estudiantes visita su restaurante. Conteste estas preguntas de los estudiantes usando un pronombre en vez de un complemento directo.

MODELO: ¿Tienen una gran variedad de vinos?
Sí, la tenemos.

1. ¿Buscan ustedes nuevas recetas cada año?
2. ¿Usan las máquinas para lavar los platos?
3. ¿Preparan muchos tamales aquí?
4. ¿Sirven vino y cerveza en la cafetería?

D. Otra vez los expertos. Explíqueles a los visitantes para qué usan estas cosas en el cultivo y la preparación de la comida. Incluya un pronombre de objecto indirecto.

MODELO: los fertilizantes
Los usamos para poner nutrientes en la tierra.

1. las recetas   **2.** los ingredientes   **3.** las semillas

Lección 9

Consejos útiles

Módulo I

A. La educación para adultos. Usted es recepcionista en un Centro de educación para adultos. Conteste las preguntas que tienen estas personas que piden información.

MODELO: Tengo un amigo que no sabe leer ni escribir, pero está determinado a aprender ahora. ¿Qué clases necesita?
Necesita clases de alfabetización.

1. Yo soy recién llegado aquí y no hablo inglés. ¿Tiene clases para mí?
2. Acabamos de llegar de Centroamérica y tenemos muchas preguntas sobre las visas y el proceso de naturalización. ¿Con quiénes hablamos?
3. Terminé mis clases de inglés y ahora quiero prepararme para una carrera como secretaria. Necesito aprender a usar una computadora. ¿Qué necesito hacer?
4. Mi esposo y yo queremos entrar en la universidad comunitaria para prepararnos para una carrera nueva, pero no sabemos qué queremos estudiar ni ser al final. ¿Cón quién debemos hablar?

B. La voz de la experiencia. El Centro de educación para adultos ofrece una orientación para los nuevos estudiantes una vez a la semana. Termine usted las recomendaciones que hace el "veterano" del centro a los nuevos participantes. Llene cada espacio con el subjuntivo del verbo indicado.

1. Les recomiendo que _____ (pasar) mucho tiempo conociendo la cultura.

2. También les sugiero que _____ (buscar) a un mentor aquí.

3. Espero que ustedes _____ (estar cómodos) aquí en este pueblo.

4. Quiero que me _____ (decir) sus impresiones.

C. Las reglas del Centro. Ahora usted tiene que explicar las reglas del Centro a los nuevos estudiantes. Llene el espacio con la forma indicada del verbo.

MODELO: El Centro exige que los estudiantes _____ (presentar) los documentos de inscripción antes de la clase.
El Centro exige que los estudiantes presenten los documentos de inscripción antes de la clase.

1. El maestro teme que no _____ (haber) más vacantes en la clase.

2. El estudiante le pide al maestro que _____ (hacer) una excepción.

3. Quiero que ustedes _____ (saber) la enorme importancia que tiene la educación.

4. Espero que el estudiante _____ (ir) a la clase mañana.

D. Éxito en la escuela para adultos. Como mentor estudiantil, usted ayuda a los nuevos estudiantes con sus estudios. Haga una recomendación positiva para cada uno de estos estudiantes.

MODELO: las estudiantes de ESL
Recomiendo que miren la televisión en inglés—sobre todo las telenovelas para aprender más vocabulario diario.

1. el estudiante que aprende a leer
2. la familia que no tiene comida
3. el joven que quiere asistir a la universidad
4. la señora que necesita trabajo

Módulo 2

A. Centro de información.   Ayude, por favor, a estos estudiantes con sus preguntas.

MODELO: Soy estudiante en la clase de computación y no comprendo la tarea. ¿Me puede ayudar?
Usted necesita ver a los tutores.

  1.   ¿Dónde podemos dejar a los niños durante nuestra clase?
  2.   ¿Dónde puedo encontrar a un médico?
  3.   Quiero inscribirme en unas clases. ¿Adónde voy?
  4.   ¿Puedo navegar por Internet aquí?

B. Más reglas.   Por favor, dé usted más consejos a los nuevos participantes en la orientación al terminar estas oraciones.

MODELO: Es normal que ustedes _____ (tener) miedo.
Es normal que ustedes tengan miedo.

  1.   Es importante que nosotros _____ (trabajar) juntos.

  2.   Es preferible que los niños _____ (ir) a la guardería durante la clase.

  3.   Es raro que una persona _____ (tener) problemas con nuestros maestros.

  4.   Es evidente que ustedes _____ (ser) personas inteligentes y

que también _____ (preocuparse) por el futuro.

C. Problemas de los estudiantes.   ¡Ay, no! Algunos de los nuevos estudiantes están nerviosos en la escuela y tienen ideas muy raras. Usted tiene que ser muy diplomático al contrariarlos. Usando el indicativo o el subjuntivo y toda la cortesía que pueda, acepte o rechace *(reject)* estas declaraciones.

MODELO: Estudiante: Esta escuela es sólo para los ricos.
Usted: No es verdad que...
No es verdad que esta escuela sea sólo para los ricos.

  1.   Estudiante: Yo soy el único estudiante inteligente aquí.
Usted: Dudo que...
  2.   Estudiante: ¡Yo no vuelvo nunca a esta clase!
Usted: Es urgente que...
  3.   Estudiante: Mi maestro es mejor que el otro maestro.
Usted: No creo que...
  4.   Estudiante: Nadie aprende nada aquí nunca.
Usted: No es verdad que...

ᴍᴍ D. Decisiones académicas. Uno de ustedes es un estudiante que quiere abandonar las clases e ir a trabajar, y el otro es el mentor que quiere retenerlo en la escuela. Cada uno de ustedes debe preparar una lista de cinco razones para ilustrar su punto de vista. Use, por favor, una de las frases impersonales para demostrar su imparcialidad.

MODELO: Estudiante: *Es importante que gane dinero.*
Mentor: *Es probable que gane más dinero con una educación más fuerte.*

Lección 10

La universidad

Módulo 1

A. El consejero viejo. Un consejero muy viejo y un poco olvidadizo quiere explicarles algunos de los términos importantes para el proceso de planificar los estudios universitarios. El problema es que usted tiene que ayudarlo a encontrar las palabras que no puede recordar.

MODELO: Hay una persona en el colegio responsable de orientar a los estudiantes durante el proceso de solicitar admisión a la universidad. *¿Un consejero?*

1. Es el formulario que los estudiantes llenan con datos personales para pedir entrada a una universidad.
2. Es el dinero que usted puede solicitar para ayudar con los gastos de la educación.
3. Esta es una reunión en persona que un estudiante tiene con representantes de la universidad para determinar si es la universidad indicada para esta persona. ¿Cuál es la palabra que busco?
4. Es el documento que el estudiante tiene que escribir con su visión personal para el futuro.

B. La visita a la universidad. Usted tiene la suerte de visitar su universidad preferida para ver cómo es la vida estudiantil. Use el pretérito para escribir un informe sobre lo que hizo.

MODELO: despertarse a las 6 de la mañana
Me desperté a las seis de la mañana.

1. buscar la cafetería
2. entregar los documentos importantes a la recepcionista del decano
3. hablar durante media hora con un estudiante de primer año
4. ir a la recepción para los padres de los estudiantes nuevos

C. Un robo en las oficinas del decano.   Usted y su guía llegaron muy temprano a la oficina del decano—antes que nadie. O casi nadie. Cuando llegaron, notaron que algo estaba mal. Escriba este Informe de incidente—usando el pretérito.

MODELO: *Venimos* a la oficina a las siete.
Vinimos a la oficina a las siete.

1. Algo *hace* ruído.
2. No *podemos* ver nada al principio.
3. Entonces *vemos* a dos personas cerca de un archivo con documentos importantes.
4. Yo *quiero* llamar a la policía y mi compañero *quiere* observar a los ladrones *(robbers)*.
5. Le *digo* al policía que *tenemos* un problema en la oficina.
6. Los policías *llegan* rápidamente y les *ponen* esposas a los criminales.
7. V*amos* con el policía para hacer una declaración.

D. Una emergencia personal.   Describa o invente una emergencia en la que participó. Use el pretérito para decirnos: 1) el problema, 2) lo que hizo y 3) el resultado.

MODELO: *Hace 10 años, yo vi un accidente de automóvil en la calle. Llamé al 911 y una ambulancia vino inmediatamente. Me llamaron un héroe.*

Módulo 2

A. En la universidad.   Explique en sus propias palabras las siguientes cosas que se encuentran en una universidad.

MODELO: becas
Las becas son dinero que dan a estudiantes dedicados para pagar los gastos de la universidad. Una beca es dinero gratis y el estudiante no tiene que pagarlo.

1. préstamos
2. bonete y toga
3. diploma
4. discurso de despedida

B. El estudiante o los profesores.   Diga si el estudiante **(Yo)** o los profesores **(Ellos)** hicieron las siguientes cosas para la clase. Use el tiempo pretérito.

MODELO: preparar los exámenes
Ellos prepararon los exámenes.

1. buscar información para el informe final en la biblioteca
2. dormir en la residencia estudiantil
3. pedir más tiempo para completar una tarea
4. seguir las instrucciones en el examen
5. traer actividades interesantes a la clase para ayudar a los estudiantes

C. ¿Qué hicieron los estudiantes ayer?   Hoy fue el examen final en una clase muy importante para su graduación. El profesor quiere saber cómo pasó usted el día ayer preparándose para el examen.

dormir	pedir	buscar	estar	encontrar	servir
decir	hacer	ir		traer	conducir

MODELO: pedir
Yo pedí las notas de clase a unos compañeros.

D. Necesitamos su ayuda.   Usted y su compañero fueron voluntarios para organizar las festividades de la ceremonia de graduación. Haga una lista de cinco actividades que hicieron para realizar este día.

MODELO: *Primero organizamos una lista de los graduados.*

Lección 11

Entonces y ahora

Módulo 1

A. Los abuelos.   Los niños de hoy no conocen el mundo sin las conveniencias modernas. Para cada innovación, dé el equivalente que usaron los abuelos.

MODELO: el teléfono inalámbrico
el teléfono de disco

1. investigación por Internet
2. copiadora electrónica
3. tiendas pequeñas: la dulcería
4. clases virtuales

B. La anticipación de Raúl.   El día de antes de volver a Menlo Park como maestro, Raúl se puso muy nervioso. Llene los espacios con la forma indicada del pretérito o imperfecto para explicarle a la Sra. Miller cómo se sentía.

Ayer, yo no (1) _____ (tener) mucha energía.

(2) _____ (estar) muy nerviosa pensando en mi clase. Durante la tarde, yo intenté comunicarme por e-mail con usted muchas veces, pero

(3) _____ (ser) imposible. Primero, (4) _____ (haber) problemas con mi computadora y después no (5) _____

(funcionar) mi servicio de Internet. Cuando me acosté, no

(6) _____ (poder) dormir pensando en los niños. Esta mañana

cuando me levanté, me (7) _____ (ponerse) muy contento pensando en mi nueva carrera y mis nuevos estudiantes.

C. La rutina de la clase.   Una hora después de empezar la clase, Raúl se tranquilizó notando que los niños ya estaban tan cómodos que podían volver a su rutina normal. Diga por qué estas personas necesitaban hacer estas acciones.

MODELO: Alejandro tomó agua.
Alejandro tomó agua porque tenía sed.

1.   Fui a la cafetería.
2.   La Sra. Miller fue al salón de maestros.
3.   Los estudiantes fueron a la biblioteca.
4.   Investigaste a Pancho Villa por Internet.

D. ¿Y usted?   ¿Recuerda su primer día de la escuela? Escriba (o invente) cómo se sentía y qué hacía el primer día de la escuela.

MODELO: *Siempre me acostaba temprano la noche antes del primer día de la escuela. Normalmente estaba nervioso.*

Módulo 2

A. Vocabulario. Raúl quiere confirmar que los estudiantes comprenden el nuevo vocabulario que necesitan para los proyectos de historia oral. Dé usted la palabra o frase que mejor identifique cada concepto.

MODELO: la comunidad (las personas, las casas, las calles y los negocios) en el área donde yo vivo
Mi barrio

1. una medicina que se preparaba en casa para curar enfermedades menores
2. una manera de solicitar información o opiniones personales hablando con otra persona
3. los miembros de mi familia de quienes soy descendiente
4. el combate entre dos naciones

B. ¿Eres tú? Cuando la ex-directora de Menlo Park, Patricia McCant, vino a visitar a su colega, la señora Miller, tuvo una gran sorpresa. Llene el espacio con la forma indicada del imperfecto o del pretérito para saber lo que pasó.

MODELO: PATRICIA: *Perdone, señor. Busco a la Sra. Miller. ¡Raúl Torres!, ¿eres tú? Hace muchos años, ¿no <u>eras</u> (ser) estudiante aquí en la escuela Menlo Park?*
RAÚL: *Sí, yo <u>asistía</u> (asistir) a Menlo Park. ¿Es usted la Directora McCant?*

PATRICIA: Sí, Raúl. Te recuerdo bien. Tú siempre (1) _____

(tener) interés en la tecnología y ¡cuánto te (2) _____ (gustar) los

juegos en el patio de recreo! Y recuerdo que siempre (3) _____

(jugar) en el gimnasio con Alicia.

RAÚL: ¡Qué buena memoria! ¿Sabe qué? Hace seis meses cuando yo

(4) _____ (graduarse) de la universidad, yo (5) _____

(casarse) con Alicia.

PATRICIA: ¡No me digas! Recuerdo como si fuera ayer un día que la secretaria me (6) _____ (llamar) de una reunión en el distrito. Ella (7) _____ (estar) muy nerviosa. Me (8) _____ (decir) que tú y Alicia (9) _____ (jugar) en el gimnasio cuando de repente (*suddenly*) tú (10) _____ (caerse). Cuando yo (11) _____ (llegar) e (12) _____ (investigar), tú (13) _____ (estar) inconsciente en el patio. La enfermera (14) _____ (trabajar) para reanimarte y Alicia y tus otros amigos (15) _____ (tener) tanto miedo que lloraban en la clase.

RAÚL: También recuerdo que usted me (16) _____ (llamar) "Corazón". ¡Qué emoción! Y, ¡qué buena memoria!

PATRICIA: Yo no lo (17) _____ (olvidar) nunca. Ésta fue la primera crisis médica de mi carrera. La primera de muchas, muchas más entre mis estudiantes.

C. ¿Y usted? ¿Recuerda alguna vez en que usted tuvo una crisis en la escuela o en el trabajo? Narre la anécdota incluyendo las circunstancias y detalles.

MODELO: *En mi primer empleo cuando tenía 17 años, contestaba los teléfonos. No sabía usar el sistema porque era complicado, y desconecté al jefe durante una llamada a Europa.*

Spanish-English Glossary

a   *to*   1
a ciencia cierta   *for sure*   9
a continuación   *following*   3
a pesar de   *in spite of*   10
¿A qué hora...?   *At what time...?*   1
a sus órdenes   *at your service; may I help you?*   PC
a través de   *through*   7
a veces   *at times*   3
A ver   *Let's see*   1
abajo   *under*   5
abandonar   *to abandon*   10
abarcar   *to cover*   9
abierto/a   *open*   7
el/la abogado/a   *attorney*   9
abogar   *to defend, to champion with*   2
abrazarse   *to embrace*   8
el abrazo   *hug*   4
abril   *April*   PC
abrir   *to open*   5
el/la abuelo/a   *grandfather/mother*   2
aburrido/a   *bored*   2
el abuso   *abuse*   5
acá   *here*   10
acabar   *to end*   8
acabar de + inf.   *to have just*   7
académico/a   *academic*   1
acceder   *to gain access to*   7
el accidente   *accident*   1
la acción   *action*   5
el aceite   *oil*   8
aceptar   *to accept*   1
acerca de   *about, concerning*   3
aclarar   *to clarify*   3
acompañar   *to accompany*   5
aconsejar   *to advise*   9
acostar (ue)   *to put to bed*   4
el acta (f.) de nacimiento   *birth certificate*   1
la actitud   *attitude*   2
la actividad   *activity*   1
actual   *current*   1
el acuario   *aquarium*   2
el acuerdo   *agreement*   10
adecuado/a   *adequate*   3
adelante   *forward*   1

además   *besides*   3
adentro   *inside*   2
el aderezo   *dressing*   8
adiós   *good-bye*   PC
adjunto/a   *enclosed*   2
la administración   *administration*   2
el/la administrador/a   *administrator*   1
admitir   *to admit*   5
el/la adolescente   *adolescent*   2
el/ la adulto/a   *adult*   1
afectar   *to affect*   5
el/la aficionado/a   *fan*   8
afuera   *outside*   2
el agente   *agent*   5
agosto   *August*   PC
agradable   *pleasant*   3
agrícola   *agricultural*   10
la agricultura   *agriculture*   10
el agua (f.)   *water*   2
ahora   *now*   1
ahorrar   *to save*   7
el aire   *air*   3
el aire acondicionado   *air conditioning*   2
al aire libre   *open air*   9
¡Ajá!   *Aha!*   1
ajustado/a   *adjusted*   10
al azar   *at random*   7
al contrario   *to the contrary*   4
al corriente   *current*   3
al por mayor   *wholesale*   9
al por menor   *retail*   9
al principio   *at the beginning*   5
al revés   *in reverse*   7
la alarma   *alarm*   5
el/la alcalde/sa   *mayor*   5
alcanzar   *to reach*   10
el alcohol   *alcohol*   2
alegrarse de que   *to be happy about*   9
alejarse de   *to move away from*   5
el alemán   *German*   8
la alergia   *allergy*   3
alérgico/a   *allergic*   3
alerto/a   *alert*   3
la alfabetización   *literacy*   9

el alfabeto   *alphabet*   1
la alfombra   *rug, carpet*   2
el álgebra (f.)   *algebra*   7
algo   *something*   1
alguien   *somebody, anybody*   5
algún/uno/a   *some*   3
el alimentador   *feeder*   7
alimentar   *to feed*   8
aliviar   *to relieve*   3
allí   *there*   5
el almacén   *department store*   5
almorzar (ue)   *to have lunch*   4
el almuerzo   *lunch*   1
el alojamiento   *lodging*   10
el alquiler   *rent*   10
alrededor de   *around, about*   7
el altavoz   *speaker*   7
alternativo/a   *alternative*   7
alto/a   *tall, high*   1, 2
el alumno/a   *student*   7
amar   *to love*   10
amarillo/a   *yellow*   2
ambicioso/a   *ambitious*   1
ambiental   *environmental*   9
el ambiente   *environment*   3
el ámbito   *sphere, field*   7
ambos   *both*   2
la ambulancia   *ambulance*   5
la amenaza   *threat*   5
americano/a   *American*   1
el/la amigo/a   *friend*   PC
la amistad   *friendship*   8
amistoso/a   *friendly*   2
el amor   *love*   2
amplio/a   *ample*   11
la ampolla   *blister*   3
el análisis   *analysis*   11
anciano/a   *elderly*   11
animado/a   *lively*   7
el/la animador/a   *cheerleader*   8
animar   *to encourage*   4
el ánimo   *encouragement*   4
anoche   *last night*   7
anotar   *to make note of*   10
la ansiedad   *anxiety*   3
anteayer   *day before yesterday*   7

el antepasado *ancestor* 11
antes *before* 11
anticipar *to anticipate* 10
antipático/a *unpleasant* 1
anunciar *to announce* 4
el anuncio *announcement* 2
el año *year* 7
apagar *to turn off* 4
el apartamento *apartment* 1
el apellido *last name* 1
aplicar *to apply* 2
aportar *to contribute* 10
apoyar *to support* 2
el apoyo *support* 7
aprender *to learn* 1
el aprendizaje *learning* 4
el apretón de manos *hand-shake* 11
apropiado/a *appropriate* 2
aprovechar *to take advantage of* 2
apuntar *to note* 9
aquel/la *that* 7
aquí *here* 4
el/la árbitro *referee* 8
el árbol *tree* 5
el archivo *file* 3
el arco iris *rainbow* 2
la arena *sand* 3
el arma (f.) *weapon* 5
el armario *closet* 1
la armonía *harmony* 5
arreglar *to arrange, to fix* 8
arriba *above* 5
el arroz *rice* 8
el arte (f.) *art* 1
las artes culinarias *culinary arts* 8
artístico/a *artistic* 2
la asamblea *assembly* 4
el ascensor *elevator* 5
así *so, thus* 1
asiático/a *Asian* 1
la asignatura *subject* 2
la asistencia *attendance* 7
el/la asistente *assistant* PC
asistir *to attend* 2
el asma *asthma* 3
la asociación *association* 1
la aspirina *aspirin* 1
el/la astronauta *astronaut* 11
el asunto *matter* 9
el ataque *attack* 3

la atención *attention* 1
atender (ie) *to assist* 8
atentamente *sincerely* 9
el/la atleta *athlete* 8
atlético/a *athletic* 1
el atletismo *athletics* 7
atraer *to attract* 8
atrás *back, behind* 11
atrasado/a *slow, backward* 4
el atún *tuna* 8
la audición *hearing* 3
el auditorio *auditorium* 1
el aula (f.) *classroom* 7
aumentar *to augment* 5
aunque *even though* 7
la ausencia *absence* 5
ausente *absent* 2
el autobús *bus* 1
el automóvil *automobile* 5
el/la autor/a *author* 2
la autorización *authorization* 2
avanzado/a *advanced* 7
el/la aventurero/a *adventurer* 2
averiguar *to find out* 8
avisar *to notify* 3
ayer *yesterday* 7
la ayuda *help* 2
el/la ayudante *helper* 2
ayudar *to help* 1
el/la azúcar *sugar* 8
azul *blue* 2

la bacteria *bacteria* 3
bailar *to dance* 2
el baile *dance* 11
bajo/a *short (height)* 1
el balón *ball* 8
la banda *band* 8
la bandeja *tray* 7
la bandera *flag* 1
el banquete *banquet* 10
bañarse *to bathe* 8
el baño *bathroom, bath* 1
la barbilla *chin* 3
la barriga *belly, tummy* 3
el barrio *neighborhood* 2
básico/a *basic* 10
el básquetbol *basketball* 1
bastante *enough* 4
beber *to drink* 2
la beca *scholarship* 8

el béisbol *baseball* 2
las bellas artes *fine arts* 7
el beneficio *benefit* 5
besar *to kiss* 2
la biblioteca *library* 1
bien *well* PC
los bienes *goods* 10
los bienes raíces *real estate* 2
el bienestar *well-being* 4
bienvenidos *welcome* PC
bilingüe *bilingual* 1
el billar *billiards, pool* 11
la biografía *biography* 11
la biología *biology* 8
el/la bisabuelo/a *great-grand-parent* 11
blanco/a *white* 1
la blusa *blouse* 5
la boca *mouth* 3
la boleta de calificaciones *report card* 4
el boletín *bulletin* 2
el bolsillo *pocket* 7
la bomba *bomb* 5
el/la bombero/a *firefighter* 5
el bonete *cap* 10
bonito/a *pretty* 1
el borrador *eraser* 1
borrar *to erase* 1
la botella *bottle* 8
el boxeo *boxing* 2
el brazo *arm* 3
brillante *brilliant* 7
bruto/a *gross (income)* 10
buenas noches *good evening, good night* PC
buenas tardes *good afternoon* PC
bueno/a *good* 1
buenos días *good morning* PC
el bufete *law firm* 9
buscar *to look for* 1
la búsqueda *search* 7

el caballo *horse* 11
la cabeza *head* 3
cada *each* 1
la cadena *chain* 8
caerse (ig) *to fall down* 3
café *brown* 2
la cafetería *cafeteria* 1
la caja *box, cash drawer* 1, 10

el/la cajero/a *cashier* 10
los calcetines *socks* 5
la calculadora *calculator* 7
la calefacción *heating* 2
el calendario *calendar* PC
la calidad *quality* 2
caliente *hot* 2
la calificación *grade* 9
la calle *street* 1
la calma *calm* 5
calmarse *to calm down* 8
el calor *heat* 2
la cama *bed* 3
la cámara *camera* 7
cambiar *to change* 8
el cambio *change* 4
caminar *to walk* 2
el camino *road* 5
la camisa *shirt* 2
la camiseta *T-shirt* 8
el campeonato *championship* 8
el campo *countryside, field* 2
la canción *song* 2
el/la candidato/a *candidate* 1
canino/a *canine* 5
cansado/a *tired* 2
el/la cantante *singer* 4
cantar *to sing* 2
capaz *capable* 3
la capital *capital* 7
el/la capitán/ana *captain* 8
la cara *face* 5
caracterizar *to characterize* 3
caro/a *expensive* 8
la carrera *career* 8
la carta *letter* 1
la casa *house* 1
el casco *helmet* 8
casero/a *homemade* 11
casi *almost* 3
castaño/a *brown (hair/eyes)* 2
el castigo *punishment* 4
católico/a *Catholic* 11
causar *to cause* 5
la ceguera *blindness* 4
celebrar *to celebrate* 4
el censo *census* 10
el centavo *cent* 10
el centro *center* 1
el centro comercial *shopping center* 11
cerca de *near* 3

el cerebro *brain* 3
la ceremonia *ceremony* 10
cerrar (ie) *to close* 3
el certificado *certificate* 1
la cerveza *beer* 7
el césped *grass* 9
el chaleco *vest* 11
la champaña *champagne* 8
el champú *shampoo* 2
la chaqueta *jacket* 5
charlar *to chat* 7
el cheque *check* 1
el chicle *gum* 6
chico/a *small (size)* 2
el/la chico/a *boy, girl* 2
el ciberespacio *cyberspace* 7
el ciclo *cycle* 2
el ciclón *cyclone* 5
ciego/a *blind* 4
la ciencia *science* 1
científico/a *scientific* 2
cierto/a *certain* 9
el cigarro *cigar, cigarette* 2
el cine *theater, cinema* 7
el círculo *circle* 5
la cita *appointment, date* 1
la ciudad *city* 1
la ciudadanía *citizenship* 9
el/la ciudadano/a *citizen* 10
claro que sí/no *of course (not)* 1
la clase *class* PC
clave *key* 7
el/la cliente/a *client* 2
el clima *climate* 9
la clínica *clinic* 1
el club *club* 10
la cobija *blanket* 5
cobrar *to charge* 9
cocinar *to cook* 5
el/la cocinero/a *cook* 2
el código *code* 1
el codo *elbow* 11
el cole(gio) *school* 2
el/la colega *colleague* 1
colocar *to place* 5
los columpios *swings* 3
comentar *to comment* 4
el comentario *comment* 4
comenzar (ie) *to begin* 4
comer *to eat* 1
el comercio *business* 8
la comezón *itch* 3

cómico/a *comical* PC
la comida *food, meal* 1
el comité *committee* 4
como *as, like* 4
¿Cómo está Ud.? *How are you? (formal)* PC
¿Cómo estás? *How are you? (familiar)* PC
¿Cómo se dice...? *How do you say...?* 1
¿Cómo se llama Ud.? *What is your name? (formal)* PC
¿Cómo te llamas? *What is your name? (familiar)* PC
cómodo/a *comfortable* 2
el/la compañero/a *companion* 4
compartir *to share* 4
la competencia *competition* 9
competitivo/a *competitive* 11
el complejo *complex* 8
completar *to complete* 5
la complicación *complication* 3
el comportamiento *behavior* 2
el/la comprador/a *buyer* 7
comprar *to buy* 1
comprender *to understand* 1
comprometer *to compromise* 7
la computación *computing* 9
la computadora *computer* 1
común *common* 3
comunicar *to communicate* 5
la comunidad *community* 1
comunitario/a *community* 9
con *with* 1
con permiso *excuse me* PC
la conciencia *conscience* 9
el concurso *competition* 11
la concusión *concussion* 3
el condado *county* 2
conducir (zc) *to drive* 3
la conducta *conduct, behavior* 5
el conejillo de Indias *guinea pig* 2
la conferencia *conference* 1
la confianza *confidence* 2
confiar *to confide* 5
el conflicto *conflict* 5
confundido/a *confused* 2

conjunto/a *joint* 2

conmigo *with me* 4

conmovido/a *moved* 11

conocer (zc) *to know, be acquainted with* 1

el conocimiento *knowledge* 2

consciente *conscious* 3

el/la consejero/a *counselor* 2

el consejo *advice* 2

el conserje *custodian* 1

consultar *to consult* 3

el consultorio *office (medical)* 1

contactar *to contact* 3

contagioso/a *contagious* 3

contar (ue) *to count* 1

el contenido *content* 11

contento/a *content, happy* 2

contestar *to answer* 1

contigo *with you* 10

contra *against* 3

la contraseña *password* 7

el/la contratista *contractor* 9

cooperar *to cooperate* 5

el/la coordinador/a *coordinator* 4

la copiadora *copier* 1

copiar *to copy* 5

el corazón *heart, sweetheart* 3

el coro *choir* 2

correcto/a *correct* 2

corregir (i) *to correct* 5

el correo *mail* 7

correr *to run* 2

cortar *to cut* 7

el corte *cut* 3

la cortesía *courtesy* 2

corto *short (length)* 5

la cosa *thing* 1

la cosecha *harvest* 8

costar (ue) *to cost* 4

el costo *cost* 2

la costumbre *custom* 2

el crayón *crayon* 1

el/la creador/a *creator* 5

crear *to create* 5

crecer (zc) *to grow* 8

creciente *growing* 5

el crecimiento *growth* 9

el crédito *credit* 10

la creencia *belief* 4

creer *to believe* 2

el crimen *crime* 5

crítico/a *critical* 3

la cruz *cross* 5

el cuaderno *notebook* 1

la cuadra *block* 11

¿Cuál es la fecha de hoy? *What's today's date?* PC

¿Cuál/es? *Which (one/s)?* 1

¿Cuándo? *When?* 1

¿Cuánto/a? *How much?* 1

¿Cuántos/as? *How many?* 1

cuarto/a *quarter, fourth* 1

cubrir *to cover* 5

el cuello *neck* 3

la cuenta *bill* 7

el cuento *story* 1

el cuerpo *body* 2

el cuidado *care* 2

cuidar *to take care of* 2

cuidarse *to take care of (oneself)* 8

culpable *guilty* 10

la cultura *culture* 9

el cumpleaños *birthday* 2

cumplir *to fulfill* 7

la cuota *fee* 2

curar *to cure* 3

cursar *to take a course* 10

el curso *course* 11

la custodia *custody* 10

cuyo/a *whose* 10

el daño *damage* 3

dar *to give* 3

los datos *data, information* 7

de *of, from* 1

de nada *you're welcome* PC

debajo de *under* 3

deber *to ought to, should* 2

débil *weak* 2

el decano *dean* 10

decidir *to decide* 5

décimo/a *tenth* 7

decir (i) (g) *to say, to tell* 2

la declaración *declaration* 5

declarar *to declare* 3

dedicado/a *dedicated* 1

el dedo *finger* 3

defender (ie) *to defend* 5

dejar *to leave (behind), to let, allow* 5, 7

la delincuencia *delinquency* 5

demasiado/a *too* 8

demostrar (ue) *to demonstrate* 1

el/la dependiente/a *dependent* 10

el deporte *sport* 1

deportivo/a *sports-related* 2

el derecho *right* 10

el desacuerdo *disagreement* 5

el desafío *challenge* 9

desanimado/a *discouraged* 4

desaparecer (zc) *to disappear* 7

desarrollar *to develop* 2

el desarrollo *development* 2

el desastre *disaster* 2

el desayuno *breakfast* 1

descansar *to rest* 2

desconocido/a *unknown* 3

descubrir *to discover* 7

desear *to wish* 9

desecho/a *ruined, shattered* 5

desempeñar *to carry out, to perform* 11

el desempeño *performance* 4

deshonesto *dishonest* 2

la despedida *farewell* 10

despedirse (i) *to say goodbye* 4

despertarse (ie) *to wake up* 8

después *after* 2

la destreza *skill* 8

detener (ie, g) *to stop* 4

la deuda *debt* 10

devolver (ue) *to return (something)* 9

el diamante *diamond* 11

diario/a *daily* 5

dibujar *to sketch, to draw* 1

el diccionario *dictionary* 1

diciembre *December* PC

el diente *tooth* 3

diferente *different* 1

difícil *difficult* 1

dinámico/a *dynamic* 11

el dinero *money* 1

el diploma *diploma* 9

la dirección *address* 1

directamente *directly* 5

el/la director/a *principal, director* 2

la directriz *directive* 11

dirigido/a *directed, supervised* 9

la discapacidad *disability* 4

discapacitado/a *disabled* 4

la disciplina *discipline* 5

el disco compacto *compact disc* 2

el disco duro *hard drive* 7

discutir *to argue* 2

el diseño *design* 4

disfrutar *to have fun* 9

disminuir (y) *to reduce* 3

disponible *available* 1

la distancia *distance* 7

el distrito *district* 1

divertido/a *fun, enjoyable* 4

el documento *document* 1

doler (ue) *to hurt, cause pain* 3

el dolor *pain* 3

el domicilio *address* 1

domingo *Sunday* PC

el dominio *control* 11

¿Dónde? *Where?* 1

dormir (ue) *to sleep* 2

el dormitorio *bedroom* 2

dotar *to provide* 11

el drama *drama* 8

la droga *drug* 2

el/la drogadicto/a *drug addict* 5

la ducha *shower* 8

ducharse *to shower* 8

la duda *doubt* 9

dudar *to doubt* 9

dudoso/a *doubtful* 9

el/la dueño/a *owner* 9

dulce *sweet* 8

la dulcería *candy store* 11

durante *during* 1

el durazno *peach* 8

la edad *age* 1

el edificio *building* 5

la educación *education* 1

eficaz *efficient* 4

la eficiencia *efficiency* 11

eficiente *efficient* 1

el ejemplo *example* 5

el ejercicio *exercise* 1

el ejército *army* 8

él *he* PC

la elección *choice* 7

el electrodoméstico *appliance* 11

electrónico/a *electronic* 7

el elefante *elephant* 11

elegir (i) *to opt, elect* 4

eliminar *to eliminate* 7

ella *she* PC

ellos/as *they* PC

elogiar *to praise* 5

el elogio *praise* 5

embellecer (zc) *to embellish* 9

la emergencia *emergency* 1

emocionado/a *emotional* 9

el emparedado *sandwich* 8

el empeño *determination* 9

el/la empleado/a *employee* 1

la empresa *enterprise* 8

en caso de *in case of* 1

en cuanto a *as regards* 9

en orden *in order* 10

en punto *exactly, on the dot* 1

en vez de *in place of* 7

encantado/a *delighted* 7

encantar *to delight* 9

encargado/a *in charge of* 8

la encía *gum (mouth)* 3

encontrar (ue) *to find* 4

la encuesta *survey* 8

la energía *energy* 11

enero *January* PC

la enfermedad *illness* 1

la enfermería *nursing* 3

el/la enfermero/a *nurse* 3

enfocado/a *focused* 9

el enfoque *focus* 9

enfrentar *to face* 10

enfrente de *in front of* 5

el enlace *link* 7

enojarse *to get angry* 8

el enrojecimiento *reddening* 3

la ensalada *salad* 8

el ensayo *essay* 8

enseguida *at once* 3

enseñar *to teach* 1

entender (ie) *to understand* 4

entero/a *whole* 8

entonces *then* 1

entorpecido/a *slowed down, dulled* 5

la entrada *entry* 8

entrar *to enter* 3

entre *between* 2

entregar *to hand over, deliver* 4

el/la entrenador/a *trainer, coach* 2

el entrenamiento *training* 2

el entretenimiento *entertainment* 2

la entrevista *interview* 1

el entusiasmo *enthusiasm* 5

enviar *to send* 7

la envidia *envy* 7

el equipo *equipment, team* 2

la equivocación *mistake* 4

el error *error* 1

la erupción *eruption* 3

es un placer *it's a pleasure* PC

la escala *scale* 11

la escalera *stairway* 5

escoger (j) *to choose* 7

escolar *school related* 1

escondido/a *hidden* 5

escribir *to write* 1

el escritorio *desk* 1

la escritura *writing* 1

escuchar *to listen* 1

la escuela *school* 1

esforzarse (ue) *to make an effort* 5

el esfuerzo *effort* 2

el español *Spanish* 1

especial *special* 1

el espejo *mirror* 8

esperar *to wait for, hope* 5

el/la esposo/a *spouse* 2

establecer (zc) *to establish* 5

las estadísticas *statistics* 9

el estado *state* 1

Estados Unidos *United States* 1

estadounidense *American (U.S.)* 3

la estancia *stay* 11

el estante *shelf* 1

estar *to be* 2

estar de acuerdo *to agree* 8

este/a *this* 1

estimado/a *dear (business letter)* 1

estimular *to stimulate* 9

el estómago *stomach* 3

estoy *I am* 1
la estrategia *strategy* 11
la estrella *star* 8
el estrés *stress* 9
estricto/a *strict* 8
el/la estudiante *student* 1
estudiantil *student* 2
estudiar *to study* 1
los Estudios sociales *Social Studies* 1
estúpido/a *stupid* 5
étnico/a *ethnic* 7
la evacuación *evacuation* 5
la evaluación *evaluation* 3
evaluar *to evaluate* 3
la evidencia *evidence* 3
evitar *to avoid* 3
exactamente *exactly* 2
el examen *test* 2
excelente *excellent* 1
la excursión *excursion* 2
exigir *to require* 9
el éxito *success* 1
la experiencia *experience* 1
el experimento *experiment* 2
explicar *to explain* 5
explorar *to explore* 9
expresar *to express* 5
el/la extranjero/a *foreigner* 10

fabuloso/a *fabulous* 7
fácil *easy* 4
la falda *skirt* 5
faltar *to lack, be missing* 3
la familia *family* 1
famoso/a *famous* 1
febrero *February* PC
la felicidad *happiness* 4
¡Felicitaciones! *Congratulations!* 10
feliz *happy* 1
la feria *fair* 7
el festival *festival* 11
la fiebre *fever* 3
la fiesta *party* 1
la fila *line, queue* 5
la firma *signature* 1
la física *physics* 7
físico/a *physical* 1
la flor *flower* 2
el folleto *pamphlet* 8
el fomento *promotion* 10

los fondos *funds* 5
la fonética *phonetics* 2
el formulario *form* 1
el foro *forum* 7
fortalecer (zc) *to fortify* 9
la foto(grafía) *photo(graph)* 4
el fracaso *failure* 4
la fractura *fracture* 3
el francés *French* 8
la frase *phrase* 11
fresco/a *cool* 8
el frío *cold* 2
la frontera *border* 7
frustrado/a *frustrated* 4
la fruta *fruit* 8
la fuente *source, fountain* 7, 8
fuera *outside* 2
fuerte *strong* 2
la fuerza *force* 9
las Fuerzas Armadas *Armed Forces* 10
la fundación *foundation* 10
el/la fundador/a *founder* 9
el fútbol *soccer* 1
el fútbol americano *football* 8
el/la futbolista *soccer player* 2
el futuro *future* 1

la galleta *cookie, cracker* 2
la gallina *chicken, hen* 11
la gana *desire, urge* 2
el/la ganador/a *winner* 4
ganar *to win, to earn* 2
la garganta *throat* 3
el gasto *expense* 7
el gato *cat* 1
la gelatina *gelatin* 8
la gente *people* 7
la geografía *geography* 2
la geometría *geometry* 8
el gimnasio *gymnasium* 1
el globo *balloon* 10
el gobierno *government* 1
golpear *to hit* 5
gordo/a *fat* 1
la gota *drop* 3
gracias *thank you* PC
el grado *grade* 1
graduarse *to graduate* 9
el grafiti *graffiti* 5
grande *big* 1

la grasa *fat* 8
gratis *free (of charge)* 3
la gripe/gripa *flu* 3
gritar *to shout* 3
el grito *shout* 1
el grupo *group* 1
guapo/a *good-looking* 1
guardar *to keep* 4
la guardería *child care* 2
el/la guardián/-diana *guardian* 2
la guerra *war* 11
el/la guía *guide* 9
gustar *to like* 7

la habilidad *skill* 9
la habitación *room* 11
hablador/a *talkative* 1
hablar *to talk, to speak* 1
hacer (g) *to do, make* 4
la hallaca *cornmeal with meat, vegetables wrapped in banana leaf* 11
el hambre (f.) *hunger* 2
la hamburguesa *hamburger* 8
hasta luego *see you later* PC
hay *there is, are* 2
la herencia *heritage* 9
la herida *wound* 5
el/la hermano/a *brother, sister* 3
el héroe/la heroína *hero* 5
el hielo *ice* 3
la hierba *herb* 11
el hierro *iron* 8
el hígado *liver* 5
el/la hijo/a *son/daughter* 1
la hinchazón *swelling* 3
hispano/a *Hispanic* 1
el/la hispanohablante *Spanish speaker* 5
la historia *history, story* 1
el hogar *home* 8
la hoja *leaf* 8
hola *hello, hi* PC
el hombre *man* 1
la hora *hour* 1
el horario *schedule* 8
hoy *today* 8
la huelga *strike* 8
el/la huérfano/a *orphan* 10
el huevo *egg* 3
el humo *smoke* 3

identificar *to identify* 10
el idioma *language* 1
igual *equal* 7
igualmente *likewise* PC
ilegal *illegal* 5
la imagen *image* 7
imaginar *to imagine* 8
impaciente *impatient* 5
el impedimento *impediment* 4
importante *important* 1
imposible *impossible* 2
la imprenta *printing press* 9
imprescindible *essential* 10
la impresora *printer* 7
imprimir *to print* 7
el impuesto *tax* 10
inalámbrico/a *wireless* 7
el incendio *fire* 5
incorporar *to incorporate* 11
la industria *industry* 8
infantil *childish* 5
la infección *infection* 3
la influencia *influence* 8
la información *information* 1
la informática *computer science* 9
la ingeniería *engineering* 9
el inglés *English* 1
el ingrediente *ingredient* 8
ingresar *to enroll* 3
el ingreso *income* 10
iniciar *to initiate* 5
la iniciativa *initiative* 11
el/la inmigrante *immigrant* 1
la inmunización *immunization* 1
innovador/a *innovative* 7
inscribir *to enroll* 9
la inscripción *registration* 1
insistir en *to insist on* 5
inspeccionar *to inspect* 5
instalar *to install* 9
instantáneo/a *instantaneous* 7
el instituto *institute* 9
el/la instructor/a *instructor* 1
insultar *to insult* 5
intelectual *intellectual* 2
inteligente *intelligent* 1
intentar *to attempt* 5
el interés *interest* 10
interferir (ie) *to interfere* 5
intermedio/a *intermediate* 5

el/la intérprete *interpreter* 4
interrumpir *to interrupt* 5
la intimidad *intimacy* 4
el invernadero *greenhouse* 9
investigar *to investigate* 7
el invierno *winter* 8
el/la invitado/a *guest* 2
invitar *to invite* 3
ir *to go* 3

el jabón *soap* 3
japonés/esa *Japanese* 2
el jardín *garden* 2
el/la jefe/a *chief, boss* 1
la jirafa *giraffe* 1
joven *young* 1
la joya *jewel* 11
el juego *game* 1
jueves *Thursday* PC
el/la juez/a *judge* 8
jugar (ue) *to play games, sports* 1
el jugo *juice* 2
el juguete *toy* 1
el juicio *judgement* 5
julio *July* PC
junio *June* PC
junto/a *together* 1
justo/a *fair* 5
juvenil *juvenile* 5

el kinder(garten) *kindergarten* 2

el laboratorio *laboratory* 2
el lado *side* 5
el ladrillo *brick* 5
la lágrima *tear* 4
la lámpara *lamp* 2
el lápiz *pencil* 1
la lástima *pity* 9
la lastimadura *injury* 3
lastimar *to injure* 5
lavarse *to wash* 8
le *to him/her/you (formal)* 5
le gusta *he, she, you (formal) like(s)* 2
la lección *lesson* 1
la leche *milk* 2
la lechuga *lettuce* 8
el/la lector/a *reader* 7
la lectura *reading* 1
leer *to read* 1

lejos *far* 5
el lenguaje *language* 1
les *to them/you (pl.)* 5
la letra *letter (alphabet)* 2
levantar *to lift* 3
leve *slight* 3
la ley *law* 3
la libra *pound* 7
la librería *bookstore* 7
el/la librero/a *bookseller* 7
el libro *book* 1
la licenciatura *bachelor's degree* 10
el/la líder *leader* 2
limpiar *to clean* 2
la limpieza *cleaning* 5
limpio/a *clean* 2
la línea *line* 7
la lista *list* 3
listo/a *ready, clever* 3
la literatura *literature* 8
la llaga *sore* 3
la llamada *call* 10
llamar *to call* 2
la llave *key* 5
llegar *to arrive* 1
llenar *to fill* 1
llevable *wearable* 11
llevar *to take (along), to carry* 2
llevarse bien, mal *to get along well, not at all* 8
llorar *to cry* 2
llover (ue) *to rain* 8
la lluvia *rain* 8
loco/a *crazy* 1
lograr *to succeed* 2
la lucha libre *wrestling* 8
luchar *to fight, to struggle* 2
el lugar *place* 1
la luna *moon* 11
lunes *Monday* PC
la luz *light* 3

la maceta *pot* 9
la madre *mother* PC
maduro/a *mature* 11
la maestría *master's degree* 10
el/la maestro/a *teacher* 1
el maíz *corn* 8
mal *not well* PC
maltratar *to mistreat* 5

la mamá   *mom*   1
el mandamiento   *command-ment*   5
mandar   *to send*   4
el mandato   *command*   5
el manejo   *use*   7
el manguito   *sleeve*   7
manifestar (ie)   *to show*   3
la mano   *hand*   1
mantener (ie) (g)   *to maintain*   3
la manzana   *apple*   8
mañana   *tomorrow*   10
el mapa   *map*   1
la máquina   *machine*   11
el/la maratón   *marathon*   11
maravilloso/a   *marvelous*   7
martes   *Tuesday*   PC
marzo   *March*   PC
más   *more*   1
la mascota   *pet*   3
masticar   *to chew*   6
las matemáticas   *mathematics*   1
la materia   *subject*   4
la matrícula   *registration*   1
mayo   *May*   PC
mayor   *older*   2
la mayoría   *majority*   3
me   *me, to me*   5
me gusta   *I like*   2
Me llamo...   *My name is ...*   PC
la medianoche   *midnight*   1
la medicina   *medicine*   3
el/la médico   *doctor*   1
la medida   *measure*   3
medio/a   *half*   1
el medio ambiente   *environ-ment*   9
el mediodía   *noon*   1
medir (i)   *to measure*   4
mejor   *better*   4
mejorar   *to improve*   2
la memoria   *memory*   1
mencionar   *to mention*   7
menor   *younger*   4
menos   *less*   4
el mensaje   *message*   3
la mente   *mind*   4
mentir (ie)   *to lie*   4
el menudo   *tripe stew*   11
el mercado   *market*   7

el mercadotecnia   *marketing*   10
la merienda   *snack (afternoon)*   2
el mes   *month*   4
la mesa   *table*   1
el/la mesero/a   *waiter, waitress*   8
la meta   *goal*   8
mexicano/a   *Mexican*   1
mezclar   *to mix*   8
mi   *my*   1
el micrófono   *microphone*   2
el miedo   *fear*   2
el/la miembro   *member*   1
mientras   *meanwhile*   7
miércoles   *Wednesday*   PC
la milla   *mile*   10
el millón   *million*   1
mirar   *to look at*   2
la misión   *mission*   2
mismo/a   *same*   7
el misterio   *mystery*   2
la mitad   *half*   3
la mochila   *backpack*   1
la moda   *fashion*   2
la modalidad   *mode, method*   11
modelar   *to model*   5
el/la modelo   *model*   5
el módem   *modem*   7
moderno/a   *modern*   1
el modo   *way, manner*   7
el módulo   *module*   7
molestar   *to bother*   9
la moneda   *coin*   7
el/la monitor/a   *monitor*   3
moreno/a   *brown (skin)*   2
morir (ue)   *to die*   3
motivado/a   *motivated*   4
moverse (ue)   *to move*   3
movilizar   *to mobilize*   11
el/la muchacho/a   *boy/girl*   PC
mucho gusto   *pleased/nice to meet you*   PC
mucho/a   *a lot*   1
la muerte   *death*   3
la mujer   *woman*   1
el/la (mujer) policía   *police officer*   1
el mundo   *world*   1
la muñeca   *doll*   1
los muñequitos   *dolls*   5

el museo   *museum*   7
la música   *music*   1
muy   *very*   PC

nacer (zc)   *to be born*   10
el nacimiento   *birth*   1
la nación   *nation*   1
nada   *nothing*   2
nadar   *to swim*   2
nadie   *nobody*   2
la nana   *grandma*   11
la naranja   *orange*   8
la nariz   *nose*   3
narrar   *to narrate*   11
la natación   *swimming*   8
la náusea   *nausea*   3
la navaja   *knife, razor*   5
navegar   *to navigate*   7
la Navidad   *Christmas*   11
necesitar   *to need*   1
negligente   *negligent*   1
los negocios   *business*   1
negro/a   *black*   2
nervioso/a   *nervous*   2
nevar (ie)   *to snow*   8
el/la nieto/a   *grandchild*   3
la nieve   *snow*   8
ningún/guno/a   *none, not one*   4
el/la niño/a   *child*   1
el nivel   *level*   5
no hay de qué   *you're welcome*   PC
el nombre   *name*   1
la norma   *norm*   5
nos   *us, to us*   5
nos gusta(n)   *we like*   2
nosotros/as   *we*   PC
la nota   *grade, note*   4
las noticias   *news*   1
notificar   *to notify*   3
la novedad   *innovation*   7
noveno/a   *ninth*   7
noviembre   *November*   PC
el/la novio/a   *boy/girlfriend*   8
nuestro/a   *our*   1
nuevo/a   *new*   1
nunca   *never*   5

el objetivo   *objective*   11
la obra   *work*   2
el/la obrero/a   *worker*   8
la obscenidad   *obscenity*   5

observar *to observe* 1
obtener (ie) (g) *to obtain* 1
octavo/a *eighth* 7
octubre *October* PC
ocupado/a *occupied* 2
ocuparse *to take charge of* 3
el oeste *west* 5
la oficina *office* 1
ofrecer (zc) *to offer* 1
el oído *ear (inner)* 4
oír (ig) (y) *to hear* 3
ojalá *I hope, Let's hope, May Allah grant* 9
el ojo *eye* 2
oler (ue) *to smell* 5
olvidarse de *to forget about* 7
opinar *to express an opinion* 7
la oportunidad *opportunity* 5
optimista *optimistic* 1
la oreja *ear (outer)* 4
la organización *organization* 1
organizar *to organize* 9
el orgullo *pride* 4
orgulloso/a *proud* 4
la orquesta *orchestra* 2
la ortografía *spelling* 1
el otoño *fall* 8
otorgar *to award* 10
otro/a *other, another* 1
el óvalo *oval* 11

la paciencia *patience* 8
paciente *patient* 1
el padre *father* 1
pagar *to pay* 1
la página *page* 2
el pago *payment* 9
el país *country* 1
el palabra *word* 2
pálido/a *pale* 3
el pan *bread* 8
la pandilla *gang* 5
la pantalla *screen* 2
los pantalones *pants* 5
el pañuelo *handkerchief* 1
la papa *potato* 8
el papá *dad* 7
el papel *paper, role* 1, 2
las paperas *mumps* 3
para *for, in order to* 2
el/la paramédico/a *paramedic* 3

parar *to stop* 5
parecer (zc) *to seem* 3
la pared *wall* 5
la pareja *pair* 9
el/la pariente *relative* 11
el párrafo *paragraph* 9
la parte *part* 7
participar *to participate* 5
particular *private* 7
el partido *game, match* 8
pasado/a *past, last* 7
el pasaje *passage* 11
pasar *to pass, to spend* 2
el pasatiempo *hobby* 11
pasear *to stroll* 5
el pasillo *hallway* 2
el paso *step* 10
el pastel *cake, pastry* 2
la patineta *skateboard* 4
el patriotismo *patriotism* 2
el/la patrocinador/a *sponsor* 11
la paz *peace* 5
el pecho *chest* 3
la pedagogía *pedagogy, teaching* 11
el pedazo *piece* 8
pedir (i) *to ask for, order* 4
el pegamento *glue* 1
pegar *to glue* 1
peinarse *to comb one's hair* 8
la pelea *fight* 5
la película *movie* 1
el peligro *danger* 2
peligroso/a *dangerous* 2
pelirrojo/a *redheaded* 2
el pelo *hair* 2
la pelota *ball* 1
pensar (ie) *to think* 2
peor *worse* 4
el pepino *cucumber* 8
pequeño/a *small (size)* 1
la pera *pear* 8
perder (ie) *to lose* 4
perdón *pardon me* PC
perezoso/a *lazy* 7
el período *period* 7
permanecer (zc) *to remain, stay* 3
el permiso *permission* 10
permitir *to permit* 9
pero *but* 1
el perro *dog* 1

la persona *person* 4
el personal *personnel* 1
pesado/a *heavy* 5
las pesas *weights* 8
pesimista *pessimistic* 1
el pez *fish* 2
picar *to itch, sting* 3
el pie *foot* 3
la piel *skin* 3
la pierna *leg* 3
la pimienta *pepper* 8
pintar *to paint* 2
la pintura *painting* 5
los piojos *lice* 3
la piscina *swimming pool* 11
el piso *floor* 2
el pito *whistle* 3
la pizarra *chalkboard* 1
el planeta *planet* 7
planificar *to plan* 9
plano/a *flat* 7
la planta *plant* 2
el plantel *staff* 11
el plomo *lead* 4
la pluma *pen* 1
la población *population* 3
¡Pobrecito/a! *Poor thing!* 3
poder (ue) *to be able, can* 4
la poesía *poetry* 2
poner (g) *to put, place* 3
por *through, by, for* 3
por eso *that's why* 2
por favor *please* PC
por fin *finally* 2
por lo menos *at least* 3
por medio de *by means of* 3
¿Por qué? *Why?* 1
porque *because* 1
el porcentaje *percentage* 9
el portafolios *briefcase* 1
portátil *portable* 7
la portería *goal (sports)* 8
el portero *custodian, doorman* 1
la potencia *power* 7
la práctica *practice* 5
practicar *to practice* 1
el precio *price* 1
precisamente *precisely* 2
preferir (ie) *to prefer* 2
la pregunta *question* 1
el premio *prize* 2
prender *to turn on* 5

preocupado/a *worried* 2

la preparatoria *prep school* 7

la presa *dam* 9

el/la presidente/a *president* 1

el préstamo *loan* 9

prestar *to lend* 5

primario/a *primary* 1

la primavera *spring* 2

primer/o/a *first* 1

los primeros auxilios *first aid* 3

el/la primo/a *cousin* 4

el principio *principle, concept* 11

la prisa *haste* 2

probar (ue) *to attempt, try; to prove* 4, 5

el problema *problem* 4

el procedimiento *procedure* 7

el procesador *processor* 7

el proceso *process* 7

producir (zc) *to produce* 3

el/la profesor/a *professor* 1

el programa *program* 1

el progreso *progress* 4

prohibir *to prohibit* 9

prolongado/a *lengthy* 7

el promedio *average* 4

la promesa *promise* 10

prometer *to promise* 2

pronto *soon* 1

pronunciar *to deliver (speech)* 10

propagar *to spread* 3

la propiedad *property* 2

propio/a *own* 7

proporcionar *to provide* 9

proteger *to protect* 1

próximo/a *next* 2

el proyecto *project* 7

la prueba *examination* 4

el/la psicólogo/a *psychologist* 1

la publicidad *advertising* 7

público/a *public* 5

el puente *bridge* 9

la puerta *door* 1

el puerto *port* 7

puertorriqueño/a *Puerto Rican* 1

pues *well* 4

la pulgada *inch* 11

la pulmonía *pneumonia* 3

la puntuación *score, grade* 10

el pupitre *student desk* 1

que *that* 1

¿Qué? *What?* 1

¡Qué alivio! *What a relief!* 1

¡Qué bueno! *That's great!* 1

¿Qué día es hoy? *What day is today?* PC

¡Qué emoción! *How exciting!* 2

¡Qué lástima! *What a shame!* 7

¡Qué maravilla! *How wonderful!* 1

quedarse *to stay, remain* 4

el quehacer *chore* 9

quejarse de *to complain about* 4

querer (ie) *to want* 4

el queso *cheese* 8

¿Quién/es? *Who?* 1

la química *chemistry* 7

químico/a *chemical* 5

quinto/a *fifth* 2

quitar *to remove* 3

quizás *perhaps* 9

el/la radio *radio* 5

la raíz *root, stem* 4

la raja *slice* 8

el ramo *bouquet* 10

rápido/a *fast* 3

rascar *to scratch* 3

el rastro *trace* 8

el ratón *mouse* 7

la rayuela *hopscotch* 3

la razón *reason* 2

la reacción *reaction* 11

realizar *to carry out* 7

la rebanada *slice* 8

el/la recepcionista *receptionist* 1

la receta *prescription, recipe* 3

recibir *to receive* 1

recoger *to pick up* 5

recomendar (ie) *to recommend* 1

reconocer (zc) *to recognize* 1

recordar (ue) *to remember* 2

el recreo *recreation* 1

el recuerdo *memory* 8

recuperarse *to recuperate* 3

el recurso *resource* 9

la Red *Web* 7

la redacción *writing* 8

reducido/a *reduced* 1

reducir (zc) *to reduce* 4

reemplazar *to replace* 7

el refresco *refreshment, soda* 2

el refugio *shelter* 5

el regalo *gift* 7

regar (ie) *to water* 8

el registro *registry* 10

la regla *ruler, rule* 1

regresar *to return* 1

el regreso *return* 2

regular *so-so* PC

el reingreso *readmit* 9

reírse de (i) *to laugh about* 10

rellenar *to fill out* 1

remediar *to fix* 5

el remedio *remedy* 11

renunciar *to renounce* 5

reparar *to repair* 9

repetir (i) *to repeat* 4

el/la reportero/a *reporter* 8

el/la representante *representative* 9

el reproductor *player, burner* 7

requerir (ie) *to require* 7

el requisito *requirement* 7

el resbalador *slide* 3

el resfriado *cold* 3

la residencia *residence* 1

resolver (ue) *to resolve* 5

respetar *to respect* 9

el respeto *respect* 1

respetuoso/a *respectful* 1

responsable *responsible* 1

la respuesta *answer, response* 2

restar *to subtract* 2

la resucitación cardiopulmonar *CPR* 3

el resultado *result* 2

resumir *to summarize* 11

el retraso mental *mental retardation* 4

la reunión *meeting* 1

reunirse *to get together* 7

la revista *magazine* 7

rico/a *rich* 8

el riesgo *risk* 10

el río *river* 11

la risa *laughter* 1

el rival *rival* 5

la roca *rock* 4

la rodilla *knee* 11

rojo/a *red* 2

la ropa *clothing* 2

rosado/a *pink* 3

rubio/a *blond* 2

la ruta *route* 5

la rutina *routine* 1

sábado *Saturday* PC

saber *to know* 1

sabio/a *wise* 5

sabroso/a *tasty* 8

sacar *to take (out)* 4

el saco *sack* 5

la sacudida *shaking* 5

la sal *salt* 8

la sala *room, living room* 2

el salario *salary* 1

la salchicha *sausage* 8

el saldo *balance* 10

la salida *exit* 5

salir (g) *to leave* 3

el salón *room* 1

saltar a la cuerda *to jump rope* 3

la salud *health* 1

saludar *to greet* 1

la sangre *blood* 3

sano/a *healthy* 2

el sarampión *measles* 3

satisfacer (g) *to satisfy* 7

secarse *to dry off* 8

seco/a *dry* 3

el/la secretario/a *secretary* PC

el secreto *secret* 2

secundario/a *secondary* 1

la sed *thirst* 2

seguir (i) *to continue, follow* 4

según *according to* 4

segundo/a *second* 1

la seguridad *security* 5

el seguro *insurance* 1

seguro/a *sure* 2

seleccionar *to select* 7

el sello *stamp* 2

la semana *week* 7

sembrar (ie) *to plant* 8

el semestre *semester* 10

la semilla *seed* 8

el seminario *seminary* 11

sensato/a *sensible* 5

la sensibilidad *sensitivity* 3

sensible *sensitive* 11

sentarse (ie) *to sit down* 8

el sentido *sense* 2

sentirse (ie) *to feel* 2

la seña *sign* 4

la señal *sign* 4

el señor *sir, Mr.* 1

la señora *ma'am, Mrs.* 1

la señorita *miss, young lady* 1

septiembre *September* PC

séptimo/a *seventh* 7

ser *to be* 1

serio/a *serious* 1

el servicio *service* 7

el servidor *server* 7

servir (i) *to serve* 4

el sexo *sex* 1

sexto/a *sixth* 3

si *if* 1

siempre *always* 1

la siesta *nap* 1

siguiente *following* 7

el silencio *silence* 1

la silla *chair* 1

la silla de ruedas *wheelchair* 4

el símbolo *symbol* 2

simpático/a *nice* 1

el simulacro *simulation* 5

sin *without* 2

sin embargo *nevertheless* 5

sin fines de lucro *non-profit* 10

el sindicato *union* 8

sino *but* 2

el síntoma *symptom* 3

el sistema *system* 2

el sitio *place* 1

el sitio amparado *shelter* 5

sobre *about, on* 2

sobresalir *to excel* 5

la sociedad *society* 11

la soga *rope* 4

el sol *sun* 8

el soldado *soldier* 11

solicitar *to apply* 9

la solicitud *application* 1

sólo *only* 1

la solución *solution* 5

el sombrero *hat* 3

la sonrisa *smile* 4

soñar (ue) *to dream* 8

la sordera *deafness* 4

sordo/a *deaf* 4

sorprender *to surprise* 9

la sorpresa *surprise* 2

el sorteo *drawing* 7

la sospecha *suspicion* 5

soy *I am* PC

su *his, her, your, their* 1

suave *smooth, great* 11

la subasta *auction* 7

el sube y baja *jungle gym* 3

subir *to go up, to climb* 2

sucio/a *dirty* 2

el sueldo *salary* 10

el sueño *sleep, dream* 2

la suerte *luck* 4

sufrir *to suffer* 2

sugerir (ie) *to suggest* 7

sumar *to add* 2

superar *to overcome* 8

el/la superintendente *superintendent* 1

supervisar *to supervise* 2

el/la supervisor/a *supervisor* 11

la supervivencia *survival* 5

el sur *south* 3

el tacto *sense of touch* 5

tal *such* 3

tal vez *perhaps* 9

el talento *talent* 10

la talla *size* 11

el tamaño *size* 8

también *also, too* 1

tampoco *neither* 5

tan *so, as* 4

tanto/a *as much* 4

tantos/as *as many* 4

la taquería *taco stand* 11

la tarea *homework, chore* 1

la tarjeta *card* 1

la tasa *rate* 10

la taza *cup* 8

te *you, to you (familiar)* 5

te gusta *you (familiar) like* 2

el teatro *theater* 1

el techo *roof, ceiling* 5

el teclado *keyboard* 11
la técnica *technique* 11
el/la técnico/a *technician* 9
la tecnología *technology* 1
el teléfono *telephone* 1
el tema *theme* 7
temer *to fear* 9
tener (ie, g) *to have* 1
tengo *I have* 1
los tenis *tennis shoes* 5
teológico/a *theological* 11
tercer/o/a *third* 7
terminar *to end* 7
el terremoto *earthquake* 5
el territorio *territory* 5
terrorista *terrorist* 5
el testimonio *proof, testimony*
    10
el tiempo *time, weather* 5, 7
la tienda *store* 7
la tierra *land* 2
las tijeras *scissors* 1
tímido/a *timid, shy* 1
la tinta *ink* 2
el/la tío/a *uncle, aunt* 4
típico/a *typical* 3
tirar *to throw* 8
el titular *headline* 11
el título *title, degree* 9
la tiza *chalk* 1
el tobillo *ankle* 3
el tobogán *slide* 3
tocar *to play (music), to touch*
    2, 5
todo/a *all* 1
la toga *gown* 10
tolerar *to tolerate* 5
tomar *to take, to drink* 2
la tonelada *ton* 7
la tontería *silly or stupid thing*
    5
tonto/a *silly, stupid* 2
torcido/a *twisted, sprained* 3
el tornado *tornado* 5
la tos *cough* 3
tosco/a *rough, unrefined* 5
toser *to cough* 2
el tostadito *toast* 8
trabajar *to work* 1
el trabajo *work, job* 1
la tradición *tradition* 11

la traducción *translation* 8
traducir (zc) *to translate* 3
traer (ig) *to bring* 3
el tranquilizante *tranquilizer*
    5
tranquilo/a *calm* 2
transformar *to transform* 5
transmitir *to transmit* 7
el transporte *transportation*
    7
tras *after* 10
el trastorno *disorder* 4
el tratamiento *treatment* 3
tratar *to try* 3
travieso/a *naughty* 6
el triángulo *triangle* 8
la trigonometría *trigonometry*
    8
triste *sad* 2
el trofeo *trophy* 8
tu *your (familiar)* 1
tú *you (familiar)* PC
el turno *shift* 8
el tutelaje *tutelage* 8
el/la tutor/a *guardian, tutor* 1

último/a *last* 3
un rato *a while* 4
único/a *unique, only* 10
la unidad *unit* 5
unificado/a *unified* 7
el uniforme *uniform* 5
la universidad *university* 1
usted *you (formal)* PC
ustedes *you (plural)* PC
el usuario *user* 7
útil *useful* 9
los útiles *supplies, tools* 1

la vaca *cow* 11
la vacante *vacancy* 9
la vacuna *vaccination* 3
el vahído *dizzy spell* 5
el valor *value* 4
vamos *we go, let's go* 1
variado/a *varied* 9
la varicela *chicken pox* 3
el varón *male* 10
el vaso *glass* 2
el/la vecino/a *neighbor* 8
el vegetal *vegetable* 2

la velocidad *speed* 7
la venda *bandage* 3
vender *to sell* 2
venir (ie) (g) *to come* 2
la venta *sale* 10
la ventaja *advantage* 1
la ventana *window* 1
ver *to see* 1
el verano *summer* 2
¿Verdad? *True? Right?* 1
verde *green* 2
la verdura *vegetable* 8
verificar *to verify* 7
el vestido *dress* 5
el vestidor *dressing room* 5
vestirse (i) *to get dressed* 8
el vestuario *changing room* 7
el/la veterano/a *veteran* 10
viajar *to travel* 9
el/la viajero/a *traveler* 9
las vías respiratorias *respirato-
    ry tract* 3
la vida *life* 2
el vídeo *video* 2
viejo/a *old* 1
el viento *wind* 8
viernes *Friday* PC
el vino *wine* 8
la violencia *violence* 5
violento/a *violent* 5
el virus *virus* 3
la vista *vision, view* 3
el vivero *nursery* 9
vivir *to live* 2
vivo/a *alive* 7
volar (ue) *to fly* 5
el vólibol *volleyball* 2
el/la voluntario/a *volunteer* 1
volver (ue) *to return* 4
el vómito *vomit* 3
votar *to vote* 4
la voz *voice* 1
la vuelta *return* 2

y *and* 1
ya *already* 1
yo *I* PC

la zanahoria *carrot* 8
el zapato *shoe* 2
la zoología *zoology* 8

English-Spanish Glossary

a lot *mucho* 1
a while *un rato* 4
to abandon *abandonar* 10
about *acerca de* 3
about, on *sobre* 2
above *arriba* 5
absence *la ausencia* 5
absent *ausente* 2
abuse *el abuso* 5
academic *académico* 1
to accept *aceptar* 1
accident *el accidente* 1
to accompany *acompañar* 5
according to *según* 4
action *la acción* 5
activity *la actividad* 1
to add *sumar* 2
address *la dirección, el domicilio* 1
adequate *adecuado* 3
adjusted *ajustado* 10
administration *la administración* 2
administrator *el/la administrador/a* 1
to admit *admitir* 5
adolescent *el/la adolescente* 2
adult *el/la adulto/a* 1
advanced *avanzado/a* 7
advantage *la ventaja* 1
adventurer *el/la aventurero/a* 2
advertising *la publicidad* 7
advice *el consejo* 2
to advise *aconsejar* 9
to affect *afectar* 5
after *después (de), tras* 2, 10
against *(en) contra (de)* 3
age *la edad* 1
agent *el/la agente* 5
to agree *estar de acuerdo* 8
agreement *el acuerdo* 10
agricultural *agrícola* 10
agriculture *la agricultura* 10
Aha! *¡Ajá!* 1
air *el aire* 3
air conditioning *el aire acondicionado* 2
alarm *la alarma* 5
alcohol *el alcohol* 2

alert *alerta* 3
algebra *el álgebra* (f.) 7
alive *vivo/a* 7
all *todo/a* 1
allergic *alérgico/a* 3
allergy *la alergia* 3
almost *casi* 3
alphabet *el alfabeto* 1
already *ya* 1
also, too *también* 1
alternative *alternativo/a* 7
always *siempre* 1
ambitious *ambicioso/a* 1
ambulance *la ambulancia* 5
American *americano/a* 1
American (U.S.) *estadounidense* 3
ample *amplio/a* 11
analysis *el análisis* 11
ancestor *el antepasado* 11
and *y* 1
ankle *el tobillo* 3
to announce *anunciar* 4
announcement *el anuncio* 2
to answer *contestar* 1
answer *la respuesta* 2
to anticipate *anticipar* 10
anxiety *la ansiedad* 3
apartment *el apartamento* 1
apple *la manzana* 8
appliance *el electrodoméstico* 11
application *la solicitud* 1
to apply *aplicar, solicitar* 2, 9
appointment *la cita* 1
appropriate *apropiado/a* 2
April *abril* PC
aquarium *el acuario* 2
to argue *discutir* 2
arm *el brazo* 3
Armed Forces *las Fuerzas Armadas* 10
army *el ejército* 8
around, about *alrededor de* 7
to arrange *arreglar* 8
to arrive *llegar* 1
art *el arte* (f.) 1
artistic *artístico/a* 2
as many *tantos/as* 4
as much *tanto/a* 4

as regards *en cuanto a* 9
as, like *como* 4
Asian *asiático/a* 1
to ask for *pedir (i)* 4
aspirin *la aspirina* 1
assembly *la asamblea* 4
to assist *atender (ie)* 8
assistant *el/la asistente* PC
association *la asociación* 1
asthma *el asma* 3
astronaut *el/la astronauta* 11
at least *por lo menos* 3
at once *de una vez* 3
at random *al azar* 7
at the beginning *al principio* 5
at times *a veces* 3
At what time . . . ? *¿A qué hora...?* 1
at your service; may I help you? *a sus órdenes* PC
athlete *el/la atleta* 8
athletic *atlético/a* 1
athletics *el atletismo* 7
attack *el ataque* 3
to attempt *intentar* 5
to attempt, try *probar (ue)* 4
to attend *asistir* 2
attendance *la asistencia* 7
attention *la atención* 1
attitude *la actitud* 2
attorney *el/la abogado/a* 9
to attract *atraer* 8
auction *la subasta* 7
auditorium *el auditorio* 1
to augment *aumentar* 5
August *agosto* PC
aunt *tía* 4
author *el/la autor/a* 2
authorization *la autorización* 2
automobile *el automóvil* 5
available *disponible* 1
average *el promedio* 4
to avoid *evitar* 3
to award *otorgar* 10

bachelor's degree *la licenciatura* 10
back *atrás* 11

backpack   *la mochila*   1
bacteria   *la bacteria*   3
balance   *el saldo*   10
ball   *la pelota, el balón*   1, 8
balloon   *el globo*   10
band   *la banda*   8
bandage   *la venda*   3
banquet   *el banquete*   10
baseball   *el béisbol*   2
basic   *básico/a*   10
basketball   *el básquetbol*   1
bath   *el baño*   2
to bathe   *bañarse*   8
bathroom   *el baño*   1
to be   *ser, estar*   1, 2
to be able, can   *poder (ue)*   4
to be born   *nacer (zc)*   10
to be happy about   *alegrarse de que*   9
because   *porque*   1
bed   *la cama*   3
bedroom   *el dormitorio*   2
beer   *la cerveza*   7
before   *antes*   11
to begin   *comenzar (ie)*   4
behavior   *el comportamiento*   2
belief   *la creencia*   4
to believe   *creer*   2
belly   *la barriga*   3
benefit   *el beneficio*   5
besides   *además*   3
better   *mejor*   4
between   *entre*   2
big   *grande*   1
bilingual   *bilingüe*   1
bill   *la cuenta*   7
billiards, pool   *el billar*   11
biography   *la biografía*   11
biology   *la biología*   8
birth   *el nacimiento*   1
birth certificate   *el acta (f.) de nacimiento*   1
birthday   *el cumpleaños*   2
black   *negro/a*   2
blanket   *la cobija*   5
blind   *ciego/a*   4
blindness   *la ceguera*   4
blister   *la ampolla*   3
block   *la cuadra*   11
blond   *rubio/a*   2
blood   *la sangre*   3
blouse   *la blusa*   5

blue   *azul*   2
body   *el cuerpo*   2
bomb   *la bomba*   5
book   *el libro*   1
bookstore   *la librería*   7
border   *la frontera*   7
bored   *aburrido/a*   2
both   *ambos*   2
to bother   *molestar*   9
bottle   *la botella*   8
bouquet   *el ramo*   10
box   *la caja*   1
boxing   *el boxeo*   2
boy, girl   *el/la muchacho/a, el/la chico/a*   PC, 2
boy/girlfriend   *el/la novio/a*   8
brain   *el cerebro*   3
bread   *el pan*   8
breakfast   *el desayuno*   1
brick   *el ladrillo*   5
bridge   *el puente*   9
briefcase   *el portafolios*   1
brilliant   *brillante*   7
to bring   *traer (ig)*   3
brother, sister   *el/la hermano/a*   3
brown   *café*   2
brown (hair/eyes)   *castaño/a*   2
brown (skin)   *moreno/a*   2
building   *el edificio*   5
bulletin   *el boletín*   2
bus   *el autobús*   1
business   *el negocio, el comercio*   1, 8
but   *pero, sino*   1, 2
to buy   *comprar*   1
buyer   *el/la comprador/a*   7
by   *por*   3
by means of   *por medio de*   3

cafeteria   *la cafetería*   1
cake, pastry   *el pastel*   2
calculator   *la calculadora*   7
calendar   *el calendario*   PC
to call   *llamar*   2
call   *la llamada*   10
calm   *tranquilo/a*   2
calm   *la calma*   5
to calm down   *calmarse*   8
camera   *la cámara*   7
candidate   *el/la candidato/a*   1
candy store   *la dulcería*   11

canine   *canino/a*   5
cap   *el bonete*   10
capable   *capaz*   3
capital   *la capital*   7
captain   *el/la capitán/ana*   8
card   *la tarjeta*   1
care   *el cuidado*   2
career   *la carrera*   8
carpet   *la alfombra*   2
carrot   *la zanahoria*   8
to carry out   *realizar, desempeñar*   7, 11
cash drawer   *la caja*   10
cashier   *el/la cajero/a*   10
cat   *el gato*   1
Catholic   *católico/a*   11
to cause   *causar*   5
ceiling   *el techo*   5
to celebrate   *celebrar*   4
census   *el censo*   10
cent   *el centavo*   10
center   *el centro*   1
ceremony   *la ceremonia*   10
certain   *cierto/a*   9
certificate   *el certificado*   1
chain   *la cadena*   8
chair   *la silla*   1
chalk   *la tiza*   1
chalkboard   *la pizarra*   1
challenge   *el desafío*   9
champagne   *la champaña*   8
championship   *el campeonato*   8
change   *el cambio*   4
to change   *cambiar*   8
changing room   *el vestuario*   7
to characterize   *caracterizar*   3
to charge   *cobrar*   9
to chat   *charlar*   7
check   *el cheque*   1
cheerleader   *el/la animador/a*   8
cheese   *el queso*   8
chemical   *químico/a*   5
chemistry   *la química*   7
chest   *el pecho*   3
to chew   *masticar*   6
chicken   *la gallina*   11
chicken pox   *la varicela*   3
chief, boss   *el/la jefe/a*   1
child   *el/la niño/a*   1
child care   *la guardería*   2

childish   *infantil*   5

chin   *la barbilla*   3

choice   *la elección*   7

choir   *el coro*   2

to choose   *escoger (j)*   7

chore   *el quehacer*   9

Christmas   *la Navidad*   11

cigar, cigarette   *el cigarro*   2

circle   *el círculo*   5

citizen   *el/la ciudadano/a*   10

citizenship   *la ciudadanía*   9

city   *la ciudad*   1

to clarify   *aclarar*   3

class   *la clase*   PC

classroom   *el aula* (f.)   7

clean   *limpio/a*   2

to clean   *limpiar*   2

cleaning   *la limpieza*   5

clever   *listo/a*   3

client   *el/la cliente/a*   2

climate   *el clima*   9

clinic   *la clínica*   1

to close   *cerrar (ie)*   3

closet   *el armario*   1

clothing   *la ropa*   2

club   *el club*   10

code   *el código*   1

coin   *la moneda*   7

cold   *el frío*   2

cold (illness)   *el resfriado*   3

colleague   *el/la colega*   1

to comb one's hair   *peinarse*   8

to come   *venir (ie) (g)*   2

comfortable   *cómodo/a*   2

comical   *cómico/a*   PC

command   *el mandato*   5

commandment   *el mandamiento*   5

comment   *el comentario*   4

to comment   *comentar*   4

committee   *el comité*   4

common   *común*   3

to communicate   *comunicar*   5

community   *la comunidad*   1

community   *comunitario/a*   9

compact disc   *el disco compacto*   2

companion   *el/la compañero/a*   4

competition   *la competencia*   9

competition (contest)   *el concurso*   11

competitive   *competitivo/a*   11

to complain about   *quejarse de*   4

to complete   *completar*   5

complex   *el complejo*   8

complication   *la complicación*   3

to compromise   *comprometer*   7

computer   *la computadora*   1

computer science   *la informática*   9

computing   *la computación*   9

concussion   *la concusión*   3

conduct   *la conducta*   5

conference   *la conferencia*   1

to confide   *confiar*   5

confidence   *la confianza*   2

conflict   *el conflicto*   5

confused   *confundido/a*   2

Congratulations!   *¡Felicitaciones!*   10

conscience   *la conciencia*   9

conscious   *consciente*   3

to consult   *consultar*   3

to contact   *contactar*   3

contagious   *contagioso/a*   3

content   *contento/a*   2

content   *el contenido*   11

to continue   *seguir (i)*   4

contractor   *el/la contratista*   9

to contribute   *aportar*   10

control   *el dominio*   11

cook   *el/la cocinero/a*   2

to cook   *cocinar*   5

cookie, cracker   *la galleta*   2

cool   *fresco/a*   8

to cooperate   *cooperar*   5

coordinator   *el/la coordinador/a*   4

copier   *la copiadora*   1

to copy   *copiar*   5

corn   *el maíz*   8

cornmeal with meat, vegetables wrapped in banana leaf   *la hallaca*   11

correct   *correcto/a*   2

to correct   *corregir (i)*   5

cost   *el costo*   2

to cost   *costar (ue)*   4

cough   *la tos*   3

to cough   *toser*   2

counselor   *el/la consejero/a*   2

to count   *contar (ue)*   1

country   *el país*   1

countryside   *el campo*   2

county   *el condado*   2

course   *el curso*   11

courtesy   *la cortesía*   2

cousin   *el/la primo/a*   4

to cover   *cubrir*   5

to cover   *abarcar*   9

cow   *la vaca*   11

CPR   *la resucitación cardiopulmonar*   3

crayon   *el crayón*   1

crazy   *loco/a*   1

to create   *crear*   5

creator   *el/la creador/a*   5

credit   *el crédito*   10

crime   *el crimen*   5

critical   *crítico/a*   3

cross   *la cruz*   5

to cry   *llorar*   2

cucumber   *el pepino*   8

culinary arts   *las artes culinarias*   8

culture   *la cultura*   9

cup   *la taza*   8

to cure   *curar*   3

current   *actual*   1

current   *al corriente*   3

custodian   *el/la conserje*   1

custodian   *el portero*   1

custody   *la custodia*   10

custom   *la costumbre*   2

cut   *el corte*   3

to cut   *cortar*   7

cyberspace   *el ciberespacio*   7

cycle   *el ciclo*   2

cyclone   *el ciclón*   5

dad   *el papá*   7

daily   *diario/a*   5

dam   *la presa*   9

damage   *el daño*   3

to dance   *bailar*   2

dance   *el baile*   11

danger   *el peligro*   2

dangerous   *peligroso/a*   2

data, information   *los datos (la información)*   7

day before yesterday   *anteayer*   7

deaf   *sordo/a*   4

deafness   *la sordera*   4

dean *el decano* 10

dear (business letter) *estima-do/a* 1

death *la muerte* 3

debt *la deuda* 10

December *diciembre* PC

to decide *decidir* 5

declaration *la declaración* 5

to declare *declarar* 3

dedicated *dedicado/a* 1

to defend *abogar, defender (ie)* 2, 5

to delight *encantar* 9

delighted *encantado/a* 7

delinquency *la delincuencia* 5

to deliver (speech) *pronunciar* 10

to demonstrate *demostrar (ue)* 1

department store *el almacén* 5

dependent *el/la dependiente/a* 10

design *el diseño* 4

desire, urge *la gana, el deseo* 2

desk *el escritorio* 1

determination *el empeño* 9

to develop *desarrollar* 2

development *el desarrollo* 2

diamond *el diamante* 11

dictionary *el diccionario* 1

to die *morir (ue)* 3

different *diferente* 1

difficult *difícil* 1

diploma *el diploma* 9

directed *dirigido/a* 9

directive *la directriz* 11

directly *directamente* 5

dirty *sucio/a* 2

disability *la discapacidad* 4

disabled *discapacitado/a* 4

disagreement *el desacuerdo* 5

to disappear *desaparecer (zc)* 7

disaster *el desastre* 2

discipline *la disciplina* 5

discouraged *desanimado/a* 4

to discover *descubrir* 7

dishonest *deshonesto* 2

disorder *el trastorno* 4

distance *la distancia* 7

district *el distrito* 1

dizzy spell *el vahído* 5

to do, make *hacer (g)* 4

doctor *el/la médico/a* 1

document *el documento* 1

dog *el perro* 1

doll *la muñeca* 1

dolls *los muñequitos* 5

door *la puerta* 1

doubt *la duda* 9

to doubt *dudar* 9

doubtful *dudoso/a* 9

drama *el drama* 8

drawing *el sorteo* 7

to dream *soñar (ue)* 8

dress *el vestido* 5

dressing *el aderezo* 8

dressing room *el vestidor* 5

to drink *beber* 2

to drive *conducir (zc)* 3

drop *la gota* 3

drug *la droga* 2

drug addict *el/la drogadicto/a* 5

dry *seco/a* 3

to dry off *secarse* 8

during *durante* 1

dynamic *dinámico/a* 11

each *cada* 2

ear (outer) *la oreja* 4

to earn, win *ganar* 2

earthquake *el terremoto* 5

easy *fácil* 4

to eat *comer* 1

education *la educación* 1

efficiency *la eficiencia* 11

efficient *eficiente, eficaz* 1, 4

effort *el esfuerzo* 2

egg *el huevo* 3

eighth *octavo/a* 7

elbow *el codo* 11

elderly *anciano/a* 11

electronic *electrónico/a* 7

elephant *el elefante* 11

elevator *el ascensor* 5

to eliminate *eliminar* 7

to embellish *embellecer (zc)* 9

to embrace *abrazarse* 8

emergency *la emergencia* 1

emotional *emocionado/a* 9

employee *el/la empleado/a* 1

enclosed *adjunto/a* 2

to encourage *animar* 4

encouragement *el ánimo* 4

to end *terminar, acabar* 7, 8

energy *la energía* 11

engineering *la ingeniería* 9

English *el inglés* 1

enough *bastante* 4

to enroll *ingresar, inscribir* 3, 9

to enter *entrar* 3

enterprise *la empresa* 8

entertainment *el entretenimiento* 2

enthusiasm *el entusiasmo* 5

entry *la entrada* 8

environment *el ambiente, el medio ambiente* 3, 9

environmental *ambiental* 9

envy *la envidia* 7

equal *igual* 7

equipment, team *el equipo* 2

to erase *borrar* 1

eraser *el borrador* 1

error *el error* 1

eruption *la erupción* 3

essay *el ensayo* 8

essential *imprescindible* 10

to establish *establecer (zc)* 5

ethnic *étnico/a* 7

evacuation *la evacuación* 5

to evaluate *evaluar* 3

evaluation *la evaluación* 3

even though *aunque* 7

evidence *la evidencia* 3

exactly *exactamente* 2

exactly *en punto* 1

examination *la prueba* 4

example *el ejemplo* 5

to excel *sobresalir* 5

excellent *excelente* 1

excursion *la excursión* 2

excuse me *con permiso* PC

exercise *el ejercicio* 1

exit *la salida* 5

expense *el gasto* 7

expensive *caro/a* 8

experience *la experiencia* 1

experiment *el experimento* 2

to explain *explicar* 5

to explore *explorar* 9

to express *expresar* 5

to express an opinion *opinar* 7

eye *el ojo* 2

fabulous *fabuloso/a* 7
face *la cara* 5
to face *enfrentar* 10
failure *el fracaso* 4
fair *justo/a* 5
fair *la feria* 7
fall *el otoño* 8
to fall down *caerse (ig)* 3
family *la familia* 1
famous *famoso/a* 1
fan *el/la aficionado/a* 8
far *lejos* 5
farewell *la despedida* 10
fashion *la moda* 2
fast *rápido/a* 3
fat *gordo/a* 1
fat *la grasa* 8
father *el padre* 1
fear *el miedo* 2
to fear *temer* 9
February *febrero* PC
fee *la cuota* 2
to feed *alimentar* 8
feeder *el alimentador* 7
to feel *sentirse (ie)* 2
festival *el festival* 11
fever *la fiebre* 3
fifth *quinto/a* 2
fight *la pelea* 5
to fight *luchar* 2
file *el archivo* 3
to fill *llenar* 1
to fill out *rellenar* 1
finally *por fin* 2
to find *encontrar (ue)* 4
to find out *averiguar* 8
fine arts *las bellas artes* 7
finger *el dedo* 3
fire *el incendio* 5
firefighter *el/la bombero/a* 5
first *primer/o/a* 1
first aid *los primeros auxilios* 3
fish *el pez* 2
to fix *remediar* 5
flag *la bandera* 1
flat *plano/a* 7
floor *el piso* 2
flower *la flor* 2
flu *la gripe/gripa* 3
to fly *volar (ue)* 5
focus *el enfoque* 9
focused *enfocado/a* 9

following *a continuación* 3
following *siguiente* 7
food, meal *la comida* 1
foot *el pie* 3
football *el fútbol americano* 8
for *por* 3
for sure *a ciencia cierta* 9
for, in order to *para* 2
force *la fuerza* 9
foreigner *el/la extranjero/a* 10
to forget about *olvidarse de* 7
form *el formulario* 1
to fortify *fortalecer (zc)* 9
forum *el foro* 7
forward *adelante* 1
foundation *la fundación* 10
founder *el/la fundador/a* 9
fountain *la fuente* 8
fracture *la fractura* 3
free (of charge) *gratis* 3
French *el francés* 8
Friday *viernes* PC
friend *el/la amigo/a* PC
friendly *amistoso/a* 2
friendship *la amistad* 8
fruit *la fruta* 8
frustrated *frustrado/a* 4
to fulfill *cumplir* 7
fun, enjoyable *divertido/a* 4
funds *los fondos* 5
future *el futuro* 1

to gain access to *acceder* 7
game *el juego* 1
game, match *el partido* 8
gang *la pandilla* 5
garden *el jardín* 2
gelatin *la gelatina* 8
geography *la geografía* 2
geometry *la geometría* 8
German *el alemán* 8
to get along well, not at all *llevarse bien, mal* 8
to get angry *enojarse* 8
to get dressed *vestirse (i)* 8
to get together *reunirse* 7
gift *el regalo* 7
giraffe *la jirafa* 1
to give *dar* 3
glass *el vaso* 2
glue *el pegamento* 1
to glue *pegar* 1

to go *ir* 3
to go up, climb *subir* 2
goal *la meta* 8
goal (sports) *la portería* 8
good *bueno/a* 1
good afternoon *buenas tardes* PC
good evening, good night *buenas noches* PC
good morning *buenos días* PC
good-bye *adiós* PC
good-looking *guapo/a* 1
goods *los bienes* 10
government *el gobierno* 1
gown *la toga* 10
grade (level) *el grado* 1
grade *la calificación* 9
grade, note *la nota* 4
to graduate *graduarse* 9
graffiti *el grafiti* 5
grandchild *el/la nieto/a* 3
grandfather/mother *el/la abuelo/a* 2
grandma *la nana* 11
grass *el césped* 9
great-grandparent *el/la bisabuelo/a* 11
green *verde* 2
greenhouse *el invernadero* 9
to greet *saludar* 1
gross (income) *bruto/a* 10
group *el grupo* 1
to grow *crecer (zc)* 8
growing *creciente* 5
growth *el crecimiento* 9
guardian *el/la guardián/-diana* 2
guardian, tutor *el/la tutor/a* 1
guest *el/la invitado/a* 2
guide *el/la guía* 9
guilty *culpable* 10
guinea pig *el conejillo de Indias* 2
gum (chewing) *el chicle* 6
gum (mouth) *la encía* 3
gymnasium *el gimnasio* 1

hair *el pelo* 2
half *medio/a* 1
half *la mitad* 3
hallway *el pasillo* 2
hamburger *la hamburguesa* 8

hand   la mano   1
to hand over, deliver   entregar   4
handkerchief   el pañuelo   1
handshake   el apretón de manos   11
happiness   la felicidad   4
happy   feliz   1
hard drive   el disco duro   7
harmony   la armonía   5
harvest   la cosecha   8
haste   la prisa   2
hat   el sombrero   3
to have   tener (ie, g)   1
to have fun   disfrutar   9
to have just   acabar de + inf.   7
to have lunch   almorzar (ue)   4
he   él   PC
he, she, you (formal) like(s)   le gusta   2
head   la cabeza   3
headline   el titular   11
health   la salud   1
healthy   sano/a   2
to hear   oír (ig) (y)   3
hearing   la audición   3
heart   el corazón   3
heat   el calor   2
heating   la calefacción   2
heavy   pesado/a   5
hello, hi   hola   PC
helmet   el casco   8
help   la ayuda   2
to help   ayudar   1
helper   el/la ayudante   2
herb   la hierba   11
here   aquí, acá   4, 10
heritage   la herencia   9
hero   el héroe/la heroína   5
hidden   escondido/a   5
high   alto/a   2
to him/her/you (formal)   le   5
his, her, your, their   su   1
Hispanic   hispano/a   1
history, story   la historia   1
to hit   golpear   5
hobby   el pasatiempo   11
home   el hogar   8
homemade   casero/a   11
homework, chore   la tarea   1
hopscotch   la rayuela   3

horse   el caballo   11
hot   caliente   2
hour   la hora   1
house   la casa   1
How are you? (familiar)   ¿Cómo estás?   PC
How are you? (formal)   ¿Cómo está Ud.?   PC
How do you say…?   ¿Cómo se dice…?   1
How exciting!   ¡Qué emoción!   2
How many?   ¿Cuántos/as?   1
How much?   ¿Cuánto/a?   1
How wonderful!   ¡Qué maravilla!   1
hug   el abrazo   4
hunger   el hambre (f.)   2
to hurt, cause pain   doler (ue)   3

I   yo   PC
I am   soy, estoy   PC, 1
I have   tengo   1
I hope, Let's hope, May Allah grant   ojalá   9
I like   me gusta   2
ice   el hielo   3
to identify   identificar   10
if   si   1
illegal   ilegal   5
illness   la enfermedad   1
image   la imagen   7
to imagine   imaginar   8
immigrant   el/la inmigrante   1
immunization   la inmunización   1
impatient   impaciente   5
impediment   el impedimento   4
important   importante   1
impossible   imposible   2
to improve   mejorar   2
in case of   en caso de   1
in charge of   encargado/a   8
in front of   enfrente de   5
in order   en orden   10
in place of   en vez de   7
in reverse   al revés   7
in spite of   a pesar de   10
inch   la pulgada   11
income   el ingreso   10
to incorporate   incorporar   11
industry   la industria   8

infection   la infección   3
influence   la influencia   8
information   la información   1
ingredient   el ingrediente   8
iniciative   la iniciativa   11
to initiate   iniciar   5
to injure   lastimar   5
injury   la lastimadura   3
ink   la tinta   2
innovation   la novedad   7
innovative   innovador/a   7
inside   adentro   2
to insist on   insistir en   5
to inspect   inspeccionar   5
to install   instalar   9
instantaneous   instantáneo/a   7
institute   el instituto   9
instructor   el/la instructor/a   1
to insult   insultar   5
insurance   el seguro   1
intellectual   intelectual   2
intelligent   inteligente   1
interest   el interés   10
to interfere   interferir (ie)   5
intermediate   intermedio/a   5
interpreter   el/la intérprete   4
to interrupt   interrumpir   5
interview   la entrevista   1
intimacy   la intimidad   4
to investigate   investigar   7
to invite   invitar   3
iron   el hierro   8
it's a pleasure   es un placer   PC
itch   la comezón   3
to itch, sting   picar   3

jacket   la chaqueta   5
January   enero   PC
Japanese   japonés/esa   2
jewel   la joya   11
joint   conjunto/a   2
judge   el/la juez/a   8
judgement   el juicio   5
juice   el jugo   2
July   julio   PC
to jump rope   saltar a la cuerda   3
June   junio   PC
jungle gym   el sube y baja   3
juvenile   juvenil   5

to keep   guardar   4
key   la llave   5

key *clave* 7
keyboard *el teclado* 11
kindergarten *el kinder(garten)* 2
to kiss *besar* 2
knee *la rodilla* 11
knife, razor *la navaja* 5
to know *saber* 1
to know (be acquainted with) *conocer (zc)* 1
knowledge *el conocimiento* 2

laboratory *el laboratorio* 2
to lack *faltar* 3
lamp *la lámpara* 2
land *la tierra* 2
language *el lenguaje, el idioma* 1
last *último/a* 3
last name *el apellido* 1
last night *anoche* 7
to laugh about *reírse de (i)* 10
laughter *la risa* 1
law *la ley* 3
law firm *el bufete* 9
lazy *perezoso/a* 7
lead *el plomo* 4
leader *el/la líder* 2
leaf *la hoja* 8
to learn *aprender* 1
learning *el aprendizaje* 4
to leave *salir (g)* 3
to leave (behind) *dejar* 5
leg *la pierna* 3
to lend *prestar* 5
lengthy *prolongado/a* 7
less *menos* 4
lesson *la lección* 1
to let, allow *dejar* 7
Let's see *A ver* 1
letter *la carta* 1
letter (alphabet) *la letra* 2
lettuce *la lechuga* 8
level *el nivel* 5
library *la biblioteca* 1
lice *los piojos* 3
to lie *mentir (ie)* 4
life *la vida* 2
to lift *levantar* 3
light *la luz* 3
to like *gustar* 7
likewise *igualmente* PC

line *la línea* 7
line, queue *la fila* 5
link *el enlace* 7
list *la lista* 3
to listen *escuchar* 1
literacy *la alfabetización* 9
literature *la literatura* 8
to live *vivir* 2
lively *animado/a* 7
liver *el hígado* 5
loan *el préstamo* 9
lodging *el alojamiento* 10
to look at *mirar* 2
to look for *buscar* 1
to lose *perder (ie)* 4
love *el amor* 2
to love *amar* 10
luck *la suerte* 4
lunch *el almuerzo* 1

ma'am, Mrs. *la señora* 1
machine *la máquina* 11
magazine *la revista* 7
mail *el correo* 7
majority *la mayoría* 3
to make an effort *esforzarse (ue)* 5
to make note of *anotar* 10
male *el varón* 10
man *el hombre* 1
map *el mapa* 1
marathon *el/la maratón* 11
March *marzo* PC
market *el mercado* 7
marketing *la mercadotecnia* 10
marvelous *maravilloso/a* 7
master's degree *la maestría* 10
mathematics *las matemáticas* 1
matter *el asunto* 9
mature *maduro/a* 11
May *mayo* PC
mayor *el/la alcalde/sa* 5
me, to me *me* 5
meanwhile *mientras* 7
measles *el sarampión* 3
measure *la medida* 3
to measure *medir (i)* 4
medicine *la medicina* 3
meeting *la reunión* 1
member *el/la miembro/a* 1

memory *la memoria* 1
memory *el recuerdo* 8
mental retardation *el retraso mental* 4
to mention *mencionar* 7
message *el mensaje* 3
Mexican *mexicano/a* 1
microphone *el micrófono* 2
midnight *la medianoche* 1
mile *la milla* 10
milk *la leche* 2
million *el millón* 1
mind *la mente* 4
mirror *el espejo* 8
miss, young lady *la señorita* 1
mission *la misión* 2
mistake *la equivocación* 4
to mistreat *maltratar* 5
to mix *mezclar* 8
to mobilize *movilizar* 11
mode, method *la modalidad* 11
model *el/la modelo* 5
to model *modelar* 5
modem *el módem* 7
modern *moderno/a* 1
module *el módulo* 7
mom *la mamá* 1
Monday *lunes* PC
money *el dinero* 1
monitor *el monitor* 3
month *el mes* 4
moon *la luna* 11
more *más* 1
mother *la madre* PC
motivated *motivado/a* 4
mouse *el ratón* 7
mouth *la boca* 3
to move *moverse (ue)* 3
to move away from *alejarse de* 5
moved *conmovido/a* 11
movie *la película* 1
mumps *las paperas* 3
museum *el museo* 7
music *la música* 1
my *mi* 1
My name is . . . *Me llamo...* PC
mystery *el misterio* 2

name *el nombre* 1
nap *la siesta* 1
to narrate *narrar* 11

nation   la nación   1
naughty   travieso/a   6
nausea   la náusea   3
to navigate   navegar   7
near   cerca de   3
neck   el cuello   3
to need   necesitar   1
negligent   negligente   1
neighbor   el/la vecino/a   8
neighborhood   el barrio   2
neither   tampoco   5
nervous   nervioso/a   2
never   nunca   5
nevertheless   sin embargo   5
new   nuevo/a   1
news   las noticias   1
next   próximo/a   2
nice   simpático/a   1
ninth   noveno/a   7
nobody   nadie   2
none, not one   ningún/uno/a   4
non-profit   sin fines de lucro   10
noon   el mediodía   1
norm   la norma   5
nose   la nariz   3
not well   mal   PC
to note   apuntar   9
notebook   el cuaderno   1
nothing   nada   2
to notify   notificar, avisar   3
November   noviembre   PC
now   ahora   1
nurse   el/la enfermero/a   3
nursery   el vivero   9
nursing   la enfermería   3

objective   el objetivo   11
obscenity   la obscenidad   5
to observe   observar   1
to obtain   obtener (ie, g)   1
occupied   ocupado/a   2
October   octubre   PC
of course (not)   claro que sí/no   1
of, from   de   1
to offer   ofrecer (zc)   1
office   la oficina   1
office (medical)   el consultorio   1
oil   el aceite   8
old   viejo/a   1

older   mayor   2
only   sólo   1
open   abierto/a   7
to open   abrir   5
open air   al aire libre   9
opportunity   la oportunidad   5
to opt, elect   elegir (i)   4
optimistic   optimista   1
orange   la naranja   8
orchestra   la orquesta   2
organization   la organización   1
to organize   organizar   9
orphan   el/la huérfano/a   10
other, another   otro/a   1
to ought to, should   deber   2
our   nuestro/a   1
outside   afuera, fuera   2
oval   el óvalo   11
to overcome   superar   8
own   propio/a   7
owner   el/la dueño/a   9

page   la página   2
pain   el dolor   3
to paint   pintar   2
painting   la pintura   5
pair   la pareja   9
pale   pálido/a   3
pamphlet   el folleto   8
pants   los pantalones   5
paper   el papel   1
paragraph   el párrafo   9
paramedic   el/la paramédico/a   3
pardon me   perdón   PC
part   la parte   7
to participate   participar   5
party   la fiesta   1
to pass, to spend   pasar   2
passage   el pasaje   11
password   la contraseña   7
past, last   pasado/a   7
patience   la paciencia   8
patient   paciente   1
patriotism   el patriotismo   2
to pay   pagar   1
payment   el pago   9
peace   la paz   5
peach   el durazno   8
pear   la pera   8
pedagogy   la pedagogía   11
pen   la pluma   1

pencil   el lápiz   1
people   la gente   7
pepper   la pimienta   8
percentage   el porcentaje   9
performance   el desempeño   4
perhaps   quizás, tal vez   9
period   el período   7
permission   el permiso   10
to permit   permitir   9
person   la persona   4
personnel   el personal   1
pessimistic   pesimista   1
pet   la mascota   3
phonetics   la fonética   2
photo(graph)   la foto(grafía)   4
phrase   la frase   11
physical   físico/a   1
physics   la física   7
to pick up   recoger   5
piece   el pedazo   8
pink   rosado/a   3
pity   la lástima   9
place   el lugar, el sitio   1
to place   colocar   5
to plan   planificar   9
planet   el planeta   7
plant   la planta   2
to plant   sembrar (ie)   8
to play (music)   tocar   2
to play games   jugar (ue)   1
player   el reproductor   7
pleasant   agradable   3
please   por favor   PC
pleased/nice to meet you   mucho gusto   PC
pneumonia   la pulmonía   3
pocket   el bolsillo   7
poetry   la poesía   2
police officer   el/la (mujer) policía   1
Poor thing!   ¡Pobrecito/a!   3
population   la población   3
port   el puerto   7
portable   portátil   7
pot   la maceta   9
potato   la papa   8
pound   la libra   7
power   la potencia   7
practice   la práctica   5
to practice   practicar   1
praise   el elogio   5
to praise   elogiar   5
precisely   precisamente   2

to prefer   *preferir (ie)*   2
prep school   *la preparatoria*   7
prescription   *la receta*   3
president   *el/la presidente/a*   1
pretty   *bonito/a*   1
price   *el precio*   1
pride   *el orgullo*   4
primary   *primario/a*   1
principal   *el/la director/a*   2
principle   *el principio*   11
to print   *imprimir*   7
printer   *la impresora*   7
printing press   *la imprenta*   9
private   *particular*   7
prize   *el premio*   2
problem   *el problema*   4
procedure   *el procedimiento*   7
process   *el proceso*   7
processor   *el procesador*   7
to produce   *producir (zc)*   3
professor   *el/la profesor/a*   1
program   *el programa*   1
progress   *el progreso*   4
to prohibit   *prohibir*   9
project   *el proyecto*   7
promise   *la promesa*   10
to promise   *prometer*   2
promotion   *el fomento*   10
proof, testimony   *el testimonio*
   10
property   *la propiedad*   2
to protect   *proteger*   1
proud   *orgulloso/a*   4
to prove   *probar (ue)*   5
to provide   *proporcionar, dotar*
   9, 11
psychologist   *el/la psicólogo/a*
   1
public   *público/a*   5
Puerto Rican   *puertorriqueño/a*
   1
punishment   *el castigo*   4
to put to bed   *acostar (ue)*   4
to put, place   *poner (g)*   3

quality   *la calidad*   2
quarter, fourth   *cuarto/a*   1
question   *la pregunta*   1

radio   *el/la radio*   5
rain   *la lluvia*   8
to rain   *llover (ue)*   8
rainbow   *el arco iris*   2

rate   *la tasa*   10
to reach   *alcanzar*   10
reaction   *la reacción*   11
to read   *leer*   1
reader   *el/la lector/a*   7
reading   *la lectura*   1
readmit   *el reingreso*   9
ready   *listo/a*   3
real estate   *los bienes raíces*   2
reason   *la razón*   2
to receive   *recibir*   1
receptionist   *el/la recepcionista*
   1
recipe   *receta*   3
to recognize   *reconocer (zc)*   1
to recommend   *recomendar
   (ie)*   1
recreation   *el recreo*   1
to recuperate   *recuperarse*   3
red   *rojo/a*   2
reddening   *el enrojecimiento*   3
redheaded   *pelirrojo/a*   2
to reduce   *disminuir (y), reducir
   (zc)*   3, 4
reduced   *reducido/a*   1
referee   *el/la árbitro*   8
refreshment   *el refresco*   2
registration   *la inscripción, la
   matrícula*   1
registry   *el registro*   10
relative   *el/la pariente*   11
to relieve   *aliviar*   3
to remain   *permanecer (zc)*   3
remedy   *el remedio*   11
to remember   *recordar (ue)*   2
to remove   *quitar*   3
to renounce   *renunciar*   5
rent   *el alquiler*   10
to repair   *reparar*   9
to repeat   *repetir (i)*   4
to replace   *reemplazar*   7
report card   *la boleta de calificaciones*   4
reporter   *el/la reportero/a*   8
representative   *el/la representante*   9
to require   *requerir (ie), exigir*
   7, 9
requirement   *el requisito*   7
residence   *la residencia*   1
to resolve   *resolver (ue)*   5
resource   *el recurso*   9
respect   *el respeto*   1

to respect   *respetar*   9
respectful   *respetuoso/a*   1
respiratory tract   *las vías respiratorias*   3
responsible   *responsable*   1
to rest   *descansar*   2
result   *el resultado*   2
retail   *al por menor*   9
return   *el regreso, la vuelta*   2
to return   *regresar, volver (ue)*
   1, 4
to return (something)   *devolver
   (ue)*   9
rice   *el arroz*   8
rich   *rico/a*   8
right   *el derecho*   10
risk   *el riesgo*   10
rival   *el rival*   5
river   *el río*   11
road   *el camino*   5
rock   *la roca*   4
role   *el papel*   2
roof   *el techo*   5
room   *el salón*   1
room, bedroom   *la habitación*
   11
room, living room   *la sala*   2
root, stem   *la raíz*   4
rope   *la soga*   4
rough, unrefined   *tosco/a*   5
route   *la ruta*   5
routine   *la rutina*   1
rug   *la alfombra*   2
ruined, shattered   *desecho/a*
   5
ruler, rule   *la regla*   1
to run   *correr*   2

sack   *el saco*   5
sad   *triste*   2
salad   *la ensalada*   8
salary   *el salario, el sueldo*   1, 10
sale   *la venta*   10
salt   *la sal*   8
same   *mismo/a*   7
sand   *la arena*   3
sandwich   *el emparedado*   8
to satisfy   *satisfacer (g)*   7
Saturday   *sábado*   PC
sausage   *la salchicha*   8
to save   *ahorrar*   7
to say goodbye   *despedirse (i)*
   4

to say, to tell   *decir (i) (g)*   2

scale   *la escala*   11

schedule   *el horario*   8

scholarship   *la beca*   8

school   *la escuela, el colegio*   1, 2

school related   *escolar*   1

science   *la ciencia*   1

scientific   *el/la científico/a*   2

scissors   *las tijeras*   1

score, grade   *la puntuación*   10

to scratch   *rascar*   3

screen   *la pantalla*   2

search   *la búsqueda*   7

second   *segundo/a*   1

secondary   *secundario/a*   1

secret   *el secreto*   2

secretary   *el/la secretario/a*   PC

security   *la seguridad*   5

to see   *ver*   1

see you later   *hasta luego*   PC

seed   *la semilla*   8

to seem   *parecer (zc)*   3

to select   *seleccionar*   7

to sell   *vender*   2

semester   *el semestre*   10

seminary   *el seminario*   11

to send   *mandar, enviar*   4, 7

sense   *el sentido*   2

sense of touch   *el tacto*   5

sensible   *sensato/a*   5

sensitive   *sensible*   11

sensitivity   *la sensibilidad*   3

September   *septiembre*   PC

serious   *serio/a*   1

to serve   *servir (i)*   4

server   *el servidor*   7

service   *el servicio*   7

seventh   *séptimo/a*   7

sex   *el sexo*   1

shaking   *la sacudida*   5

shampoo   *el champú*   2

to share   *compartir*   4

she   *ella*   PC

shelf   *el estante*   1

shelter   *el refugio*   5

shift   *el turno*   8

shirt   *la camisa*   2

shoe   *el zapato*   2

shopping center   *el centro comercial*   11

short (height)   *bajo/a*   1

short (length)   *corto*   5

shout   *el grito*   1

to shout   *gritar*   3

to show   *manifestar (ie)*   3

shower   *la ducha*   8

to shower   *ducharse*   8

side   *el lado*   5

sign   *la seña, la señal*   4

signature   *la firma*   1

silence   *el silencio*   1

silly or stupid thing   *la tontería*   5

silly, stupid   *tonto/a*   2

simulation   *el simulacro*   5

sincerely   *atentamente*   9

to sing   *cantar*   2

singer   *el/la cantante*   4

sir, Mr.   *el señor*   1

to sit down   *sentarse (ie)*   8

sixth   *sexto/a*   3

size   *el tamaño, la talla*   8, 11

skateboard   *la patineta*   4

to sketch, to draw   *dibujar*   1

skill   *la destreza, la habilidad*   8, 9

skin   *la piel*   3

skirt   *la falda*   5

to sleep   *dormir (ue)*   2

sleep, dream   *el sueño*   2

sleeve   *la manga*   7

slice   *la rebanada, la raja*   8

slide   *el tobogán, el resbalador*   3

slight   *leve*   3

slow, backward   *atrasado/a*   4

slowed down, dulled   *entorpecido/a*   5

small (size)   *pequeño/a, chico/a*   1

to smell   *oler (ue)*   5

smile   *la sonrisa*   4

smoke   *el humo*   3

smooth   *suave*   11

snack (afternoon)   *la merienda*   2

snow   *la nieve*   8

to snow   *nevar (ie)*   8

so, as   *tan*   4

so, thus   *así*   1

soap   *el jabón*   3

soccer   *el fútbol*   1

soccer player   *el/la futbolista*   2

Social Studies   *los Estudios sociales*   1

society   *la sociedad*   11

socks   *los calcetines*   5

soldier   *el soldado*   11

solution   *la solución*   5

some   *algún/uno/a*   3

somebody, anybody   *alguien*   5

something   *algo*   1

son/daughter   *el/la hijo/a*   1

song   *la canción*   2

soon   *pronto*   1

sore   *la llaga*   3

so-so   *regular*   PC

source   *la fuente*   7

south   *el sur*   3

Spanish   *el español*   1

Spanish speaker   *el/la hispanohablante*   5

to speak   *hablar*   1

speaker   *el altavoz*   7

special   *especial*   1

speed   *la velocidad*   7

spelling   *la ortografía*   1

sphere, field   *el ámbito*   7

sponsor   *el/la patrocinador/a*   11

sport   *el deporte*   1

sports-related   *deportivo/a*   2

spouse   *el/la esposo/a*   2

to spread   *propagar*   3

spring   *la primavera*   2

staff   *el plantel*   11

stairway   *la escalera*   5

stamp   *el sello*   2

star   *la estrella*   8

state   *el estado*   1

statistics   *las estadísticas*   9

stay   *la estancia*   11

to stay, remain   *quedarse*   4

step   *el paso*   10

to stimulate   *estimular*   9

stomach   *el estómago*   3

to stop   *detener (ie, g), parar*   4, 5

store   *la tienda*   7

story   *el cuento*   1

strategy   *la estrategia*   11

street   *la calle*   1

stress   *el estrés*   9

strict   *estricto/a*   8

strike   *la huelga*   8

to stroll   *pasear*   5

strong   *fuerte*   2

student   el/la estudiante, el/la alumno/a   1, 7
student   (adj.)   estudiantil   2
student desk   el pupitre   1
to study   estudiar   1
stupid   estúpido/a   5
subject   la asignatura, la materia   2, 4
to subtract   restar   2
to succeed   lograr   2
success   el éxito   1
such   tal   3
to suffer   sufrir   2
sugar   el/la azúcar   8
to suggest   sugerir (ie)   7
to summarize   resumir   11
summer   el verano   2
sun   el sol   8
Sunday   domingo   PC
superintendent   el/la superintendente   1
to supervise   supervisar   2
supervisor   el/la supervisor/a   11
supplies, tools   los útiles   1
support   el apoyo   7
to support   apoyar   2
sure   seguro/a   2
surprise   la sorpresa   2
to surprise   sorprender   9
survey   la encuesta   8
survival   la supervivencia   5
suspicion   la sospecha   5
sweet   dulce   8
swelling   la hinchazón   3
to swim   nadar   2
swimming   la natación   8
swimming pool   la piscina   11
swings   los columpios   3
symbol   el símbolo   2
symptom   el síntoma   3
system   el sistema   2

table   la mesa   1
taco stand   la taquería   11
to take (along), to carry   llevar   2
to take (out)   sacar   4
to take a course   cursar   10
to take advantage of   aprovechar   2
to take care of   cuidar   2

to take care of (oneself)   cuidarse   8
to take charge of   ocuparse   3
to take, to drink   tomar   2
talent   el talento   10
to talk   hablar   1
talkative   hablador/a   1
tall   alto/a   1
tasty   sabroso/a   8
tax   el impuesto   10
to teach   enseñar   1
teacher   el/la maestro/a   1
tear   la lágrima   4
technician   el/la técnico/a   9
technique   la técnica   11
technology   la tecnología   1
telephone   el teléfono   1
tennis shoes   los tenis   5
tenth   décimo/a   7
territory   el territorio   5
terrorist   terrorista   5
test   el examen   2
thank you   gracias   PC
that   que   1
that   aquel/lla   7
That's great!   ¡Qué bueno!   1
that's why   por eso   2
to the contrary   al contrario   4
theater   el teatro   1
theater, cinema   el cine   7
to them/you (pl.)   les   5
theme   el tema   7
then   entonces   1
theological   teológico/a   11
there   allí   5
there is, are   hay   2
they   ellos/as   PC
thing   la cosa   1
to think   pensar (ie)   2
third   tercer/o/a   7
thirst   la sed   2
this   este/a   1
threat   la amenaza   5
throat   la garganta   3
through   a través de   7
through   por   3
to throw   tirar   8
Thursday   jueves   PC
time   el tiempo   5
timid, shy   tímido/a   1
tired   cansado/a   2
title, degree   el título   9

to   a   1
toast   el tostadito   8
today   hoy   8
together   junto/a   1
to tolerate   tolerar   5
tomorrow   mañana   10
ton   la tonelada   7
too   demasiado/a   8
tooth   el diente   3
tornado   el tornado   5
to touch   tocar   5
toy   el juguete   1
trace   el rastro   8
tradition   la tradición   11
trainer, coach   el/la entrenador/a   2
training   el entrenamiento   2
tranquilizer   el tranquilizante   5
to transform   transformar   5
to translate   traducir (zc)   3
translation   la traducción   8
to transmit   transmitir   7
transportation   el transporte   7
to travel   viajar   9
traveler   el/la viajero/a   9
tray   la bandeja   7
treatment   el tratamiento   3
tree   el árbol   5
triangle   el triángulo   8
trigonometry   la trigonometría   8
tripe stew   el menudo   11
trophy   el trofeo   8
True? Right?   ¿Verdad?   1
to try   tratar   3
T-shirt   la camiseta   8
Tuesday   martes   PC
tuna   el atún   8
to turn off   apagar   4
to turn on   prender   5
tutelage   el tutelaje   8
twisted, sprained   torcido/a   3
typical   típico/a   3

uncle   el tío   4
under   debajo de, abajo   3, 5
to understand   comprender, entender (ie)   1, 4
unified   unificado/a   7
uniform   el uniforme   5
union   el sindicato   8

unique, only *único/a* 10
unit *la unidad* 5
United States *Estados Unidos* 1
university *la universidad* 1
unknown *desconocido/a* 3
unpleasant *antipático/a* 1
us, to us *nos* 5
use *el manejo* 7
useful *útil* 9
user *el usuario* 7

vacancy *la vacante* 9
vaccination *la vacuna* 3
value *el valor* 4
varied *variado/a* 9
vegetable *el vegetal, la verdura* 2, 8
to verify *verificar* 7
very *muy* PC
vest *el chaleco* 11
veteran *el/la veterano/a* 10
video *el vídeo* 2
view *la vista* 3
violence *la violencia* 5
violent *violento/a* 5
virus *el virus* 3
vision *la vista* 3
voice *la voz* 1
volleyball *el vólibol* 2
volunteer *el/la voluntario/a* 1
vomit *el vómito* 3
to vote *votar* 4

to wait for, hope *esperar* 5
waiter, waitress *el/la mesero/a* 8
to wake up *despertarse (ie)* 8
to walk *caminar* 2
wall *la pared* 5
to want *querer (ie)* 4
war *la guerra* 11
to wash *lavarse* 8

water *el agua* (f.) 2
to water *regar (ie)* 8
way, manner *el modo* 7
we *nosotros/as* PC
we go, let's go *vamos* 1
we like *nos gusta(n)* 2
weak *débil* 2
weapon *el arma* (f.) 5
wearable *llevable* 11
weather *el tiempo* 7
Web *la Red* 7
Wednesday *miércoles* PC
week *la semana* 7
weights *las pesas* 8
welcome *bienvenidos* PC
well *bien* PC
well (conj.) *pues* 4
well-being *el bienestar* 4
west *el oeste* 5
What? *¿Qué?* 1
What a relief! *¡Qué alivio!* 1
What a shame! *¡Qué lástima!* 7
What day is today? *¿Qué día es hoy?* PC
What is your name? (familiar) *¿Cómo te llamas?* PC
What is your name? (formal) *¿Cómo se llama Ud.?* PC
What's today's date? *¿Cuál es la fecha de hoy?* PC
wheelchair *la silla de ruedas* 4
When? *¿Cuándo?* 1
Where? *¿Dónde?* 1
Which (one/s)? *¿Cuál/es?* 1
whistle *el pito* 3
white *blanco/a* 1
Who? *¿Quién/es?* 1
whole *entero/a* 8
wholesale *al por mayor* 9
whose *cuyo/a* 10
Why? *¿Por qué?* 1

to win, to earn *ganar* 2
wind *el viento* 8
window *la ventana* 1
wine *el vino* 8
winner *el/la ganador/a* 4
winter *el invierno* 8
wireless *inalámbrico/a* 7
wise *sabio/a* 5
to wish *desear* 9
with *con* 1
with me *conmigo* 4
with you *contigo* 10
without *sin* 2
woman *la mujer* 1
word *la palabra* 2
work *la obra* 2
work (job) *el trabajo* 1
to work *trabajar* 1
worker *el/la obrero/a* 8
world *el mundo* 1
worried *preocupado/a* 2
worse *peor* 4
wound *la herida* 5
wrestling *la lucha libre* 8
to write *escribir* 1
writing *la escritura, la redacción* 1, 8

year *el año* 7
yellow *amarillo/a* 2
yesterday *ayer* 7
you (familiar) like *te gusta* 2
you (familiar) *tú* PC
you (formal) *usted* PC
you (plural) *ustedes* PC
you, to you (familiar) *te* 5
you're welcome *de nada, no hay de qué* PC
young *joven* 1
younger *menor* 4
your *tu* 1

zoology *la zoología* 8

Index

Credits

Page 39: Patricia Rush; **page 55:** Patricia Rush; **page 83:** AP/Wide World Photos; **page 88:** Courtesy of Miami Children's Hospital, Kidsville Pediatric Care; **page 99:** Patricia Rush; **page 113:** Courtesy of the U.S. Department of Health and Human Services; **page 146:** © 2000 Heartsprings, Inc.; **page 151:** Courtesy of the U.S. Department of Health and Human Services; **page 156:** American Red Cross of Ventura County, printing by Farmers Insurance; **page 160:** Courtesy of JIST Publishing, Inc.; **page 166:** U.S. Department of Health and Human Services; **page 167:** U.S. Department of Health and Human Services; **p. 168:** U.S. Census Bureau; **p. 212:** We would like to thank MCI WorldCom for allowing us to use Tecnoguía, the industry's first on-line searchable English-Spanish glossary of over 1000 frequently used technological terms. To learn more about Tecnoguía, please visit www.mci.com/tecnoguia. **page 213:** Courtesy of Washington Mutual Bank; **page 235:** AP/Wide World Photos; **page 244:** United States Postal Service; **page 253:** Patricia Rush; **page 271:** Photo courtesy of Ernie and Lorie Chapa; **page 276:** U.S. Department of Education; **page 281:** Copyright 1995 by Hispanic Scholarship Fund. Reproduced with permission. All rights reserved www.hsf.net; **page 290:** Patricia Rush; **page 302:** Courtesy of Armando Garcia Martinez; **page 313:** Courtesy St. John's Seminary College; **page 325:** Courtesy of The Latino Book & Family Festival.